Human Metabolism

Human Metabolism
Functional Diversity and Integration

J. R. Bronk

Addison Wesley Longman Limited
Edinburgh Gate
Harlow
Essex CM20 2JE
England

*and Associated Companies throughout
the World*

© Addison Wesley Longman Limited 1999

· ·

First published 1999

ISBN 0 582 026555

· ·

**British Library Cataloguing-in-
Publication Data**
A catalogue record for this book is
available from the British Library.

Set by 30 in 10/12 Garamond
Printed in Singapore (KKP)

SHORT CONTENTS

CONTENTS

In the early years of biochemical research many of the important discoveries revealed the details of reactions responsible for providing cells with key metabolic requirements. Most of those who carried out this early research had been trained as physiologists so that their aim was to understand the metabolic processes that enabled an organism to carry out particular functions. More recently biochemistry has become increasingly concerned with investigation of the molecular basis of particular reactions and the ways in which they can be initiated and controlled. These exciting investigations have tended to make biochemists focus on the details of a particular metabolic event and to ignore the way in which it contributes to the function of the whole cell or tissue in which the process takes place. The complexity of modern biochemical research has also made it increasingly difficult for those studying biology or medicine to acquire a basic understanding of the metabolic processes responsible for particular physiological processes.

The aim of this book is to provide an overview of the ways in which metabolism supports the physiological functions of the major tissues in the body. In the first part I have attempted to provide a summary of the ways in which metabolic processes support the basic functions of mammalian cells. The second part of the book describes how the particular physiological functions of eight different human tissues are supported by specialized metabolic processes. However, Part 2 also aims to show how the various tissues cooperate to satisfy the physiological requirements of the body as a whole. The basis of the integration of the different tissues is introduced in the first chapter of Part 2 (Chapter 5), and it becomes the main theme of Part 3 which illustrates how tissue integration is altered by changes in diet, and by trauma, disease, starvation and exercise. Overall I hope that this book will help biochemistry students to understand how metabolism supports the important physiological functions of the human body. It should enable students of medicine and biology to see which metabolic pathways are essential for the physiological processes that occur in major body tissues. Also, the overview of human metabolism provided should help to explain the effects of metabolic diseases and how various diets can influence human health.

I would like to thank three of my colleagues at York, Henry Leese, George Kellett and Martin Rumsby, for their help in revising the manuscript of *Human Metabolism*. I am also very grateful to some of my biochemistry students at the University of York for their comments on many of the diagrams which I used in teaching my course on Tissue Metabolism. Finally I would like to thank my wife for her support and the editorial staff at Addison Wesley Longman for their help with the publication of this book.

J. Ramsey Bronk
Department of Biology,
University of York

PREFACE

General features of metabolism

PART 1

An overview of metabolism

Metabolism has two main functions for all cells:

- *it provides the energy required to maintain the internal composition of the cell and support its specialized functions, and*
- *it provides the metabolites the cell needs for the biosynthesis of its constituents and any products released by the cell.*

Metabolism is usually subdivided into a number of distinct areas, but it is important to gain an overall view of the way metabolism supports the needs of a cell.

1.1 Why do we need to understand metabolism?

Most of us take comfort from the knowledge that modern medicine can deal in a very sophisticated way with any threats to our health, but fundamentally medicine is a fire-fighting service ready to step in to help us in the event of accident, disease or even a defective genetic inheritance. We need to recognize that at least some of the health problems we are likely to face as we grow older can be avoided or at least postponed if we pay more attention to our diet and lifestyle. There is no shortage of dietary advice or warnings about ways in which we can damage our health, but many consider such advice alarmist, and take refuge in the thought that the 'experts' often disagree, and in any case will probably change their views. It is true that theories about health do change as research provides us with more information that can lead to new interpretations. One of the aims of this book is to approach these questions from a different angle by helping the reader to understand some of the reasons for the statements about the ways in which diet and lifestyle can affect our health. We must admit that because we do not have all the facts at present our conclusions about what constitutes the healthiest lifestyle are bound to change as new information is discovered. Nevertheless a sound factual background should help us to evaluate the significance of new data that become available in the future and to make more informed decisions about whether to accept the inevitable changes in guidance that accompany new findings.

CHAPTER 1

An example may help to illustrate the problem. A city taxi driver has a potentially dangerous lifestyle. He or she is often trapped in heavy traffic with an impatient client. At one time the driver would have tried to keep calm by smoking heavily, but now recognizes that this is too great a danger to health. In order to stop smoking the driver has taken to eating sweets, and is becoming fat as a consequence. Sadly, the sweets are not effective in preventing the driver from becoming angry and frustrated with the traffic, and the resulting secretion of adrenaline together with the steady intake of sucrose will tend to make the driver even fatter and probably increase the chances of a serious vascular accident in either the heart or the brain.

At least a third of all serious health problems such as coronary heart disease, strokes and diabetes are a consequence of metabolic disorders. In order to provide the background necessary to understand these problems the first chapter gives a general description of the purposes and functions of pathways common to most mammalian cells and introduces the system of metabolic schemes used in the book. This will provide an opportunity to discuss the subdivision of metabolism into separate areas and the effects of cell compartmentation. ATP formation by substrate-level phosphorylation and by oxidative phosphorylation is considered together with the processes responsible for transporting solutes across membranes. The general principles of metabolic control are also introduced.

1.2 What is metabolism?

Metabolism is the sum total of all the enzyme-catalysed reactions that occur in a cell. The large number of reactions in a cell are organized into a relatively small number of sequences or pathways. Individual reactions are catalysed by specific enzymes. The genes coding for the enzymes catalysing individual reactions often appear to be expressed in a coordinated manner so that each pathway can operate as a unit.

What are the functions of metabolism?

In all cells metabolism enables the cell to perform its vital functions. These include the formation of covalent bonds during the synthesis (and recycling) of the cell constituents and provision of the energy necessary to maintain the internal environment of the cell and to make it possible for the cell to fulfil its specialized functions. These features of metabolism are closely interrelated since the synthesis of the molecules that make up cell constituents requires an input of energy, while at the same time it is obvious that the cell constituents, such as those that make up the cell membrane and its constituent transport proteins, are needed to provide the energy supply and to control intracellular solute concentrations. The specialized functions of a cell such as movement, the secretion of a particular type of molecule or the stimulation of an adjacent cell also require biosynthetic processes as well as a supply of energy.

In single-celled organisms it is obvious that metabolism must satisfy all the organism's requirements. Each cell must take in nutrients and use them to form new cell constituents, if it is growing, or to recycle existing ones if it is not. The cell needs energy for biosynthesis as well as for other functions, and it must also ensure that the necessary compounds are available in the cytoplasm for the synthesis of cell constituents and products. In a complex integrated organism such as a mammal many cells carry out special functions for the body as a whole, and there are significant metabolic differences between different types of mammalian cells. The main purpose of this book is to show how the specialized functions of a number of mammalian tissues are related to their metabolic differences.

The synthesis of cell constituents begins with the metabolic pathways which supply the building blocks

The major cell constituents are proteins, nucleic acids, lipids and complex carbohydrates and, as indicated schematically in Figure 1.1, they are formed from relatively simple starting materials. In mammalian cells these key metabolites will come from one of three sources:

- Absorption of the metabolites from outside the cell and by implication, if we consider the organism as a whole, by absorption of the metabolites as dietary constituents from the digestive tract.

- Release of the metabolite from a source stored within the cell. The metabolite may be released either from a molecule used exclusively for storage, such as glycogen or triacylglycerol, or from a molecule that has another function within the cell such as an enzyme or a membrane lipid.

- The metabolite may be formed by the metabolism of a simple precursor. However the precursor must be absorbed by the cell or derived from a source stored within the cell.

Metabolism enables the cell to convert some of the energy found in nutrients into a form which will support biosynthesis, the maintenance of the internal environment and the cell's other energy-requiring processes

Biosynthetic reaction sequences in the cell require an input of energy, and this will normally be in the form of ATP (adenosine-5'-triphosphate), one of the other triphosphates or a reduced coenzyme (e.g. NADH, the reduced form of nicotinamide adenine dinucleotide, or NADPH, the reduced form of NAD phosphate). As discussed in section 1.7 it is important to recognize that the usefulness of ATP as a source of energy is not a consequence of any special or 'high-energy' form of the phosphate bond, but is merely a function of how far the hydrolysis of ATP is displaced from equilibrium. Mammalian cells have five reaction schemes which are capable of supplying cells with substantial amounts of energy conserved in one of these forms. These pathways are listed below:

- The glycolytic pathway which converts glucose into the three-carbon compounds, pyruvate or lactate.

- The tricarboxylic acid (TCA) cycle which converts two-carbon acetate units into carbon dioxide.

- The pentose phosphate pathway which converts glucose-6-phosphate into pentose phosphate, and reduces the $NADP^+$ coenzyme.

- The β-oxidation of fatty acids which converts fatty acids into two-carbon units, and reduces the coenzymes FAD (flavin adenine dinucleotide) and NAD^+.

5

- Oxidative phosphorylation, the electron transport phosphorylation process in which molecular oxygen is used to oxidize the coenzymes, which are reduced in the other four pathways, with the production of water and the conversion of ADP (adenosine-5'-diphosphate) plus phosphate into ATP.

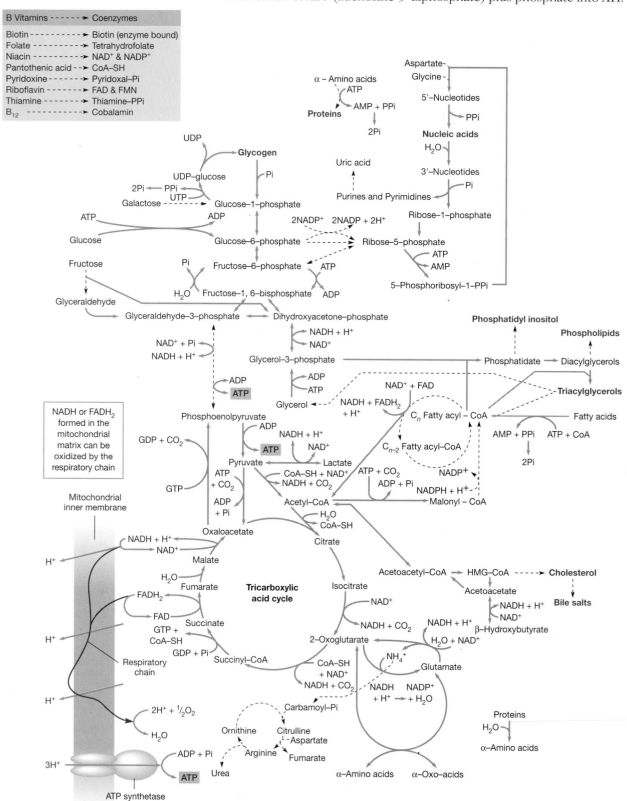

Figure 1.1 Overview of metabolism. The major cell constituents are in blue and the points of ATP formation are shaded.

One of the five energy-supplying processes, the glycolytic pathway, can be distinguished from the others because it is able to operate independently of a supply of oxygen. Unfortunately this has led people to consider that it is an anaerobic pathway, which is misleading since the pathway can (and does!) function in an oxygen-independent mode even when oxygen is plentifully available. The other four energy-supplying pathways lack this flexibility since they can only operate with oxygen present.

Metabolism provides key metabolites which are required for the synthesis of many essential cell constituents

The central metabolic pathways in Figure 1.1 include all five of the energy-conserving pathways listed in the previous section. In addition to supplying the cell with energy, these central pathways provide precursors required for the formation of the carbohydrates, lipids, nucleic acids and proteins from which the cell is made. Most of the pathways shown in Figure 1.1 are found in almost all mammalian cells, but some reactions which occur only in specialized cells have been included for completeness (e.g. the metabolism of fructose and galactose, the formation of urea and glycogen, and the hydrolysis of glucose-6-phosphate).

Glycolysis, which is responsible for the conversion of glucose into three-carbon compounds, illustrates the dual role of these central metabolic pathways. The glycolytic pathway supplies the cell with ATP and also provides the acetyl-coenzyme A (acetyl-CoA) and glycerol-3-phosphate needed to form the phospholipids required for cell membranes.

The pentose phosphate pathway provides a different sort of example since it is responsible for supplying energy (as NADPH) for fatty acid synthesis, but it also supplies the phosphoribosyl-1-pyrophosphate required for the formation of nucleotides, the precursors of the nucleic acids.

Classical subdivisions of metabolism

One aim of this book is to persuade you to think of metabolism as an integrated set of pathways within the cell rather than emphasizing the artificial subdivisions between the different areas of metabolism. However, the metabolism of the cell is too complex to consider all at once and there are some advantages in using the classical subdivisions of carbohydrate, lipid and nitrogen metabolism. Figure 1.2 shows how the metabolic pathways in Figure 1.1 are divided into the three main areas of metabolism.

Within each of these major areas Figure 1.2 also identifies the figure that gives details of particular pathways with defined functions, such as the the energy-supplying pathways mentioned previously. This is done for carbohydrate metabolism in Figure 1.3, but a comparison of Figures 1.2 and 1.3 illustrates the artificiality of the three classical subdivisions. Most of the major energy-conserving pathways fall within carbohydrate metabolism, except the β-oxidation scheme from lipid metabolism which is not included in Figure 1.3. Furthermore, as we shall see in Chapter 4, the carbon skeletons of amino acids provide an important source of substrate for the TCA cycle although they are part of nitrogen metabolism.

When we come to examine the metabolic pathways found in particular tissues in Part 2, the links between the various pathways which are shown in Figure 1.1 are emphasized and Chapter 5 outlines these relationships. The integration of metabolism is even more evident in Part 3 when we consider how the balance between the various organs changes when the body is stressed by food intake, disease, starvation, trauma or the effects of exercise.

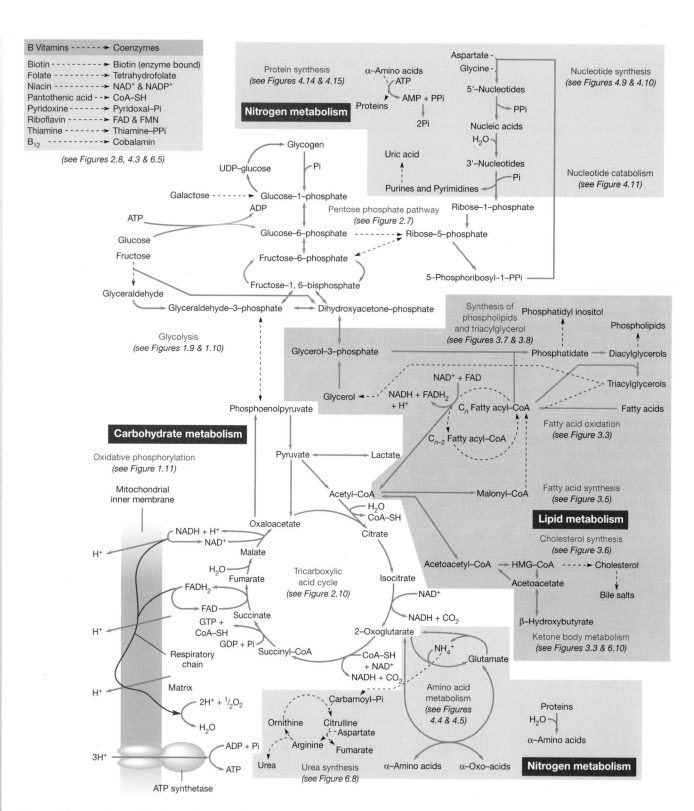

Figure 1.2 Classical subdivisions of metabolism. Nitrogen metabolism is shown in the blue tint and lipid metabolism in the grey tint. The remaining areas show carbohydrate metabolism plus the final common pathways of the tricarboxylic acid cycle and oxidative phosphorylation.

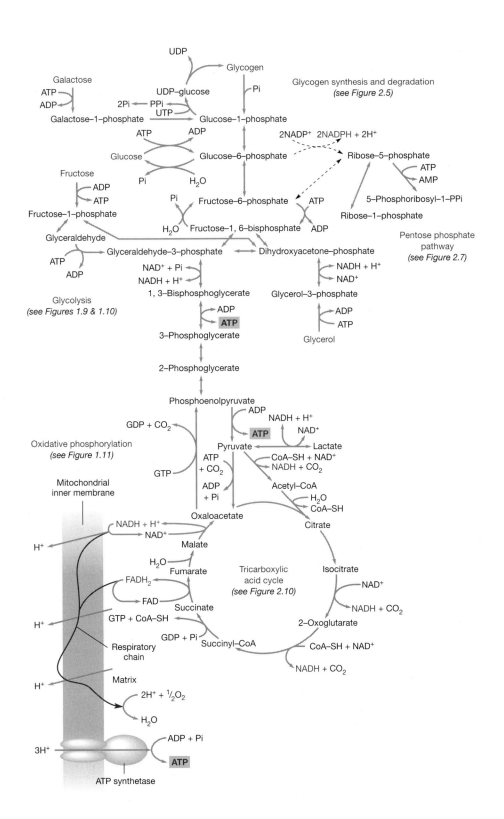

Figure 1.3
Carbohydrate metabolism.
The points of ATP formation are
blue and in a shaded box.

1.3 Organization and presentation of metabolic pathways

A number of overall schemes have been devised for this book to emphasize the links between individual metabolic pathways. This type of overview requires presentation of many of the pathways in abbreviated form to avoid burdening the schemes with too much detail. The missing material is provided in subsequent schemes and, so that the reader is not misled, a system similar to computer windows has been used to help the reader find the detailed material omitted from the general schemes. Those sections of the pathways that are subsequently explained in greater detail are often enclosed in boxes which identify the figure giving the additional information. In some cases a reaction sequence enclosed in a box in one figure may itself contain steps that are expanded in later figures. This technique of nested diagrams is employed to display the molecular mechanisms in key steps of a metabolic pathway. It is also a useful way to show the crucial roles of coenzyme structures.

For the overview of cell metabolism provided in Figure 1.1 it was necessary to omit many details in order to give the general picture. Figures 1.3, 1.9 and 1.10 indicate how the technique of nested diagrams has been used to provide increasingly detailed information concerning part of the pathway responsible for the conversion of glucose or glycogen into pyruvate or lactate. Figure 1.3 shows how the glycolytic pathway fits into the overall scheme of carbohydrate metabolism. Figure 1.9 shows the detailed steps of glycolysis and the names of the enzymes responsible for each step. Figure 1.10 provides the molecular structures of the intermediates responsible for the substrate-level phosphorylation of ADP during the conversion of glyceraldehyde-3-phosphate to pyruvate. Boxes 1 and 2 in Figure 1.10 give the structure of NAD^+ and show the reduction of the nicotinamide region of the coenzyme during the oxidation of glyceraldehyde-3-phosphate.

1.4 Maintenance of cell volume and ion content

The maintenance of a cell's volume and ion content requires about one-third of the ATP produced by cell metabolism. Cells have many macromolecules and other large solutes which cannot cross the plasma membrane. These impermeable solutes plus the ions and low molecular weight solutes in the cytoplasm must be balanced by an equivalent mix of solutes in the blood and extracellular fluid. In part, the contribution of the intracellular macromolecules to the total osmolarity of the cell contents is matched by plasma proteins such as serum albumin, but ions make up a higher proportion of the solute concentration in the plasma than they do in the cytoplasm. This means that the passive entry of Na^+ down the concentration gradient into the cell will lead to an increase in solute concentration in the cytoplasm, and as a consequence water will enter causing the cell to swell, whereas the exit of K^+ would cause the reverse effect.

The sodium pump

The net inward movement of Na^+ ions is countered by the Na^+/K^+ ATPase or 'Na$^+$ pump' in which the hydrolysis of ATP is responsible for pumping three Na^+ ions out and two K^+ ions in for each ATP hydrolysed to ADP and phosphate (see Figure 1.4a). The net export of cations from the cell by the Na$^+$ pump is largely matched by a net outward movement of anions (chiefly chloride) through specific channels in the membrane. However, this compensatory anion transfer lags behind the electrogenic cation transfer driven by the Na$^+$ pump, so that an electrical charge (the membrane potential) is established across the membrane with the outside positive. If the Na$^+$ pump is blocked by a specific inhibitor (e.g. the cardiac glycoside ouabain), the membrane potential falls to zero and in a short time the continued passive movement of extracellular ions into the cell through a variety of ion channels and transport systems causes it to swell.

It is clearly important that the net export of ions as a result of the activity of the Na$^+$ pump is limited in some way, otherwise its continued activity could cause the cell to shrink as a result of the net outward movement of solute. The mechanism responsible for limiting the activity of the Na$^+$ pump is a direct consequence of the energetics of the transport process. The maximum amount of energy available for moving the Na$^+$ and K$^+$ ions against their respective concentration gradients is provided by the energy available from the hydrolysis of ATP at the concentrations of ATP, ADP and phosphate at the cell membrane. The Na$^+$/K$^+$ ATPase is known as a P-type ATPase because, as shown in Figure 1.4(a), the enzyme is phosphorylated by ATP during the transport process and as a consequence the stoichiometry of ion movement and ATP hydrolysis is fixed. The rate at which the Na$^+$ pump operates will decrease as the Na$^+$ and K$^+$ gradients increase, so that, in principle, net ion movement would cease when the energy

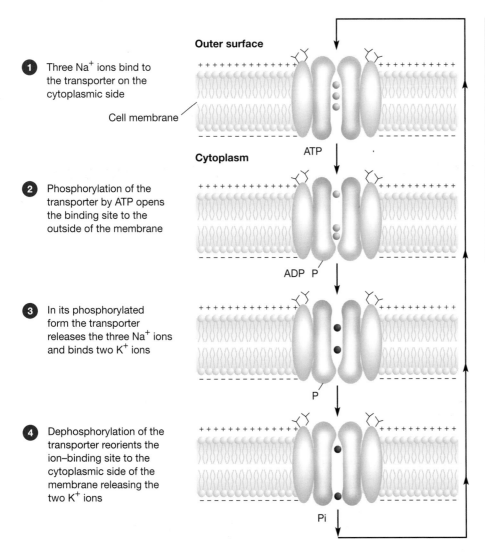
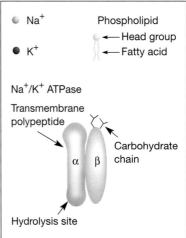

Figure 1.4(a)
The sodium/potassium ATPase.

11

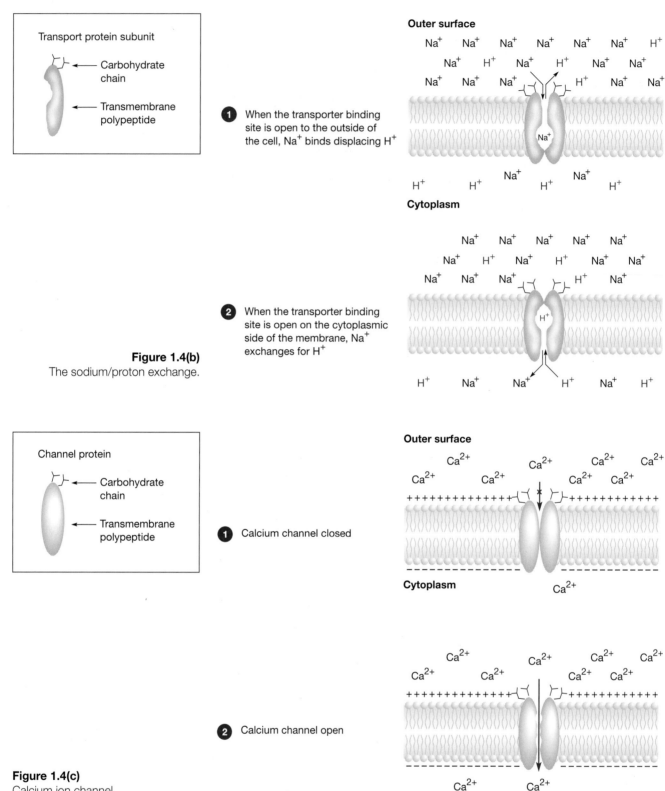

Figure 1.4(b)
The sodium/proton exchange.

Figure 1.4(c)
Calcium ion channel.

required for ion movement exactly balances that for ATP hydrolysis under the prevailing conditions. However, the net effect of the operation of the Na⁺ pump is also limited in another way: as the Na⁺ and K⁺ gradients increase, the rate at which these ions can move back passively across the membrane will also rise. Thus, as the concentration of Na⁺ in the cytoplasm declines and the ratio of cytoplasmic to extracellular K^+ rises, the rate of Na^+ pump activity will decline to the point at which it is balanced by the rate at which the ions are moving back across the cell membrane. This means that the Na^+ pump must continue to operate at a rate sufficient to compensate for the inward movement of ions through channels and transporters in the membrane.

As pointed out in the next section the Na^+ pump is important for the uptake of amino acids in order to remove the Na^+ ions which enter with many of the amino acids. The inwardly directed Na^+ gradient must be maintained to enable the cell to achieve sufficiently high intracellular amino acid concentrations to support protein synthesis. A high intracellular K^+ concentration is necessary to maintain the stability of the ribosomes which serve as the site of protein synthesis in the cytoplasm. The outwardly directed K^+ gradient can also serve as an energy source for the entry or exit of other solutes.

The sodium/proton exchange

Some compounds found in the cytoplasm are transported into the cell together with a proton, and the generation of an inwardly directed proton gradient across the cell membrane is linked to the hydrolysis of ATP by an Na^+/H^+ exchange transport system (Figure 1.4b). This Na^+/H^+ exchange makes it possible for negatively charged phosphate ions to enter the cell as uncharged phosphoric acid which then becomes ionized again as soon as it enters the cytoplasm. The cell membrane also has an exchange transporter for the bicarbonate anion produced by carbonic anhydrase (Eq. 1.1) from the CO_2 resulting from the oxidation of carbon compounds in the cell:

$$CO_2 + H_2O \rightarrow H_2CO_3 \rightarrow HCO_3^- + H^+ \qquad (1.1)$$

Bicarbonate ions leave the cell in exchange for the entry of chloride anions. The protons produced together with the bicarbonate leave the cell by the Na^+/H^+ exchange process.

Calcium channels

The other cations required by the cell, such as Mg^{2+} and Ca^{2+}, are present in the blood plasma and they can enter the cell passively through ion channels because of the membrane potential which is negative inside the membrane. In the case of Ca^{2+} the intracellular concentration is normally kept very low by an outwardly directed Ca^{2+} pump at the expense of ATP hydrolysis. Entry occurs via a Ca^{2+} channel which opens in a highly controlled way to permit a small amount of Ca^{2+} to enter the cell driven by both the concentration gradient and the membrane potential (see Figure 1.4c).

1.5 Uptake of nutrients

All mammalian cells must acquire essential nutrients from the blood or interstitial fluid. The epithelial cells that line the lumen of the small intestine have the additional function of absorbing the dietary constituents which provide the entire body with its source of essential nutrients (see Chapter 10). In this section we are concerned with the way in which simple non-specialized cells acquire the basic mix of nutrients required for their metabolic processes. The plasma concentrations of many of these constituents are maintained at reasonably constant levels by the liver and adipose tissue (see Chapters 6 and 7). There are two patterns of nutrient entry into a cell which differ in the relationship between the intracellular concentration of the nutrient and that in the surrounding fluid. If the solute concentration in the cell exceeds that outside, an energy-dependent transport process is essential. However, a solute with an intracellular concentration below that in the surrounding fluid can enter by passive diffusion (normally with the aid of a transporter). It is important to note that this alternative applies to the entry of most nutrients since once inside the cell they effectively disappear as a result of conversion to metabolic intermediates, thus maintaining an inwardly directed concentration gradient.

Facilitated transport of glucose

Glucose, which has the potential to serve as an energy source for all cells, follows the normal entry pattern for a hydrophilic solute. Glucose crosses the cell membrane with the aid of a specific transport protein (one of the family of glucose transporters (GLUT)). These transporters facilitate glucose transfer into the cell at a rate dependent on the inwardly directed concentration gradient (see Figure 1.5). In order to enter the glycolytic pathway glucose is phosphorylated by the enzyme hexokinase at the expense of ATP:

$$\text{Glucose} + \text{ATP} \rightarrow \text{Glucose-6-phosphate} + \text{ADP} \qquad (1.2)$$

In humans the blood level of glucose is maintained at about 5 mM by the liver (see Chapters 5 and 6) so that the rate of glucose uptake into the cell will depend mainly on the number of active transporters and the rate of the phosphorylation reaction. Normally both factors are important, but if there is an insufficient number of transporters the intracellular glucose concentration will be effectively zero and only a change in the number of active transporters in the membrane will alter the entry rate (and hence the availability of glucose-6-phosphate). On the

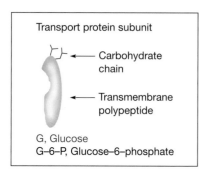

Transport protein subunit

Carbohydrate chain

Transmembrane polypeptide

G, Glucose
G–6–P, Glucose–6–phosphate

① Glucose binds to the transporter on the outer surface of the membrane where the glucose concentration is high

② Reorientation of the transporter exposes the glucose-binding site to the cytoplasmic side of the membrane. Because of the low intracellular glucose concentration, glucose diffuses away from the transporter. The glucose concentration in the cytoplasm is kept low by its conversion to glucose-6-phosphate by hexokinase at the expense of ATP

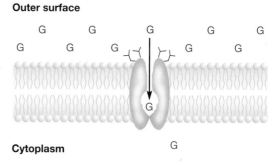

Outer surface

Cytoplasm

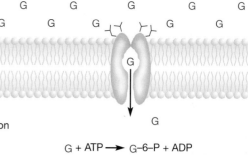

$$G + ATP \longrightarrow G{-}6{-}P + ADP$$

Figure 1.5
Facilitated transport of glucose.

other hand, an excess of active transporters will allow the glucose concentration in the cell to rise and reduce the rate of entry by cutting the concentration gradient. Under such conditions the uptake rate will be chiefly controlled by the rate of phosphorylation which will, in turn, be influenced by the subsequent fate of the glucose-6-phosphate.

Fatty acid uptake

The entry of fatty acids can be by passive diffusion because these molecules are lipophilic and can cross the cell membrane without a transporter. However, it is likely that specific fatty acid transporters are present in the plasma membrane of most cells. Once inside the cell the fatty acids are activated by attachment to coenzyme A (CoA–SH) which is derived from the B vitamin pantothenic acid. Fatty acid activation is ATP-dependent and serves to keep the cytoplasmic concentrations of free fatty acids at very low levels. This is important for uptake since fatty acids are bound to albumin in the bloodstream with the consequence that the concentration of free fatty acids in blood plasma is only about 10^{-6} M. Thus, the rate of fatty acid uptake will depend on both the blood concentration and the rate of conversion to a coenzyme A derivative. There are also binding proteins for free fatty acids in the cytoplasm. The activation of fatty acids by ATP results in the loss of pyrophosphate (PPi) which is subsequently split to inorganic phosphate (Pi), thus ensuring that the reaction, shown below, proceeds to the right even at low concentrations of fatty acid and coenzyme A:

$$R—COOH + ATP + CoA—SH \rightarrow R—CO—S—CoA + AMP + PPi \qquad (1.3)$$

Once attached to coenzyme A fatty acids can participate in reactions responsible for the biosynthesis of triacylglycerols or phospholipids in the cytoplasm. Alternatively they can be transferred to carnitine in order to cross the impermeable mitochondrial inner membrane to the site of oxidation within the mitochondrial matrix (see Figure 3.2).

Vitamin uptake

Micronutrients such as vitamins and trace elements enter the cell by passive diffusion so that their uptake will also depend on both the concentration in the plasma and the rate at which they are converted to derivatives or bound to enzymes. The only source of most vitamins is from the diet, and particularly in the case of the water-soluble B vitamins it is important that they be taken in regularly in order to keep the cells supplied with these essential precursors for coenzyme structures (see Figures 1.1 and 1.2).

Amino acid transport

Amino acids have to enter the cell against a concentration gradient. This is a consequence of the low plasma concentrations of the individual amino acids, and the fact that relatively high amino acid concentrations are necessary inside the cell to ensure an adequate rate of protein synthesis. Under these conditions amino acid uptake obviously requires both transport proteins and a source of energy. Eight different amino acid transporters have been identified and between them they are responsible for the uptake of all 20 amino acids. The transport of most amino acids is coupled to Na^+ entry (see Figure 1.6) which provides the energy needed to move the amino acids against a concentration gradient since the Na^+/K^+

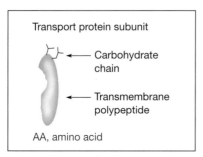

Transport protein subunit

— Carbohydrate chain

— Transmembrane polypeptide

AA, amino acid

Figure 1.6
Sodium-dependent amino acid transport.

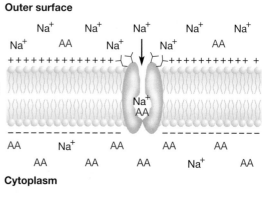

Outer surface

1 When the binding site of the amino acid transporter is exposed to the outside of the cell it binds the amino acid plus an Na^+ ion

Cytoplasm

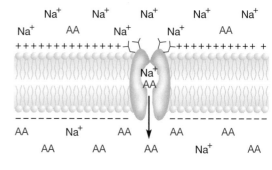

2 The menbrane potential (negative inside) causes the transporter to reorient because of the Na^+ bound to it. With the binding site exposed to the cytoplasm where the Na^+ concentration is low, the Na^+ leaves the transporter, causing the amino acid to detach even though the amino acid concentration in the cytoplasm is high

ATPase maintains the intracellular Na^+ concentration at less than 10% of that in the plasma and the membrane potential (negative inside) helps to drive the Na^+ into the cell. In principle this means that cytoplasm/plasma concentration ratios of up to 10 are possible for individual amino acids. In order to calculate the apparent intracellular concentration of an amino acid for a group of cells the amount measured in the cells is divided by the total volume of cell water. Such measurements give ratios considerably higher than 10 for some amino acids, but this can be explained by the fact that these amino acids are further concentrated within an intracellular compartment, such as the mitochondrial matrix.

1.6 Cell compartmentation

Except for admitting that the nucleus conveniently separates the genetic material from the cytoplasm, most summaries of metabolic pathways tend to treat the cell as though it were a single compartment. Of course such a view is a gross over-simplification, since the cytoplasm of most cells is packed with a variety of organelles. From the metabolic point of view the most important point to establish is the extent to which the various cytoplasmic organelles provide genuine compartmentation of the various metabolic processes that occur in the cell. The picture of cell structure that is given by electron micrographs is of a range of membrane-bound structures, shown diagrammatically in Figure 1.7. The effects that each of these structures has on metabolism depend on the enzymes that make up the pathways within the organelle and the permeability of its membranes to the metabolites. For example, it is clear that the nucleus contains the chromosomal DNA, and even though the nuclear membrane is permeable to

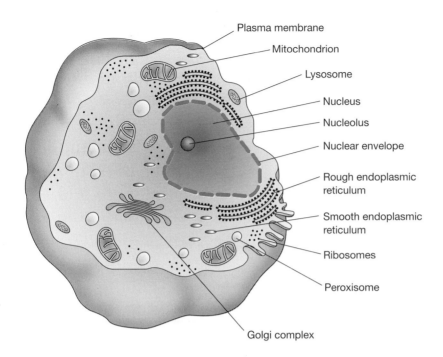

Plasma membrane
Mitochondrion
Lysosome
Nucleus
Nucleolus
Nuclear envelope
Rough endoplasmic reticulum
Smooth endoplasmic reticulum
Ribosomes
Peroxisome
Golgi complex

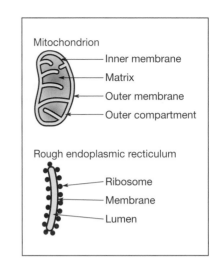

Mitochondrion
Inner membrane
Matrix
Outer membrane
Outer compartment

Rough endoplasmic recticulum
Ribosome
Membrane
Lumen

Figure 1.7
Schematic representation of the principal structural features in a mammalian cell.

nucleotides, enzymes and relatively large RNA molecules, all the DNA-dependent RNA synthesis must occur in the nucleus since that is where the DNA template is trapped. It is also clear that many enzymes are located on membranes, and this can influence the way they function since the active site of the enzyme may be on the outer face or inner face of the membrane or it may even be within the lipid environment in the centre of the membrane.

From a metabolic point of view, the most important compartmentation in the cell is provided by the mitochondria because the inner compartment (or matrix) provides the location for pathways dedicated principally to the oxidation of substrates and the conservation of some of the energy released during oxidation to form ATP by the phosphorylation of ADP as shown in Figure 1.8. It is true that the glycolytic pathway in the cytoplasm also includes steps responsible for substrate oxidation and the synthesis of ATP, but if conditions are right these steps can operate in the reverse direction reducing the substrate and using up ATP. The dedicated nature of mitochondrial metabolism is a consequence of the presence of the respiratory chain on the mitochondrial inner membrane (see Figure 1.11). This collection of oxidative enzymes ensures that metabolites such as pyruvate or fatty acids in the mitochondrial matrix are oxidized rather than used for biosynthetic processes. Localization of substrate oxidation within the mitochondria means that pathways responsible for the biosynthesis of carbohydrates and fatty acids can operate in the cytoplasm at the same time that other fatty acids and carbohydrates are being oxidized in the mitochondrial matrix to provide the necessary ATP. Control over the oxidative activity of the respiratory chain is normally provided by the demand for ATP, as measured by the availability of ADP, hence the description of the process as 'oxidative phosphorylation'. Mitochondria have two membranes. The inner membrane, which is the site of the respiratory chain and the ATP synthetase complex, has a much larger surface area than the outer membrane, as shown by the extensive folds called cristae extending into the matrix. Only the inner membrane serves as a permeability barrier to ions and small molecules. The mitochondrial outer membrane is freely permeable to ATP, ADP and other nucleotides as well as the substrates and products of the reactions that occur in the mitochondria. Since ATP produced inside the mitochondrial matrix is exported into the outer compartment in exchange for ADP, the ATP/ADP ratio in the outer compartment and the cytoplasm will be very high. The only nucleotide to be formed by the synthetase on

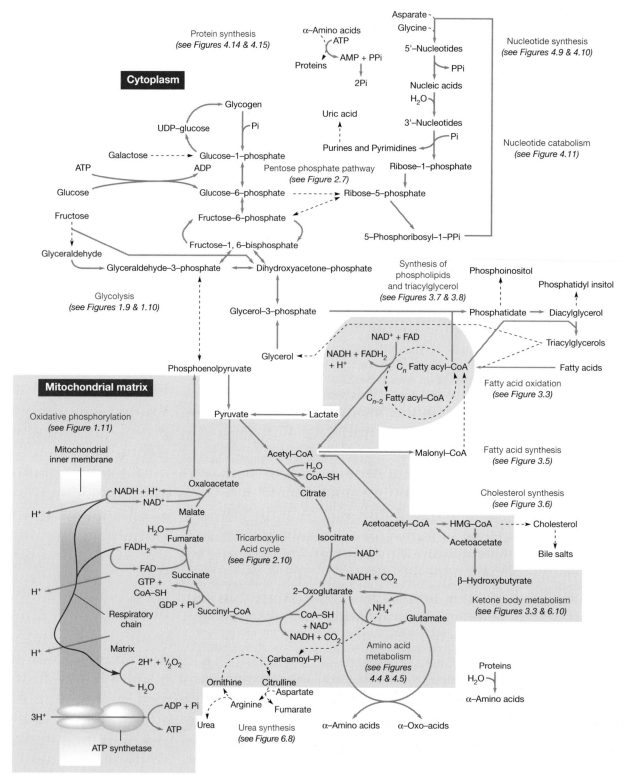

Figure 1.8 Distribution of metabolic pathways between the mitochondria and cytoplasm. The blue area shows those pathways that operate in the mitochondrial matrix.

the inner membrane is ATP and the other triphosphates (cytidine-5'-triphosphate (CTP), guanosine -5'-triphosphate (GTP), uridine -5'-triphosphate (UTP), thymidine -5'-triphosphare (TTP)) are formed from their respective diphosphates by the nucleoside diphosphokinase reactions, shown below:

$$CDP + ATP \longleftrightarrow CTP + ADP \qquad (1.4)$$

$$GDP + ATP \longleftrightarrow GTP + ADP \qquad (1.5)$$

$$UDP + ATP \longleftrightarrow UTP + ADP \qquad (1.6)$$

$$TDP + ATP \longleftrightarrow TTP + ADP \qquad (1.7)$$

These reactions will be driven to the right by the high ATP/ADP ratio, thereby ensuring a steady supply of all nucleoside triphosphates in the cytoplasm. The fact that the mitochondrial outer membrane is freely permeable to nucleotides and other low molecular weight molecules does not mean that the concentrations of the metabolites in the outer compartment will necessarily equilibrate with those in the general cytoplasm. The cell is not at equilibrium, and the respiratory activity on the mitochondrial inner membrane effectively drives the nucleotides and other ions in and out of the matrix. The concentration of ATP in the various compartments outside the mitochondria will be determined by the rate at which the ATP is used. Even when the respiration rate is constant a steady state will be established in which gradients of concentration will be determined by the rates at which the nucleotides are used in the various parts of the cell and the distance from the mitochondria.

Lysosomes provide another compartment separated from the rest of the cytoplasm by an effective permeability barrier which allows these spherical organelles to maintain a low internal pH so that they can carry out the acid hydrolysis of cell constituents such as membrane fragments and ribosomes. Many cells also contain spherical peroxisomes in which potentially damaging oxidation and peroxidation reactions are separated from the remainder of the cytoplasm. The oxidation of very long chain fatty acids also occurs in peroxisomes.

Apart from the mitochondria, the most obvious structural features in the cytoplasm are ribosomes and membranes of the endoplasmic reticulum and the Golgi. These structures provide the sites of protein and membrane synthesis. The endoplasmic reticulum membranes have specific receptors for the ribosomes synthesizing proteins destined to be secreted or incorporated into membranes. Although the endoplasmic reticulum membranes do not present a barrier to small molecules, they do entrap newly synthesized proteins within membrane vesicles which are then used to transfer these proteins to other organelles or to the Golgi for subsequent modification before they are transferred to other organelles. Some of these proteins are carried to the plasma membrane in vesicles and secreted by fusion of the vesicle with the boundary membrane of the cell.

1.7 Glycolysis and the supply of energy by substrate-level phosphorylation and NAD⁺ reduction

The most straightforward processes responsible for the synthesis of ATP are the two substrate-level phosphorylations that occur in the glycolytic pathway, since they involve phosphorylation of an intermediate in the pathway followed by the transfer of the phosphate to ADP. Figure 1.9 shows the steps of the glycolytic pathway and indicates that each end of the hexose ring must be phosphorylated by an ATP before it is split to two triose phosphates, setting the stage for the direct formation of ATP by transfer of phosphate from the substrate to ADP. Substrate-level

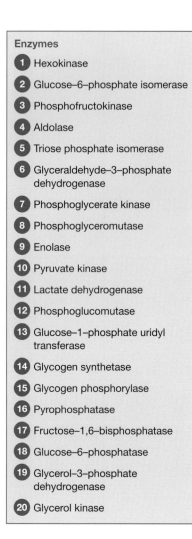

Enzymes

1. Hexokinase
2. Glucose–6–phosphate isomerase
3. Phosphofructokinase
4. Aldolase
5. Triose phosphate isomerase
6. Glyceraldehyde–3–phosphate dehydrogenase
7. Phosphoglycerate kinase
8. Phosphoglyceromutase
9. Enolase
10. Pyruvate kinase
11. Lactate dehydrogenase
12. Phosphoglucomutase
13. Glucose–1–phosphate uridyl transferase
14. Glycogen synthetase
15. Glycogen phosphorylase
16. Pyrophosphatase
17. Fructose–1,6–bisphosphatase
18. Glucose–6–phosphatase
19. Glycerol–3–phosphate dehydrogenase
20. Glycerol kinase

Figure 1.9
The glycolytic pathway.

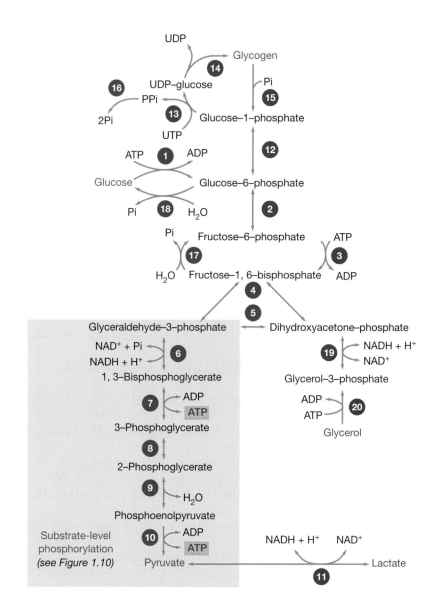

phosphorylations occur at two points in the glycolytic pathway, since both 1,3-bis-phosphoglycerate and phosphoenolpyruvate can transfer phosphates to ADP. Figure 1.10 shows the molecular structures in this part of the glycolytic pathway; those in the remainder of the pathway are shown in Figure 2.3.

Energy conservation

As mentioned earlier, there is nothing special about the two terminal phosphate bonds of ATP and ADP, which are shown below in the ionized form that they normally have in the cytoplasm at pH 7.0. Equation 1.8 shows the hydrolysis of ATP^{4-} to yield ADP^{3-} and Pi$^-$, although at pH 7.0 the phosphate would normally have about 1.5 negative charges.

$$\text{Adenine-ribose}-O-\overset{\overset{O}{\|}}{\underset{\underset{O^-}{|}}{P}}-O-\overset{\overset{O}{\|}}{\underset{\underset{O^-}{|}}{P}}-O-\overset{\overset{O}{\|}}{\underset{\underset{O^-}{|}}{P}}-O^- + H_2O \rightarrow \text{Adenine-ribose}-O-\overset{\overset{O}{\|}}{\underset{\underset{O^-}{|}}{P}}-O-\overset{\overset{O}{\|}}{\underset{\underset{O^-}{|}}{P}}-O^- + HO-\overset{\overset{O}{\|}}{\underset{\underset{OH}{|}}{P}}-O^- \quad (1.8)$$

ATP   ADP   Pi

The equilibrium constant (K') at pH 7 for this reaction is 10^{-5} and is given by the following equation:

$$K' = \frac{[\text{ADP}]\,[\text{Pi}]}{[\text{ATP}]} \qquad (1.9)$$

where the concentrations used are the total molar concentrations of each compound at equilibrium. Considering that the normal phosphate concentration in the cell is about 10^{-2} M, the ratio of ADP/ATP has to be 10^7 for hydrolysis to be at equilibrium. The total adenine nucleotide pool in the cytoplasm is less than 10^{-2} M and in fact the cytoplasmic ADP/ATP ratio is 10^{-1} or less, showing how far from equilibrium the reaction in Eq. 1.8 will be under physiological conditions.

It is the displacement of a reaction from equilibrium which determines the extent of the Gibbs free energy change (ΔG) in the reaction and we can express this quantitatively by defining the observed mass action ratio, Γ, as follows:

$$\Gamma' = \frac{[\text{ADP}]_{\text{obs}}\,[\text{Pi}]_{\text{obs}}}{[\text{ATP}]_{\text{obs}}} \qquad (1.10)$$

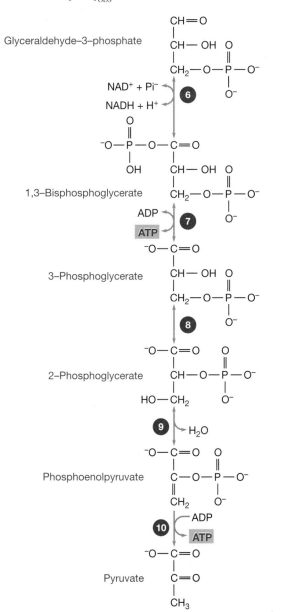

Enzymes

⑥ Glyceraldehyde–3–phosphate dehydrogenase (see Boxes 1 and 2)

⑦ Phosphoglycerate kinase

⑧ Phosphoglyceromutase

⑨ Enolase

⑩ Pyruvate kinase

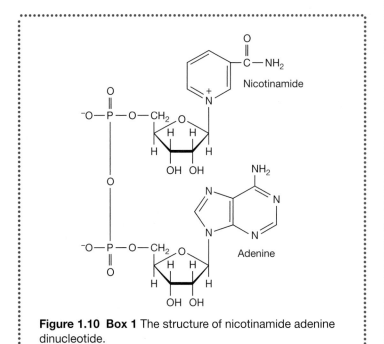

Figure 1.10 Box 1 The structure of nicotinamide adenine dinucleotide.

Figure 1.10
Details of substrate-level phosphorylation in glycolysis.

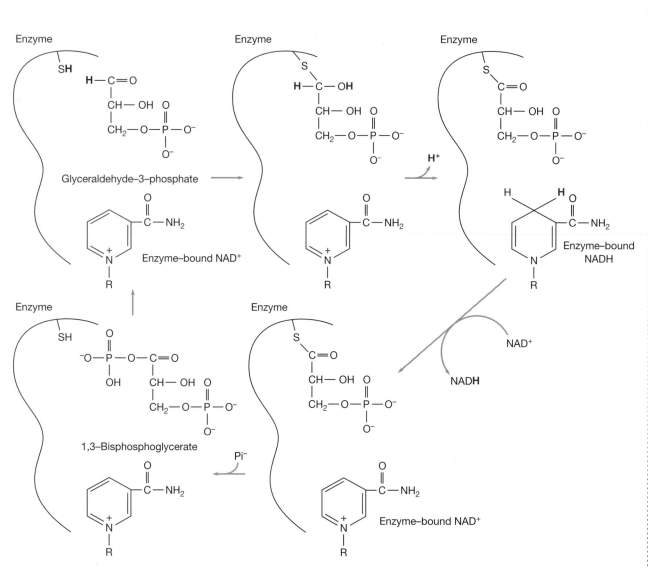

Figure 1.10 Box 2 Reduction of NAD+ in the oxidation of glyceraldehyde–3–phosphate by glyceraldehyde–3–phosphate dehydrogenase. During the reaction the enzyme reduces an enzyme-bound NAD+ and this coenzyme molecule becomes reoxidized when it reduces a soluble NAD+.

where Γ' indicates that the concentrations are now those actually observed at pH 7. The relationship between the Gibbs free energy change and the mass action ratios (Γ) at equilibrium (K'), and under real conditions ($\Delta G'$) is given by Eq. 1.11:

$$\Delta G' = -RT\ln K'/\Gamma' = -2.3RT\log_{10}K'/\Gamma' \tag{1.11}$$

Thus, with this equation it is possible to calculate the Gibbs free energy change for any reaction, provided that we know both the equilibrium constant and the actual concentrations of the reactants and products. Needless to say this information is almost impossible to obtain in a cell under physiological conditions. This has led biochemists to compare the free energy changes in reactions under arbitrary 'standard conditions', that is when the concentrations of all of the reactants and products are at 1 M. This makes Γ' equal to 1 so that the free energy change under standard conditions, which we call $\Delta G^{o'}$, equals $-RT\log_{10}K'$. Although a comparison of $\Delta G^{o'}$ values will show how two reactions may differ under the same conditions, this can be very misleading since the two processes may deviate from standard conditions in very different ways. Furthermore, both the sign and the magnitude of a particular $\Delta G^{o'}$ will give no indication of the behaviour of that reaction under real conditions. If we take the hydrolysis of ATP (Eq. 1.8) as an example, the value of $\Delta G^{o'}$ is -28.5 kJ/mol under standard conditions whereas in the cytoplasm at 37 °C, when the phosphate concentration is 10^{-2} M and the ATP/ADP ratio is 10, $\Delta G'$ would be equal to -47.3 kJ/mol. The ratio of ATP/ADP is not likely to fall below 1, and even then the $\Delta G'$ would be -41.4 kJ/mol which is far above the $\Delta G^{o'}$ value.

Substrate-level phosphorylation

The first of the substrate-level phosphorylations, shown in Figure 1.10, involves the conversion of glyceraldehyde-3-phosphate into 1,3-bisphosphoglycerate. If the $\Delta G^{o'}$ values for the two phosphates on 1,3-bisphosphoglycerate are compared with that for the terminal phosphate of ATP, they give an indication of the usefulness of ATP as a means of transferring energy from one reaction to another in the cell. The standard free energy of hydrolysis of the acyl-phosphate on carbon 1 is -49.3 kJ/mol which is much larger than the $\Delta G^{o'}$ value for the terminal phosphate of ATP, whereas the $\Delta G^{o'}$ value for hydrolysis of the phosphate ester of glycerol-3-phosphate is only -9.2 kJ/mol. Although the $\Delta G^{o'}$ values do not represent the true situation in the cytoplasm, the relationship among the standard free energies of hydrolysis of these three compounds explains why it is possible, at least under some conditions, for ADP to accept a phosphate from an acyl-phosphate and to use the energy conserved in this way as ATP to form phosphate esters with a lower free energy of hydrolysis.

Glyceraldehyde-3-phosphate dehydrogenase

In order to generate the acyl-phosphate of 1,3-bisphosphoglycerate from glyceraldehyde-3-phosphate it is necessary to couple the energetically unfavourable phosphate addition to a reaction which releases energy, namely the oxidation of the aldehyde group and the reduction of the coenzyme NAD^+ by glyceraldehyde-3-phosphate dehydrogenase. Box 2 in Figure 1.10 shows that this reaction involves the formation of a covalent bond between the enzyme and substrate by attachment of the glyceraldehyde-3-phosphate to a cysteine side chain on the enzyme. The thioester bond is then split by phosphate rather than water, to yield the acyl-phosphate.

When glycolysis is operating in the glucose to pyruvate direction, the relatively high free energy of hydrolysis of 1,3-bisphosphoglycerate makes it possible for the cell to maintain a high ATP/ADP ratio which, as shown above, increases the energy required to form the ATP. It is also important to appreciate the fact that despite the large difference between the standard free energies of hydrolysis of ATP and the acyl-phosphate of 1,3-bisphosphoglycerate, glycolysis can operate in the reverse direction using ATP to generate the acyl-phosphate! This is possible because the actual free energy changes of all the reactions shown in Figures 1.9 and 1.10 are strongly dependent on the relative concentrations of all the reactants and products involved.

The pyruvate kinase reaction

The importance of relative concentrations is shown in the second of the two substrate-level phosphorylations which is made possible by the dehydration of 2-phosphoglycerate to yield phosphoenolpyruvate. The standard free energy change on hydrolysis of 2-phosphoglycerate is similar to that of glycerol-3-phosphate whereas that of phosphoenolpyruvate is $-61.9\,kJ/mol$, and this is a measure of the fact that the pyruvate kinase reaction in which phosphoenolpyruvate donates its phosphate to ADP is very strongly displaced from equilibrium. As a consequence this is one of the few steps in the glycolytic pathway which is effectively irreversible under normal conditions. Figure 1.3 indicates that pyruvate can only be converted back to phosphoenolpyruvate by way of oxaloacetate, a route that requires the expenditure of GTP as well as ATP (see Figure 2.4).

1.8 Oxidative phosphorylation

The process responsible for the formation of ATP from ADP and phosphate in the mitochondria is known as oxidative phosphorylation to distinguish it from the substrate-level phosphorylation in the glycolytic pathway that can take place in the absence of oxygen. The energy required for ATP synthesis in the mitochondria is released by the removal of pairs of hydrogens from a range of substrates including pyruvate, glutamate and intermediates in the TCA cycle and in the β-oxidation pathway for fatty acids. These substrate oxidations are coupled to the reduction of the coenzymes NAD^+ or FAD in the mitochondrial matrix. The reduced forms of these coenzymes are reoxidized by molecular oxygen using a series of electron carriers on the inner membrane known as the respiratory chain, shown schematically in Figure 1.11.

The respiratory chain and the ATP synthetase complex

The mitochondrial inner membrane is also the site of the ATP synthetase enzyme complex. The location of both the respiratory chain and ATP synthetase on the inner membrane was shown by Peter Mitchell to be an essential feature of energy coupling in oxidative phosphorylation. If the structure of the membrane is disrupted, or if the permeability to protons is increased, the oxidative reactions in the respiratory chain may still occur but they can no longer yield ATP so that substrate oxidation is said to be uncoupled from the phosphorylation of ADP.

Since both the respiratory chain and the ATP synthetase are proton translocating systems, the link between them is provided by the proton gradient and membrane potential generated across the inner membrane by the activity of the respiratory chain. Protons are translocated out of the matrix during the oxidation of the reduced coenzymes and their movement back into the matrix through the ATP synthetase complex generates ATP. The fact that proton transport provides the link between respiration and ATP synthesis has a number of additional useful features. First of all it is important to recognize that the vectorial movement of protons across the mitochondrial inner membrane will result in both a pH gradient and a potential difference across the membrane provided there is no compensatory movement of anions. As Mitchell pointed out in the chemiosmotic theory he developed, and for which he was awarded a Nobel Prize, the effective force driving the protons back into the matrix depends on both the difference in proton concentration and the size of the potential difference (negative inside). He emphasized that it made no difference which contributed the major fraction of the total force which he named the *proton motive force*. Actual measurements on mitochondria indicate that the membrane potential contributes most of the proton motive force, leaving a relatively small pH difference across the mitochondrial inner membrane.

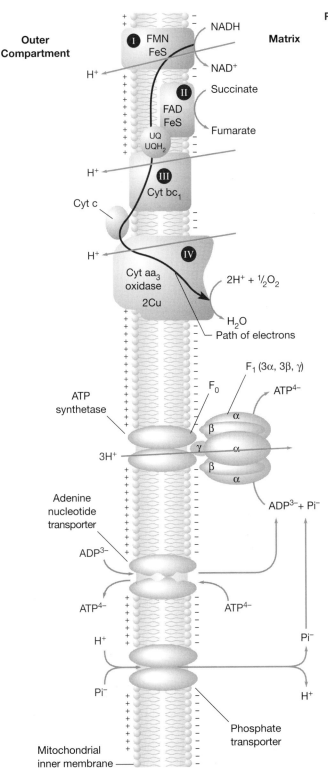

Respiratory chain (complexes **I**, **II**, **III**, **IV**)

FMN	Flavin mononucleotide
FeS	Iron sulphur protein
FAD	Flavin adenine dinucleotide
UQ	Ubiquinone
UQH_2	Reduced ubiquinone
Cyt	Cytochromes (c, b, c_1, a, a_3)

When the respiratory chain oxidizes NADH or succinate the electrons flow along the path shown until they reduce oxygen to form water. Movement of electrons down the respiratory chain causes the transfer of protons from the matrix to the outer compartment.

As a consequence of proton transport out of the matrix, the pH is lower outside the mitochondrial inner membrane. However, since the protons move back into the matrix with phosphate, most of the pH gradient is converted into a membrane potential across the inner membrane (negative inside).

Entry of ADP and phosphate
ADP^{3-} enters in exchange for ATP^{4-} and because of the difference in charge an extra H^+ must be transported out of the matrix for each ADP that enters.

Phosphate enters the matrix in an uncharged state with protons, but because the phosphate is ionized within the matrix, its entry increases the membrane potential so that no extra H^+ transport is needed.

ATP synthesis
The membrane potential drives protons back into the matrix through the F_0 and F_1 parts of the ATP synthetase and generates ATP from ADP plus phosphate.

Figure 1.11 Diagrammatic representation of oxidative phosphorylation, the transport of phosphate ions and adenine nucleotides across the mitochondrial inner membrane, and the synthesis of ATP. The pathway of electron transport along the respiratory chain is shown in dark blue.

Transport across the mitochondrial inner membrane

In addition to linking the respiratory chain to the ATP synthetase the proton motive force is also responsible for the transport of ions and other charged solutes into the mitochondrial matrix and this can lead to solute concentrations in the matrix far above those in the cytoplasm. These transport processes are particularly important for the uptake of phosphate and ADP, since the synthesis of ATP occurs on the matrix side of the inner membrane whereas most ATP hydrolysis takes place in the cytoplasm. Since phosphate is negatively charged and the membrane potential is negative inside, it is clear that phosphate cannot enter by diffusion, and in fact it enters effectively in an uncharged form since it is transported across the membrane with a proton. This means that phosphate uptake is effectively driven by the proton gradient generated by the respiratory chain. The proton motive force drives the uptake of ADP in a different way. The adenine nucleotide transporter is responsible for the exchange of an ADP^{3-} from the cytoplasmic side of the membrane for an ATP^{4-} from the matrix side. Since there is a difference of one negative charge between the two forms of adenine nucleotide, the exchange results in the export of a negative charge and is driven by the membrane potential, which is negative inside. The net result of taking a phosphate ion and an ADP into the matrix and exporting an ATP to the cytoplasm is to use up one of the protons pumped out of the matrix by the respiratory chain for each ATP delivered. Although the proton enters with the phosphate, this has no effect on the proton motive force since the phosphate immediately ionizes in the matrix, thus replacing a portion of the pH gradient with an equivalent addition to the membrane potential. However, the export of one negative charge for each ATP exchanged for a cytoplasmic ADP can only be recouped by export of an additional proton.

Stoichiometry of ATP synthesis in mitochondria

Although the chemiosmotic theory has become generally accepted, there has been considerable doubt about the exact number of ATPs which are formed from ADP and phosphate for each pair of hydrogens oxidized by the respiratory chain to form water. Empirical measurements on isolated mitochondria in the past have indicated that approximately three ATPs are formed as a result of the oxidation of $NADH + H^+$, and that two ATPs are formed when FAD-linked oxidations occur (such as the oxidation of succinate in the TCA cycle). However, these stoichiometries have been brought into question as a result of direct measurements of the proton-translocating capacities of the ATP synthetase and the various parts of the respiratory chain. It seems fairly clear that three protons must pass through the synthetase to form each ATP and with the additional proton required for the uptake of the phosphate and ADP, a total of four protons will be needed for each ATP exported to the cytoplasm. On the other hand, the maximum estimate for the number of protons pumped out of the matrix during the transfer of a pair of electrons from NADH to oxygen is thought to be 10 and that for the FAD-linked oxidation of succinate is only six. These $H^+/2e^-$ ratios indicate that a maximum of 2.5 ATPs will be formed for each NADH oxidized and 1.5 ATPs for each succinate oxidized, which is significantly less than the normally accepted figures of three and two, respectively. Furthermore, the number of ATPs produced will be further reduced by any conditions that increase the permeability of the mitochondrial inner membrane to protons, or result in the electrogenic uptake of charged solutes or ions such as Ca^{2+}.

1.9 Biosynthesis and degradation of cell constituents

During their growth phase all cells synthesize their nucleic acids, proteins, lipids and complex carbohydrates, and most mature cells, unless they have a limited life span such as the red blood cells, continually renew these essential constituents. In those cells that must be maintained throughout the life of the individual, such as nerve cells, the recycling of cell constituents must be balanced by the degradation of existing material. In order to support these biosynthetic processes the cell needs to synthesize or acquire an adequate supply of starting materials. It is also important to recognize that even when cell constituents are recycled some of the essential precursors are lost. The principal requirements for forming macromolecules are listed in Table 1.1.

Nucleic acid synthesis and degradation

For the synthesis of either DNA or RNA, it is necessary to have a DNA template to determine the sequence of bases in the nucleic acid plus a supply of the 5'-triphosphate forms of the four nucleotides required in each case. The nucleotides are built up from simple starting materials such as amino acids and 5-phosphoribosyl-1-pyrophosphate, although there is some salvage of the purines released during nucleic acid breakdown. Biosynthesis of the nucleotides yields the nucleoside monophosphates which must be converted into triphosphates by phosphotransferase reactions at the expense of ATP. The DNA double helix provides the template for its own replication by a complex process described in Chapter 4. DNA also provides the template for RNA synthesis, although in this case only one of the two strands of the DNA serves as a template.

Degradation of the nucleic acids yields 3'-nucleotides which are normally degraded rather than reused. Since the purines and pyrimidines contain nitrogen, their catabolism results in the formation of ammonia which must be detoxified by conversion to urea in the liver. In humans the purines are only partially degraded to uric acid, which is excreted.

Protein synthesis and breakdown

Proteins provide the basis of biological specificity and as enzymes they operate the metabolic pathways. In order to ensure that cellular processes are accurately maintained, proteins are continually resynthesized from their constituent amino acids. The information needed to specify the amino acid sequence in protein synthesis is supplied from DNA by means of an RNA template. In addition all 20 amino acids must be available, together with a source of energy in the form of ATP and GTP. In humans provision of the amino acids is normally from the diet, although in principle the 11 non-essential amino acids can be formed from the essential amino acids or from metabolites in the central metabolic pathways provided that sufficient nitrogen is available.

Protein breakdown is accompanied by reuse of most of the amino acids released on hydrolysis, although some amino acids are normally degraded, yielding ammonia which must be converted to urea. Any nitrogen lost in this way must be replaced by dietary intake so that a balance of nitrogen compounds is maintained. Equally, it must be recognized that excess amino acid intake must be balanced by increased catabolism and excretion of the nitrogen released during degradation.

Table 1.1 List of basic requirements for the synthesis of macromolecules and other complex cell constituents

	Starting materials	Other requirements
1. Nucleic acids		
(a) Nucleotide synthesis	Amino acids (aspartate, glycine and glutamine) 5-Phosphoribosyl-1-pyrophosphate	ATP
(b) DNA	Deoxyribonucleoside triphosphates (dATP, dCTP, dGTP and dTTP)	DNA template
(c) RNA	Ribonucleoside triphosphates (ATP, CTP, GTP and UTP)	DNA template
2. Proteins	All 20 amino acids	RNA template ATP and GTP
3. Membrane lipids		
(a) Phospholipids	Fatty acids, glycerol-3-phosphate or dihydroxyacetone-phosphate, sphingosine, choline, serine, ethanolamine and inositol	CTP
(b) Glycolipids	Fatty acids, sphingosine, glucose and sialic acid	UTP
(c) Cholesterol	Acetyl-coenzyme A	ATP
4. Polysaccharides		
(a) Glycosaminoglycans	N-acetyl glucosamine and glucose, uronic acids, sulphate	ATP and UTP
(b) Oligosaccharides (linked to proteins and lipids)	Glucose, galactose, mannose, fucose, N-acetylamino glucose and galactose, sialic acid	ATP and UTP
5. Storage molecules		
(a) Glycogen	Glucose	ATP and UTP
(b) Triacylglycerols	Fatty acids, glycerol-3-phosphate	ATP and NADPH
6. Coenzymes	B vitamins, amino acids, ribose phosphate	ATP

Lipid biosynthesis and catabolism

Three major types of lipids occur in all cells: cholesterol, phospholipids and tri-acylglycerols. Cholesterol, which is formed from acetyl-CoA, is an important constituent of membranes and it also serves as a starting material for the forma-tion of bile salts and steroid hormones. The requirements for the biosynthesis of the membrane phospholipids and storage triacylglycerols are relatively simple since both glycerol and fatty acids can be formed from glucose. Phospholipids also need a supply of phosphate and amino acids to supply the nitrogen for the basic part of the molecule. However, there are three essential fatty acids, containing conjugated double bonds, which must be obtained from the diet since they are not synthesized in humans. The unsaturated fatty acids are particularly important constituents of phospholipids because they help to maintain the fluidity of membranes.

The degradation of triacylglycerols yields fatty acids and glycerol which help to supply energy to most of the cells in the body. The same is true of the products of phospholipid catabolism, although the nitrogen component will be degraded yielding ammonia which must be detoxified. Cholesterol and the bile salts derived from it are not degraded but are excreted by the liver in the bile which passes into the top end of the small intestine. Some of this cholesterol and most of the bile salts are reabsorbed by the small intestine and returned to the liver by a process known as the enterohepatic circulation, but a proportion is lost in the faeces.

Synthesis and catabolism of complex carbohydrates

Some cells contain storage polysaccharides, but all cells require short chains of carbohydrates for the outward-facing membrane glycoproteins and glycolipids. Carbohydrate, in the form of inositol, is also required for the inositol phospholipids. Most carbohydrates can be formed from glucose or, if that is not available, the glucose itself can be formed from amino acids. In some cases amino sugars are formed and the nitrogen must be acquired from amino acids. The carbohydrate ascorbic acid (vitamin C) is required from the human diet. Although it has a number of specialized functions, vitamin C is particularly essential as a reducing agent in key areas of metabolism.

In addition to glycogen there are are other carbohydrate polymers, such as the glycosaminoglycans (see Figure 2.6a) which are important in connective tissue and as lubricants in the digestive tract.

Degradation of polysaccharides and other carbohydrates yields intermediates that feed into the central metabolic pathways and provide the cell with a source of energy and precursors for other cell constituents.

Coenzymes and other minor cell constituents

None of the biosynthetic processes listed above can be carried out without a supply of the coenzymes derived from the B vitamins. Also it is clear that a variety of inorganic anions and cations must be acquired from the diet.

The coenzymes are continually recycled and some of the essential components derived from the vitamins are lost in the urine. It is therefore essential to ensure that there is a continuing supply of the vitamins from which they are formed.

1.10 The central core of metabolic pathways

In order to present a general overview of metabolism, the pathways shown in Figures 1.1 and 1.2 contain a number of reactions and reaction sequences that are not found in most cells. If the picture is restricted to those processes that supply the cell with energy and provide for the synthesis of nucleic acids, proteins, lipids and carbohydrates, the general scheme can be simplified to that shown in Figure 1.12. These processes represent a central core of metabolic pathways which provide the minimum requirements for almost all cells, namely supplies of ATP and the precursors for cell constituents. Figure 1.12 also includes pathways for the synthesis of glycogen and ketone bodies which are absent from some cells but have been included here because of their great importance in human metabolism as a whole.

The supply of ATP comes either from substrate-level phosphorylation in the glycolytic pathway or from oxidative phosphorylation in the mitochondria. The major nutrients available to most cells are glucose, fatty acids and amino acids. Glucose is the most versatile nutrient since it is the substrate for the glycolytic pathway (which can yield ATP in the absence of oxygen) and the pentose phosphate pathway. Glucose also supplies acetyl-CoA for the TCA cycle. Fatty acids, on the other hand, are only able to supply ATP through oxidative phosphorylation. They provide reduced coenzymes for the respiratory chain from the β-oxidation pathway and acetyl-CoA for the TCA cycle. This is also true for two of the amino acids, leucine and lysine, which yield only acetyl-CoA. Although all the other amino acids are capable of producing intermediates of the TCA cycle which can be converted into phosphoenolpyruvate and which in turn can yield an ATP by substrate-level phosphorylation, the GTP required for the formation of the phosphoenolpyruvate from oxaloacetate means that in this case the substrate-level phosphorylation gives no net gain in ATP.

The central core of metabolic pathways are organized to provide acetyl-CoA from a wide range of sources. In addition to the obvious routes described above (from glucose, fatty acids and amino acids) acetyl-CoA can also come from glycerol, ribose-phosphate and the ketone bodies (acetoacetate and β-hydroxybutyrate).

In most cases there are alternate pathways for supplying the most crucial components of biosynthetic processes so that their availability is not restricted by changes in conditions. This is well illustrated by the supply of ribose-phosphate for nucleotide synthesis which can either come by oxidation of glucose-6-phosphate or, if there is no need for the NADPH formed, indirectly from fructose-6-phosphate by a series of aldolase and ketolase reactions (see Figure 2.7).

The organization of the central core of pathways emphasizes both its versatility and its limitations. All of the major nutrients, carbohydrates, lipids and proteins, can feed carbon into the TCA cycle to supply the cell with ATP. Furthermore, because they yield acetyl-CoA, all the nutrients can support the formation of the most efficient storage molecule, triacylglycerol. But even here we can begin to see limitations, since the glycerol-phosphate, which provides the backbone of the storage molecules, comes from the glycolytic pathway and cannot be made from acetyl-CoA. This means that even for the formation of triacylglycerols the cell needs a supply of glucose, or amino acids as an alternative. (Of course it should be pointed out that the breakdown of triacylglycerols will also yield some glycerol.) The other crucial limitation of the central pathways is the need to have a steady supply of dietary protein to keep up the levels of amino acids for protein synthesis and for the formation of nucleic acids.

The central core of metabolic pathways shown in Figure 1.12 contains some reaction sequences that are reversible and a number that are not. Examples of the reversible pathways are the interconversion of fructose-6-phosphate and ribose-5-phosphate, the amination and deamination of amino acids and the glycolytic pathway, although in the last case some alternate steps are required for reversal. The major examples of irreversible sequences are the TCA cycle, the β-oxidation of fatty acids in the mitochondria and the oxidative steps of the pentose phospate pathway. As we shall see in the next two chapters, the irreversible nature of these processes is usually a consequence of a linked series of reactions carried out by an enzyme complex and involving several coenzymes which are only present at very low concentrations.

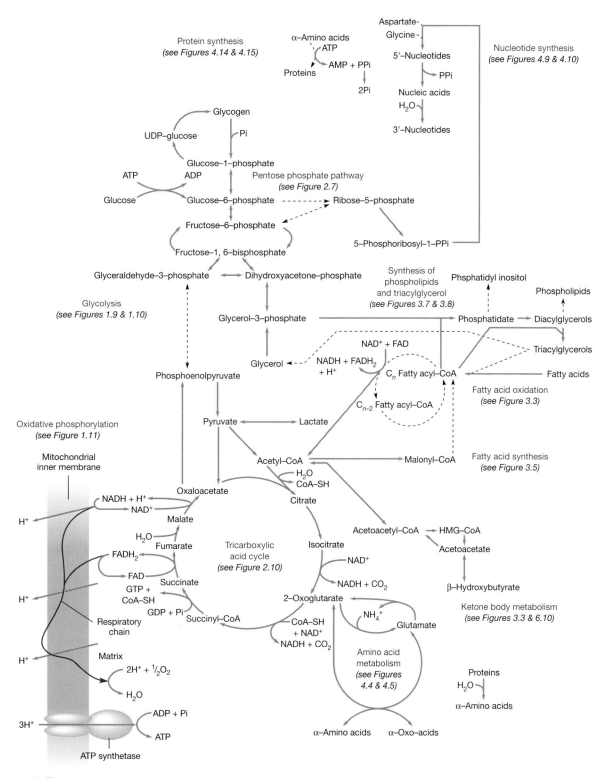

Figure 1.12 The central core of metabolic pathways. A summary of the relationships among these pathways is shown in Figure 5.1.

1.11 The basis of metabolic control

A detailed consideration of the integration and control of metabolism is given in the final part of this book. The purpose of this section is to consider in general terms some of the ways in which metabolism is controlled within the cell and to look briefly at the formation and breakdown of glycogen as an example of the way such controls can operate in response to external stimuli and changes in internal conditions. This basic information about control mechanisms should be helpful in considering the details of tissue metabolism in Part 2.

As we have seen in Figure 1.9, glycogen is formed from glucose by way of glucose-6-phosphate, glucose-1-phosphate and UDP-glucose. For each hexose unit one ATP and one UTP are converted to their respective diphosphates and two inorganic phosphates are released. The first and the last of the four enzymes responsible for this pathway, hexokinase and glycogen synthetase, are important in controlling it. In common with other biopolymers, glycogen is synthesized and degraded by different routes. Phosphorylase, the enzyme responsible for the conversion of glycogen back to glucose-1-phosphate, is also an important regulatory enzyme. The interconversion of glucose-1-phosphate and glucose-6-phosphate is freely reversible, but the production of free glucose from the latter requires the presence of glucose-6-phosphatase, an enzyme that is lacking from most types of cells except those in the liver.

Before considering the details of the control of the activity of the enzymes responsible for the formation and breakdown of glycogen, it is important to look at some more basic ways in which this process can be regulated. Most obvious, perhaps, is control by the availability of substrate. If there is no glucose, or if its entry into the cell is restricted, this will of course limit glycogen formation. The effects of competing pathways provide another form of control. Figure 1.3 shows clearly that, in addition to forming glycogen, glucose-6-phosphate can be converted to pyruvate or glycerol-phosphate or take part in the pentose phosphate pathway. If any of these pathways is proceeding at a high rate there will be little or no glucose-1-phosphate formed to serve as a substrate for glycogen synthesis. Finally, the ultimate control is exerted by whether or not the appropriate enzymes are synthesized. If glycogen synthetase is not present in a cell no glycogen can be formed.

The first enzyme in the pathway from glucose, hexokinase, is inhibited by the product of the reaction, so that as glucose-6-phosphate accumulates in a cell the phosphorylation of glucose will become progressively slower. The consequence of this simple form of control is that when glucose is present in the cell, hexokinase will rapidly form glucose-6-phosphate until the concentration rises sufficiently to inhibit the enzyme.

Figure 1.13 indicates that the regulation of glycogen synthetase and phosphorylase is much more complicated than that of hexokinase because the activity of both enzymes is influenced by phosphorylation of the enzymes and by the concentrations of substrates, products or other soluble factors. Furthermore, it must be admitted that the regulation of these two enzymes is considerably more complex than indicated in Figure 1.13.

To put the case most simply: both enzymes can be controlled in two ways, by conditions within the cell or by changes in hormone levels outside the cell. Taking the case of phosphorylase first, the internal stimulation of the activity of phosphorylase b, the inactive form, is in response to increases in the concentration of phosphate (one of its substrates) and 5'-AMP. In effect this is a response to an increase in the utilization of ATP which requires a higher rate of glycolysis to restore the ATP level. When ATP is hydrolysed ADP is produced, but the widely distributed adenylate kinase enzyme is responsible for the reaction shown in Eq. 1.12:

$$2\text{ADP} \longleftrightarrow \text{ATP} + \text{AMP} \qquad (1.12)$$

As a consequence an increase in ATP hydrolysis, or a decrease in the concentration of ATP, will lead to a rise in AMP levels. As the level of ATP recovers, the activity of phosphorylase b decreases since the 5'-AMP concentration declines. Glycogen synthetase is stimulated by a rise in the concentration of glucose-6-phosphate, which changes in the same way as glucose-1-phosphate.

The other way in which phosphorylase activity can be increased is by phosphorylation of the enzyme by ATP. As indicated in Figure 1.13, the enzyme has two forms: a relatively inactive dimer, phosphorylase b, which responds to phosphate and 5'-AMP, and the fully active tetramer, phosphorylase a, which only forms when each monomer has been phosphorylated. The covalent activation of phosphorylase b is brought about by a cascade of enzymes. The initial stimulus is provided by the binding of a hormone, e.g. adrenaline, to a receptor on the membrane. This stimulates the α subunit of the G protein to dissociate, replacing bound GDP with GTP and activating adenylate cyclase to form the intracellular effector cyclic 3',5'-AMP from ATP. The cyclic AMP activates protein kinase A (PKA), which in turn activates phosphorylase kinase, the enzyme responsible for phosphorylation of phosphorylase b. As a consequence of this sequence of events glycogen breakdown will cause a sharp rise in the concentrations of glucose-phosphates. Figure 1.13 indicates that phosphatase enzymes are also present to remove the activating phosphates from both phosphorylase kinase and phosphorylase a.

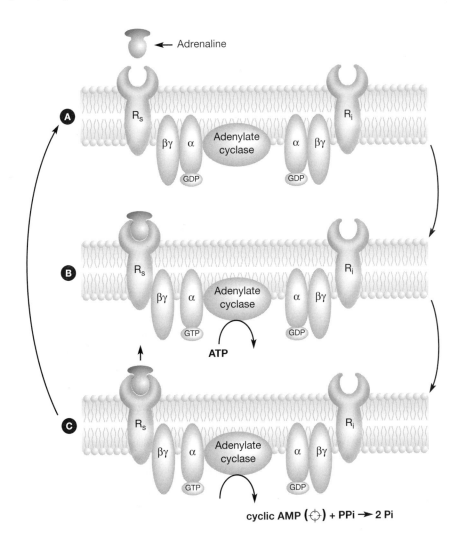

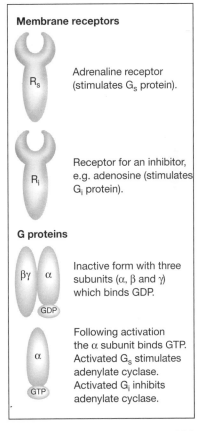

Membrane receptors

R_s — Adrenaline receptor (stimulates G_s protein).

R_i — Receptor for an inhibitor, e.g. adenosine (stimulates G_i protein).

G proteins

βγ α GDP — Inactive form with three subunits (α, β and γ) which binds GDP.

α GTP — Following activation the α subunit binds GTP. Activated G_s stimulates adenylate cyclase. Activated G_i inhibits adenylate cyclase.

cyclic AMP (⬡) + PPi → 2 Pi

Figure 1.13(a)
Mechanism responsible for the formation of cyclic AMP as a result of the binding of adrenaline to its membrane receptor.

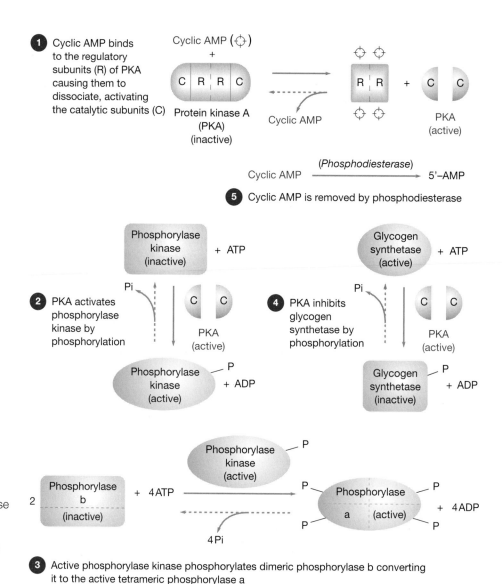

1 Cyclic AMP binds to the regulatory subunits (R) of PKA causing them to dissociate, activating the catalytic subunits (C)

Cyclic AMP ( )
+

C R R C
Protein kinase A (PKA) (inactive)

R R + C C
PKA (active)

Cyclic AMP

Cyclic AMP $\xrightarrow{\text{(Phosphodiesterase)}}$ 5'–AMP

5 Cyclic AMP is removed by phosphodiesterase

Phosphorylase kinase (inactive) + ATP

2 PKA activates phosphorylase kinase by phosphorylation

Pi

C C
PKA (active)

Phosphorylase kinase (active) — P + ADP

Glycogen synthetase (active) + ATP

4 PKA inhibits glycogen synthetase by phosphorylation

Pi

C C
PKA (active)

Glycogen synthetase (inactive) — P + ADP

Phosphorylase kinase (active) — P

2 Phosphorylase b (inactive) + 4 ATP $\longrightarrow$ Phosphorylase a (active) + 4 ADP

4 Pi

3 Active phosphorylase kinase phosphorylates dimeric phosphorylase b converting it to the active tetrameric phosphorylase a

Figure 1.13(b)
Mechanisms responsible for the activation of glycogen phosphorylase and the inhibition of glycogen synthetase by cyclic AMP. Dephosphorylation of each enzyme occurs by the action of phosphatases (dashed arrows).

Adrenaline is secreted in anticipation of a big increase in the demand for energy by the muscles. It is therefore important that the rise in the concentration of glucose-phosphates is not immediately reversed by resynthesis of the glycogen. This is accomplished in part, as indicated in Figure 1.13, by the phosphorylation of glycogen synthetase, which serves both to decrease the activity of the enzyme and to decrease its sensitivity to glucose-6-phosphate as an activator. As with phosphorylase a, the phosphate groups added to glycogen synthetase are removed by phosphatase enzymes. The control of glycogen synthetase by phosphorylation of the enzyme differs from that of phosphorylase a in that the enzyme is phosphorylated in several different places by a number of enzymes including both a protein kinase and phosphorylase kinase. The decrease in its activity is proportional to the number of sites that are phosphorylated.

The fact that phosphorylase is stimulated and glycogen synthetase is inhibited by the same cyclic AMP-dependent protein kinase A means that adrenaline can produce a massive increase in the availability of glucose phosphates for glycolysis without causing too much wasteful recycling. On the other hand, the residual phosphatase activity will ensure that if the glucose-6-phosphate is not needed much of it will eventually be converted back to glycogen since the residual phosphatase activity will reactivate glycogen synthetase and convert active phosphorylase back into phosphorylase b.

This chapter started with a story highlighting the problems of an angry and frustrated taxi driver caught in heavy traffic. The description given above should explain why the adrenaline secreted under these circumstances floods the glycolytic pathway with a large amount of substrate which is unnecessary for the taxi driver. Of course, the action of the phosphatases will allow some of the excess substrate to be converted back to glycogen, but meanwhile the extra glycolytic substrate will produce a burst of acetyl-coenzyme A to be converted into fatty acid, and this effect will be reinforced by the additional hexoses provided by the taxi driver's sweets.

E X E R C I S E S

1. What are the major functions of metabolism?

2. List five major energy-supplying pathways found in mammalian cells.

3. Distinguish between the sodium pump and the sodium/proton exchange in terms of mode of operation and energy supply.

4. Compare the entry of glucose into an ordinary mammalian cell with the processes responsible for the uptake of amino acids.

5. What are the principal metabolic processes that occur in the mitochondrial matrix?

6. How would you distinguish between oxidative phosphorylation and substrate-level phosphorylation?

7. What determines the number of ATPs formed from ADP and phosphate during the oxidation of one NADH?

8. In general terms how do the mechanisms responsible for the synthesis of macromolecules differ from those responsible for their catabolism?

9. Choose one of the B vitamins and show its importance in metabolism.

10. Describe, in general terms, how the hormone adrenaline can influence processes in the cytoplasm when it is present outside the cell.

Further reading

Cross, P.C. & Mercer, K.L. (1993) *Cell and Tissue Ultrastructure*, W.H. Freeman.

Dow, J., Lindsay, G. & Morrison, J. (1996) *Biochemistry, Molecules, Cells and the Body*, Addison-Wesley, Chapters 3 and 7.

de Duve, C. (1984) *A Guided Tour of the Living Cell*, Volumes 1 & 2, Scientific American Books.

Ernster, L. ed. (1992) *Molecular Mechanisms in Bioenergetics*, Elsevier.

Godsell, D.S. (1991) Inside a living cell, *Trends in Biochemical Sciences* **16**, 203–206.

Junge, W., Lill, H. & Engelbrecht, S. (1997) ATP synthase: an electrochemical transducer with rotary mechanics, *Trends in Biochemical Sciences* **22**, 420–423.

Malandro, M.S. & Kilberg, M.S. (1996) Molecular biology of mammalian amino acid transporters, *Annual Review of Biochemistry* **65**, 305–336.

Nicholls, D.G. & Ferguson, S.J. (1992) *Bioenergetics 2*, Academic Press.

Salway, J.G. (1994) *Metabolism at a Glance*, Blackwell Scientific.

Stryer, L. (1995) *Biochemistry*, 4th edition, W.H. Freeman, Chapter 17.

Tzagoloff, A. (1982) *Mitochondria*, Plenum.

Carbohydrate metabolism

Within the central core of metabolic pathways carbohydrate metabolism occupies an important position because it supplies the cell with ATP as well as key metabolites.

The metabolism of carbohydrates is also important because carbohydrates are the major component of the human diet.

2.1 Introduction

Carbohydrate metabolism has three main functions: to supply the cell with ATP and reduced coenzymes, to provide the cell with a range of precursors for the synthesis of cell constituents and to form polysaccharides. As shown in Figure 2.1 many of the pathways of carbohydrate metabolism are within the central core of metabolism because of their role in energy supply and because they form the link between glucose, which is the basic unit of the most common form of food, and many of the reaction sequences which are responsible for the formation of other classes of cell constituents. Although the polysaccharide glycogen is a bulky storage molecule that is extensively hydrated, it has the unique advantage of being highly branched so that there are numerous points from which glucose units can be released. In this way glycogen stores can be mobilized quickly in response to a sudden demand for additional supplies of ATP. Glycogen can also be resynthesized quickly once the requirement for extra energy has been satisfied.

2.2 The importance of carbohydrates

The value of carbohydrates is normally thought to be due to their role as energy sources for the cell but they also play a key role in biosynthesis as indicated in Figure 2.1. Carbohydrates are important for the formation of cell constituents for two main reasons. First, because these molecules are versatile in providing a wide range of starting materials for biosynthetic pathways. Secondly, the shapes of the five- and six-membered rings formed by the hexose sugars and their derivatives form the carbohydrate groups attached to membrane proteins which help to provide cells with their unique structural features, as indicated below.

CHAPTER 2

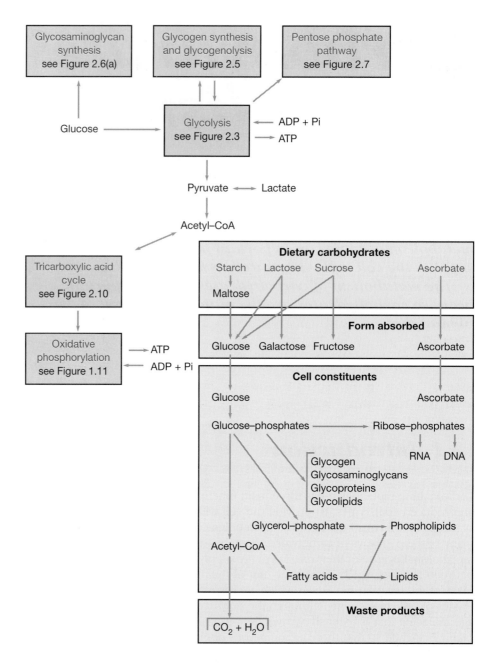

Figure 2.1
Overview of carbohydrate metabolism.

Since starch, which is a polymer of glucose, is the predominant carbohydrate available from plant sources for the human diet, it is not surprising to find that most metabolic intermediates used in the biosynthesis of cell constituents can be formed from compounds on the pathways responsible for glucose catabolism. These pathways are subjected to carefully regulated sets of control mechanisms which are designed to interrupt glucose catabolism whenever the demands on metabolism have been met. These controls permit glucose catabolism either to satisfy the demand for energy or to provide the precursors of cell constituents. It follows from these considerations that metabolism will become unbalanced, and less well controlled, in individuals consuming a diet in which the main source of calories is triacylglycerol or protein instead of carbohydrate.

Short chains of hexose rings can adopt stable and reproducible three-dimensional shapes. These carbohydrate structures play a crucial role as cell-surface markers and antigenic determinants. In this way the addition of specific groups of carbohydrate units to newly synthesized membrane proteins gives cells the unique features that identify them with a particular individual.

2.3 Details of glycolysis and gluconeogenesis: points of control

Glycolysis is the initial stage in the metabolism of the dietary carbohydrates and therefore it requires effective controls. Entry of glucose units into the glycolytic pathway is regulated in two ways. Since the glucose must be phosphorylated in order to take part in the reactions, the addition of phosphate serves as a control point. The hexose unit may be phosphorylated either by hexokinase at the expense of ATP or by phosphorolysis of glycogen (if that is present) through the action of the phosphorylase enzyme. It was pointed out in the final section of Chapter 1 that the activity of phosphorylase is controlled both by internal conditions and external stimuli. In the absence of an external stimulus, mobilization of the glycogen requires a fairly marked dephosphorylation of ATP. On the other hand the phosphorylation of glucose by hexokinase is driven by the high ATP/ADP ratio in the cytoplasm and is only inhibited by high levels of glucose-6-phosphate, a condition that will not occur except when there is little demand for ATP. Consequently, in most circumstances the major control over glucose entry into glycolysis will be the availability of glucose and this normally depends on the rate of sugar transport into the cell.

All glycolytic intermediates are phosphorylated, with only the initial substrate, glucose (or glycogen), and the final product, pyruvate (or lactate), lacking a phosphate group. The phosphorylated intermediates, which have a negative charge, are important for the integrity of the pathway because charged intermediates are hydrophilic and less likely to diffuse out of the cell or into membrane-bound compartments. The phosphorylated intermediates are also essential for the energy-conserving steps responsible for the substrate-level phosphorylation of ADP (see section 1.7).

As pointed out in the first chapter, the glycolytic pathway is unique because it combines the capacity to form ATP by substrate-level phosphorylation with the potential to be oxygen independent. Although the latter point is of little significance in most cells, glycolysis is an essential feature of the metabolism of red blood cells and is important for the metabolism of muscle cells, the epithelial lining of the small intestine and in part of the kidney tubule, despite the fact that a shortage of oxygen does not occur in all of these examples. The pathway can operate independently of oxygen because its product, pyruvate, can be reduced to lactate, thus regenerating NAD^+ from the NADH formed in the glyceraldehyde-3-phosphate reaction. Once formed the lactate is released from the cell into the blood, but it is important to recognize that lactate formation represents a dead-end since it must be reoxidized to pyruvate in order to be removed (a process that normally occurs in the liver). It is also important to note that in the conversion of glucose to pyruvate or lactate no carbon is lost.

Another feature of the glycolytic pathway is its reversibility. This requires the participation of alternate enzymes at four points in the pathway: conversion of pyruvate to phosphoenolpyruvate, conversion of fructose-1,6-bisphosphate to fructose-6-phosphate, synthesis of glycogen and the hydrolysis of glucose-6-phosphate. In effect this means that reversal of the glycolytic pathway, known as gluconeogenesis, not only requires the addition of the NADH and ATP molecules formed during the conversion of glyceraldehyde-3-phosphate into 3-phosphoglycerate but imposes an additional energy demand in the form of an ATP for the pyruvate carboxylase reaction forming oxaloacetate and a GTP to convert this into phosphoenolpyruvate. In addition, the actions of fructose-1,6-bisphosphatase and glucose-6-phosphatase mean that there is no regeneration of the two ATPs used in the conversion of glucose to fructose-1,6-bisphosphate.

Apart from the four cell types mentioned above, most cells do not convert the pyruvate formed by the glycolytic pathway into lactate. This means that some other way must be found to oxidize the NADH produced during the oxidation of glyceraldehyde-3-phosphate. The mitochondrial respiratory chain is ultimately responsible for the reoxidation, but as we shall see later in this chapter (section 2.8) the NADH cannot cross the mitochondrial inner membrane, so that the hydrogens must be transferred into the matrix by another route.

Glucose and glycogen are not the only substrates for glycolysis

Two other common hexoses, galactose and fructose, can also serve as substrates for glycolysis in some cells. Galactose is particularly important for infants since it represents half the sugar present in the milk disaccharide lactose. Lactase on the surface membrane of the small intestine converts lactose to glucose plus galactose prior to absorption. After phosphorylation by galactokinase to yield galactose-1-phosphate (see Figure 2.2), the galactose is converted to glucose-1-phosphate by the following two reactions:

$$\text{Galactose-1-phosphate} + \text{UDP-glucose} \rightarrow$$
$$\text{UDP-galactose} + \text{Glucose-1-phosphate} \quad (2.1)$$

$$\text{UDP-galactose} \rightarrow \text{UDP-glucose} \quad (2.2)$$

There are a number of genetic defects in humans which can disrupt the entry of galactose into the glycolytic pathway. The resulting galactosaemia prevents babies from developing normally and may cause permanent damage to the brain or eyes if galactose is not excluded from the diet. The most common form of galactosaemia is due to the failure of the reaction in Eq. 2.1 because the enzyme responsible for it, galactose-1-phosphate uridyl transferase, is absent, but in some cases it is the loss of galactokinase or the epimerase responsible for Eq. 2.2 that causes galactosaemia. In many regions of the world apart from northern Europe and North America people do not tolerate lactose well, but this is due to the disappearance of the disaccharidase, lactase, in the adult population rather than a defect in the pathway for galactose metabolism.

Humans have no problem in hydrolysing the disaccharide sucrose which is rapidly split into glucose plus fructose by sucrase on the surface of the epithelial lining of the small intestine. However, human metabolism is not well adapted to the high levels of sucrose which are a feature of the modern diet. Once it has been absorbed, fructose enters the metabolic pathways at the three-carbon level unlike glucose and galactose (see Figure 1.3). Although in most tissues the hexose sugars glucose, fructose and the less common mannose are phosphorylated on carbon 6 by the enzyme hexokinase, the liver lacks hexokinase and has separate enzymes for the phosphorylation of both glucose and fructose. Glucokinase converts glucose to glucose-6-phosphate, but fructokinase forms fructose-1- phosphate which is not a member of the glycolytic pathway and is cleaved by an aldolase to yield dihydroxyacetone-phosphate and glyceraldehyde (see Figure 2.2). Triose kinase completes the entry of the fructose carbon into the glycolytic pathway by converting the glyceraldehyde into glyceraldehyde-3-phosphate. The effect of bringing the fructose carbon into glycolysis at the three-carbon level is to bypass the control point at phosphofructokinase (see below). Thus the metabolism of glucose and galactose is controlled, whereas that of fructose is not, and will yield large amounts of acetyl-CoA for potential conversion to fatty acids. Of course it can be argued that fructose metabolism is controlled in most tissues since the hexokinase in tissues such as muscle and kidney feeds fructose into glycolysis as fructose-6-phosphate before the control point, but it must be recognized that fructose absorbed by the small intestine will pass first to the liver through the hepatic portal vein so that most of it will never reach the other tissues.

Mannose is a constituent of many glycoproteins, and after absorption or release following the recycling of glycoproteins mannose can be converted to manose-6-phosphate by hexokinase. Action of phosphomannose isomerase then permits the sugar to enter glycolysis at the level of fructose-6-phosphate, before the phosphofructokinase control point (see Figure 2.2).

Figure 2.2 shows one specialized hexose which does not enter the glycolytic pathway: ascorbate. This important molecule is the only vitamin related to the hexose sugars and humans are among the few mammals unable to form it from glucose. Ascorbate plays a crucial role as an antioxidant and it can also serve as a cofactor in hydroxylation reactions. These processes result in the oxidation of ascorbate to dehydroascorbate.

Phosphofructokinase: the central control point of glycolysis

It was pointed out above that the availability of glucose provides the first control point for the glycolytic pathway, and this control may operate by regulation of glucose entry into the cell or at the initial phosphorylation step. However, the main regulation of the pathway is at the conversion of fructose-6-phosphate to fructose-1,6-bisphosphate by phosphofructokinase. This phosphorylation reaction is an ideal control point since the conversion of fructose-1,6-bisphosphate back to fructose-6-phosphate is a separate reaction catalysed by fructose-1,6-bisphosphatase (see Figure 2.3). Two metabolites which act as inhibitors for phosphofructokinase, ATP (one of the substrates for the reaction) and citrate, reflect the dual role of glycolysis. The concentration of ATP, or more accurately the ratio of ATP/AMP, provides a measure of the energy supply and will only be high when the pool of adenine nucleotides is fully phosphorylated. Under these conditions the rate of the TCA cycle will slow down, and the concentration of the cycle intermediates such as citrate will rise unless some of the intermediates are being diverted to satisfy the demand for metabolic building blocks (such as glutamate, for example). Thus, phosphofructokinase will only be inhibited when the energy supply function and the requirements for building blocks have been satisfied.

Phosphofructokinase activity is stimulated by a specific activator, fructose-2,6-bisphosphate (see Figure 2.3), which increases the affinity of the enzyme for its principal substrate, fructose-6-phosphate. The activator also increases the concentration of ATP that is needed to inhibit phosphofructokinase. These effects occur principally in the liver and enable the glycolytic pathway to respond to changes in glucose concentration in the blood. Higher levels of glucose will lead to increased amounts of fructose-6-phosphate which in turn stimulates the synthesis of fructose-2,6-bisphosphate by a separate phosphofructokinase enzyme (known as PFK2). Hydrolysis of fructose-2,6-bisphosphate is catalysed by a phosphatase reaction, known as fructose bisphosphatase 2 (FBPase2) to differentiate it from fructose-1,6-bisphosphatase. The two enzyme reactions which regulate the formation and breakdown of fructose-2,6-bisphosphate are catalysed by the same multifunctional enzyme. Reduced blood glucose concentrations cause release of the hormone glucagon which acts in the liver to reduce the concentration of the activator fructose-2,6-bisphosphate. The activity of PFK2 is inhibited, and that of FBPase2 is stimulated, by phosphorylation of a serine side chain of the enzyme complex which decreases the concentration of fructose-2,6-bisphosphate.

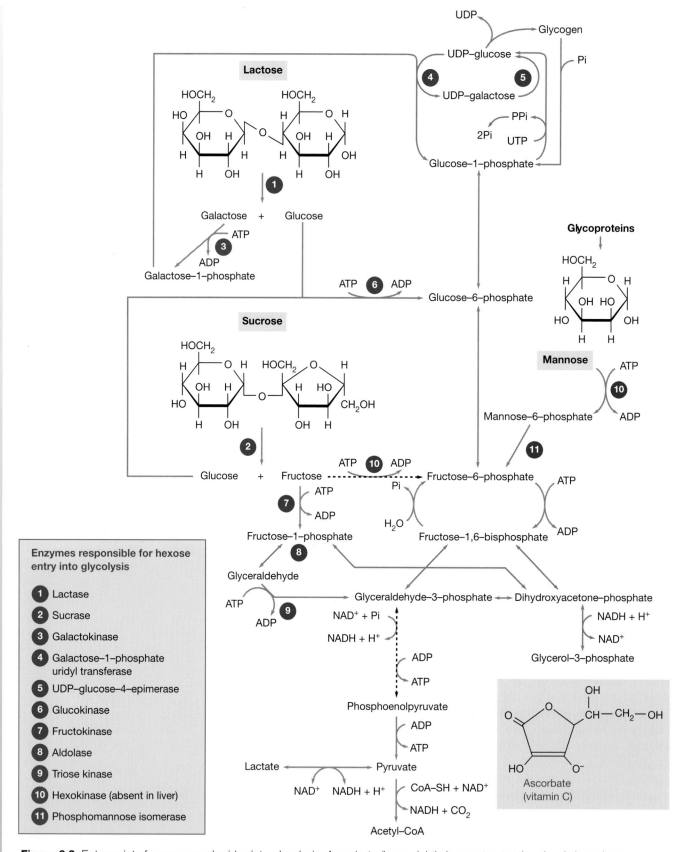

Figure 2.2 Entry points for monosaccharides into glycolysis. Ascorbate (lower right) does not enter the glycolytic pathway.

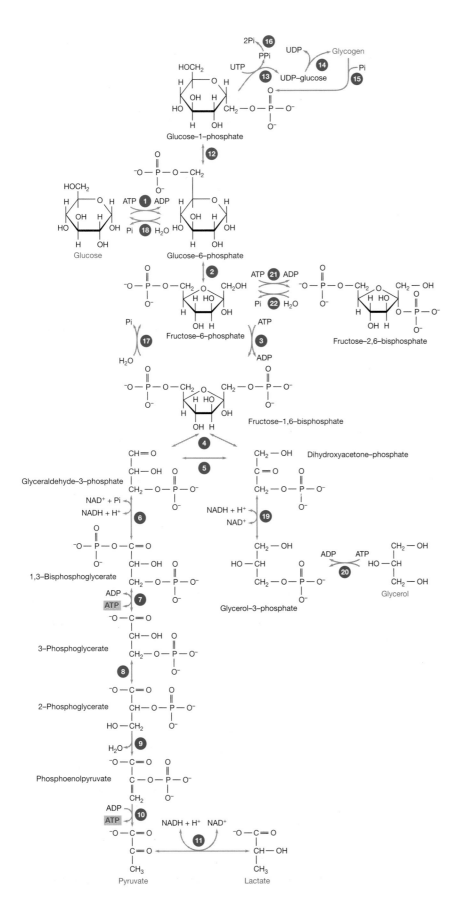

Enzymes

1. Hexokinase
2. Glucose–6–phosphate isomerase
3. Phosphofructokinase
4. Aldolase
5. Triose phosphate isomerase
6. Glyceraldehyde–3–phosphate dehydrogenase
7. Phosphoglycerate kinase
8. Phosphoglyceromutase
9. Enolase
10. Pyruvate kinase
11. Lactate dehydrogenase
12. Phosphoglucomutase
13. Glucose–1–phosphate uridyl transferase
14. Glycogen synthetase
15. Glycogen phosphorylase
16. Pyrophosphatase
17. Fructose–1,6–bisphosphatase
18. Glucose–6–phosphatase
19. Glycerol–3–phosphate dehydrogenase
20. Glycerol kinase
21. Phosphofructokinase–2
22. Fructose bisphosphatase–2

Figure 2.3
Details of the reactions in glycolysis.

Energy conservation steps of glycolysis and links to other pathways

Once fructose-1,6-bisphosphate is split to yield dihydroxyacetone-phosphate and glyceraldehyde-3-phosphate, the stage is set for the energy-conserving reactions of glycolysis which form ATP by substrate-level phosphorylation. This section of the pathway also provides important links with lipid metabolism through the formation of glycerol-3-phosphate, with amino acid metabolism through pyruvate and 3-phosphoglycerate, and with nucleic acid biosynthesis as a result of the links between glyceraldehyde-3-phosphate and ribose-5-phosphate (see Figure 2.7).

The details of the glyceraldehyde-3-phosphate dehydrogenase reaction (Figure 1.10) and the subsequent formation of ATP by substrate-level phosphorylation have been considered in Chapter 1 (section 1.7). Despite the important role of these reactions in energy conservation it should be emphasized that the section of the glycolytic pathway between fructose-1,6-bisphosphate and phosphoenolpyruvate (see Figure 2.3) is fully reversible. The direction that the pathway takes in a particular cell will depend on the relative concentrations of these two metabolites and on the NAD^+/NADH and ATP/ADP ratios.

As will be described in section 12.4 dealing with the metabolism of red blood cells, the three-carbon part of the glycolytic pathway has a shunt in which bisphosphoglyceromutase converts 1,3-bisphosphoglycerate (also called 3-phosphoglycerol phosphate) into 2,3-bisphosphoglycerate, which is subsequently dephosphorylated to 3-phosphoglycerate by the action of a phosphatase. The principal function of the 2,3-bisphosphoglycerate is to alter the oxygen-binding affinity of oxyhaemoglobin so that it will give up its oxygen at a higher partial pressure of oxygen. However, in other cells trace amounts of 2,3-bisphosphoglycerate act as a cofactor in the phosphoglyceromutase-dependent conversion of 3-phosphoglycerate into 2-phosphoglycerate.

Gluconeogenesis

Although many of the reactions of the glycolytic pathway are reversed in order to form glucose or glycogen from pyruvate or lactate, gluconeogenesis is not a simple reversal of glycolysis since it involves a number of alternative steps. Thus the synthesis of glucose from two molecules of lactate takes the equivalent of six ATPs per glucose formed (see Figure 2.4). Gluconeogenesis occurs chiefly in liver and kidney. In muscle, lactate is not converted back to glucose because these cells lack glucose-6-phosphatase, but some of the lactate formed in muscle is normally converted back into glycogen since this does not involve free glucose (Figure 2.4). It can be advantageous for rapidly contracting muscle cells to convert some of their glycogen into lactate in order to generate ATP more quickly than could occur by the oxygen-dependent pathways. The net energy cost to the muscle cell of recycling this lactate back to glycogen is four ATPs per glucose unit. Because gluconeogenesis is a particularly important feature of liver metabolism it will be considered in detail in Chapter 6. However, in the overall view of carbohydrate metabolism it is worth noting that the initial stage of gluconeogenesis requires the carboxylation of pyruvate to oxaloacetate within the mitochondria. As will be emphasized in section 2.6 the conversion of the oxaloacetate to phosphoenolpyruvate either requires the transfer of the oxaloacetate to the cytosol as malate (see Figures 2.8 and 2.11) or the export of the phosphoenolpyruvate. There is evidence that in humans both processes must occur since about half of the phosphoenolpyruvate carboxykinase (PEP-carboxykinase) is intramitochondrial.

As we shall see in the next section the glucose formed by gluconeogenesis or derived from dietary sources is used to form glycogen and a variety of complex carbohydrates. However, before going on to the polysaccharides it is worth pointing out that mammals synthesize one disaccharide, the milk sugar lactose.

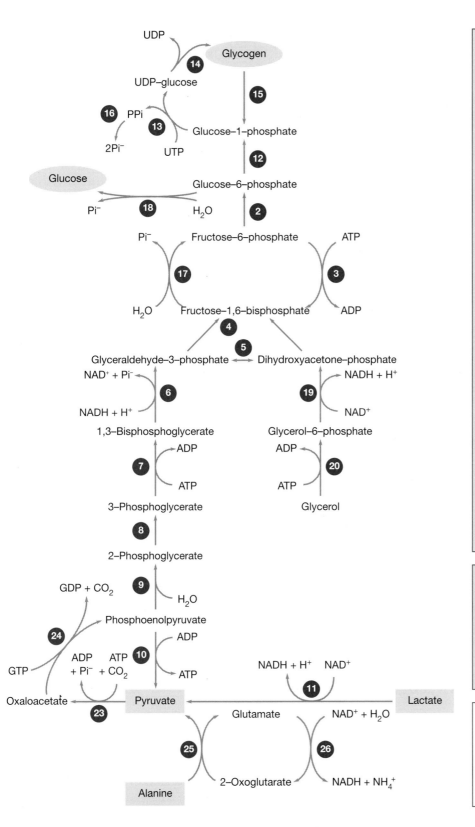

This is actually formed from two glucose units: one is converted to UDP-glucose (see Figure 2.4) which is then converted to UDP-galactose by the UDP-glucose 4-epimerase (see Figure 2.2). The final step is the addition of galactose to glucose:

$$UDP\text{-}galactose + glucose \rightarrow lactose + UDP \qquad (2.3)$$

Figure 2.4
Gluconeogenesis.

2.4 Polysaccharide synthesis: storage and utilization of glycogen

Chains of carbohydrates are known as polysaccharides, although when they are short chains of different carbohydrate units they are usually called oligosaccharides. Polysaccharides can be divided into three main types on the basis of their functions. Metabolically the most important are the storage polysaccharides: glycogen in animals and starch in plants. The second group are the glycosaminoglycans, which are polymers of more than one type of sugar, and are normally associated with at least a small amount of protein. These polysaccharides are important in connective tissue and in the digestive tract as lubricants. Third, there are the relatively small but structurally complex oligosaccharides which are attached to proteins and lipids located on the surface membranes of cells or linked to proteins that are secreted. These oligosaccharide molecules provide the unique antigenic specificity of the molecules or cells to which they are attached.

Glycogen synthesis

The formation of glycogen occurs in two stages. As we have seen in the various versions of the glycolytic pathway the activated intermediate for each new glucose unit is UDP-glucose. The enzyme glycogen synthetase transfers the glucose from UDP to carbon 4 on the end of an existing glycogen chain of at least four units to form a new α-1,4-glycosidic linkage. It is the second stage of glycogen synthesis that makes the molecule such an effective storage molecule. After glycogen synthetase has produced a chain of at least 11 glucose residues, a branching enzyme (1,6-α-glucosyltransferase) transfers a group of seven glucose residues to form a new branch at least four units away from the nearest one. These operations are shown diagrammatically in Figure 2.5(a). As a consequence of the branching activity the glycogen molecule acquires a large number of free ends, each of which can serve as a site for the addition of further glucose units by glycogen synthetase or, as we shall see in the next section, as substrates from which phosphorylase can release glucose units. Because glycogen synthetase can only add glucose to existing chains, glycogen synthesis can only begin if there is a suitable primer. This function is performed by a protein to which another enzyme has previously linked a number of oligosaccharide units to the hydroxyl groups on tyrosine residues.

Glycogen degradation

In common with all macromolecules glycogen is degraded by a different pathway and not by a reversal of its synthesis. For existing 1,4-glucosidic chains the phosphorylase enzyme releases glucose-1-phosphate by phosphorolysis (see Figure 2.5b). However, the widespread branching means that when the branches have been reduced to four glucose residues the 1,6-α-glucosyltransferase transfers three of the four units to another chain and then a debranching enzyme (α-1,6-glucosidase) removes the final glucose residue (see Figure 2.5b). As indicated at the end of Chapter 1, the activities of both phosphorylase and glycogen synthetase are regulated by a complex set of controls. This control is essential to prevent wasteful cycling between glucose-1-phosphate and glycogen, which effectively acts as a UTPase reaction. Nevertheless a certain amount of recycling does occur in both liver and muscle to ensure that adequate levels of glucose phosphates are always available to meet a sudden demand for energy.

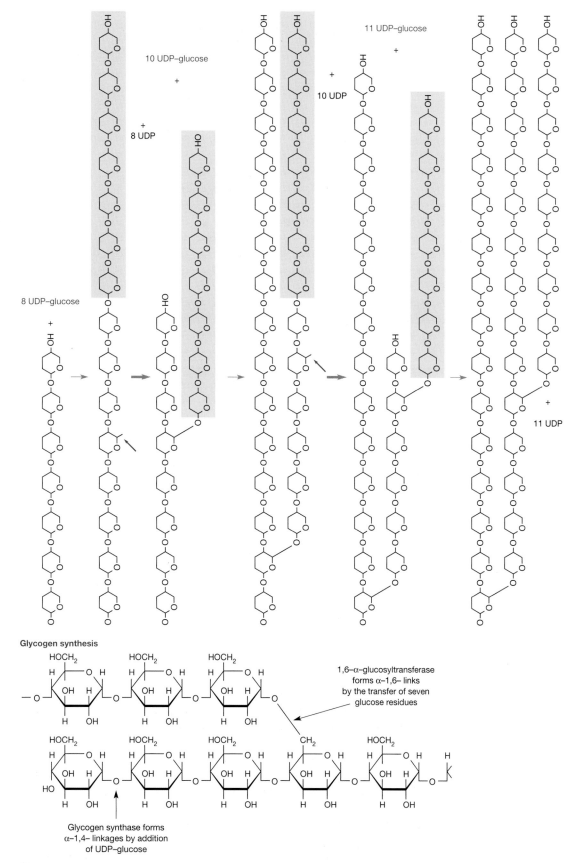

10 UDP–glucose

+

+

8 UDP

8 UDP–glucose

+

11 UDP–glucose

+

10 UDP

+

11 UDP

Glycogen synthesis

HOCH₂

HOCH₂

HOCH₂

1,6–α–glucosyltransferase forms α–1,6– links by the transfer of seven glucose residues

HOCH₂

HOCH₂

HOCH₂

CH₂

HOCH₂

Glycogen synthase forms α–1,4– linkages by addition of UDP–glucose

Figure 2.5(a) Glycogen synthesis. It is important to note that the chains of glucose residues do not remain straight or parallel.

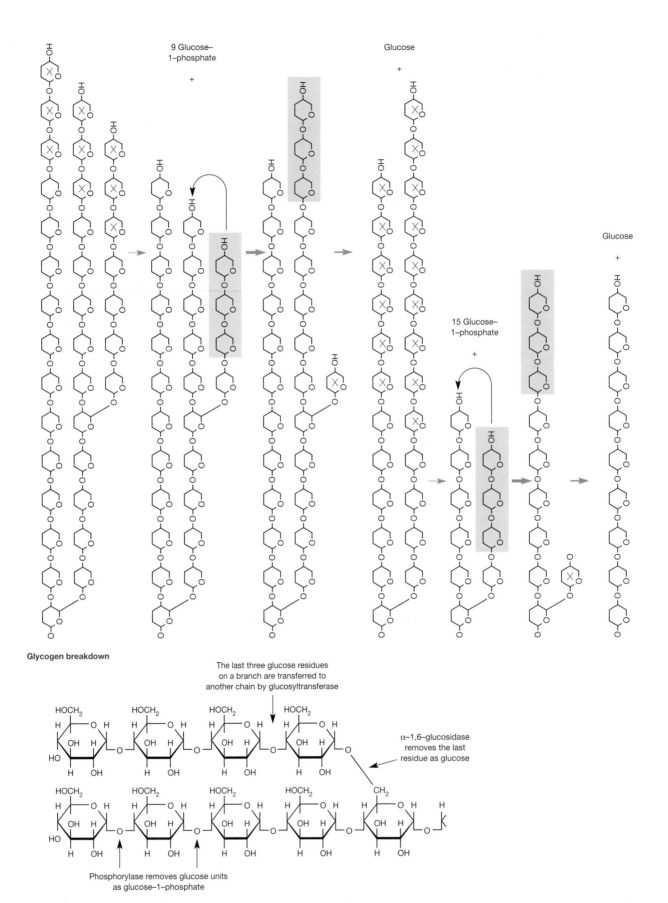

Glycogen breakdown

The last three glucose residues
on a branch are transferred to
another chain by glucosyltransferase

α–1,6–glucosidase
removes the last
residue as glucose

Phosphorylase removes glucose units
as glucose–1–phosphate

Figure 2.5(b) Glycogen degradation. Those glucose residues marked with a cross are removed by hydrolysis or phosphorolysis before the blocks of three glucose residues are transferred.

Synthesis of glycosaminoglycans

Although glycogen grows to be a very large molecule, its structure is much simpler than that of the other mammalian polysaccharides because glucose is the only basic unit. In the glycosaminoglycans the repeating unit is a disaccharide consisting of an N-acetylamino sugar (either glucose or galactose) linked to a uronic acid (a sugar with a carboxyl group), or in the case of hyaluronic acid to a galactose. Figure 2.6(a) shows in outline the way in which these precursors are formed. Although the repeating unit is a disaccharide, the sugars are added singly so that amino sugars alternate with the uronic acid or galactose. As indicated in Figure 2.6(a) the basic mechanism for the formation of the precursors starts with an intermediate from the glycolytic pathway (either fructose-6-phosphate or UDP-glucose). UDP-glucuronate is formed from UDP-glucose in two oxidative steps, the first converting the carbon 6 alcohol group to an aldehyde and the second oxidizing it to the acid. To form UDP-N-acetylglucosamine, glutamine first donates its amide nitrogen to fructose-6-phosphate and this is then acetylated by acetyl-CoA. After isomerization of the phosphate to the 1-position the UDP derivative is formed from UTP with the release and subsequent hydrolysis of pyrophosphate. UDP-N-acetylgalactosamine is formed by an additional isomerization step through the action of a 4-epimerase.

The formation of the polymers requires the action of specific glycosyltransferase enzymes which add the amino sugars and uronic acids alternately to form the particular polysaccharide attached to a protein core. The final step is the addition of a sulphate group to either the 4 or 6 position on the ring of the N-acetylgalactosamine or N-acetylglucosamine. The sulphate is added to the finished polysaccharide by a modified form of ATP in which the terminal phosphate has been replaced by a sulphate. The proportion of protein and the length of polysaccharide chain in the glycosaminoglycans varies with the different types. For example, hyaluronate in the vitreous humour of the eye has 5000 sugar units and little protein, whereas the polysaccharide chains of the ground substance of connective tissue, chondroitin sulphate, are less than 100 units although a large number of these are attached to each core protein.

The carbohydrate associated with glycoproteins

A great many different sorts of proteins have carbohydrates associated with them and there is no simple classification system by which they can be described. Furthermore the proportion of carbohydrate varies widely and does not normally have any regular repeating structure. Because of the lack of regularity the carbohydrate chains, which are normally quite short, are called oligosaccharides. Nevertheless the glycoprotein oligosaccharides do have a number of common features: they are usually branched structures made up of simple sugars (glucose, galactose, mannose and fucose) plus N-acetylgalactosamine, N-acetylglucosamine and N-acetylneuraminate (sialic acid). The oligosaccharide structures give the proteins to which they are attached (by a glycosidic linkage to a serine or threonine side chain) a highly individual structural feature. Therefore it should be no surprise that glycoproteins are found on cell surfaces where they provide stable external structural features that are important in cell–cell interactions and antibody recognition. Oligosaccharides are also frequently found on secreted proteins such as antibodies, blood clotting factors and lubricating molecules such as mucin.

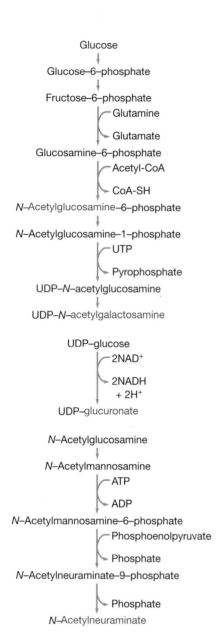

Glucose
↓
Glucose–6–phosphate
↓
Fructose–6–phosphate
⤷ Glutamine
⤷ Glutamate
Glucosamine–6–phosphate
⤷ Acetyl-CoA
⤷ CoA-SH
N–Acetylglucosamine–6–phosphate
↓
N–Acetylglucosamine–1–phosphate
⤷ UTP
⤷ Pyrophosphate
UDP–N–acetylglucosamine
↓
UDP–N–acetylgalactosamine

UDP–glucose
⤷ 2NAD⁺
⤷ 2NADH + 2H⁺
UDP–glucuronate

N–Acetylglucosamine
↓
N–Acetylmannosamine
⤷ ATP
⤷ ADP
N–Acetylmannosamine–6–phosphate
⤷ Phosphoenolpyruvate
⤷ Phosphate
N–Acetylneuraminate–9–phosphate
⤷ Phosphate
N–Acetylneuraminate

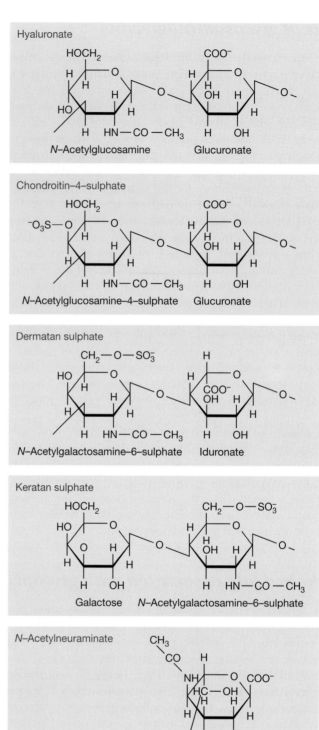

Figure 2.6(a) Pathways responsible for the synthesis of glycosaminoglycans and N-acetylneuraminate. The boxes show the strucures of the repeating units.

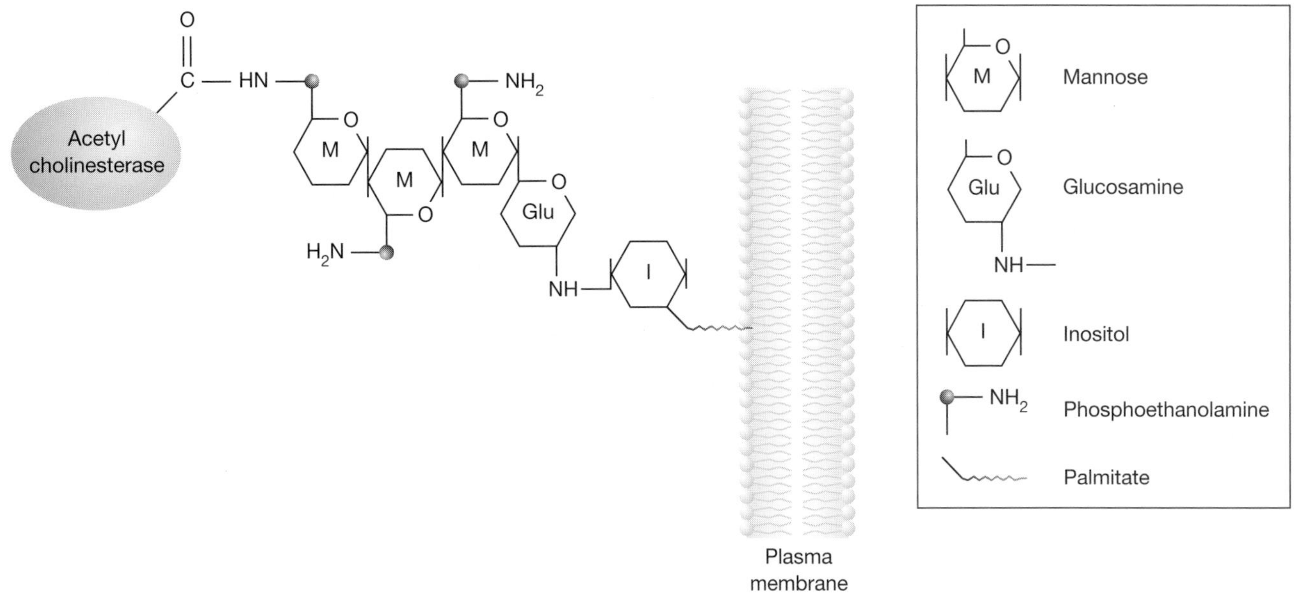

Figure 2.6(b) Structure of the glycolipid anchor for acetylcholinesterase on human erythrocytes.

Carbohydrate groups associated with glycolipids

Another type of carbohydrate-containing structure found in membranes are the glycolipids. As we shall see in the next chapter these may be membrane lipids such as sphingosine derivatives with a single carbohydrate unit such as galactose or glucose. Recently it has become clear that a number of enzymes and receptor proteins are anchored to membranes by a glycolipid anchor. An example of this type of glycolipid anchor is shown in Figure 2.6(b) where a short oligosaccharide chain links the acetylcholinesterase enzyme to the membrane. In this example the C-terminal amino acid (glycine) is linked to the oligosaccharide.

2.5 The pentose phosphate pathway

If considered in isolation, the pentose phosphate pathway can provide an alternative to glycolysis plus the TCA cycle for the complete oxidation of glucose. However, despite the fact that it is an oxidative process the pathway is restricted to the cytoplasm and consequently it can only operate if there is some mechanism for the reoxidation of the NADPH produced.

The oxidative steps of the pentose phosphate pathway

In fact, the main purpose of the pathway is not to oxidize glucose but to satisfy two other requirements for the cell: to provide the cytoplasm with a source of NADPH for biosynthetic reactions and to supply pentose phosphate for the synthesis of nucleotides. Figure 2.7 shows that the first three steps of the pathway fulfil both of these functions. Glucose-6-phosphate dehydrogenase is responsible for the first oxidative step and, after the addition of water by lactonase, the oxidative decarboxylation of 6-phosphogluconate produces the second NADPH and pentose phosphate.

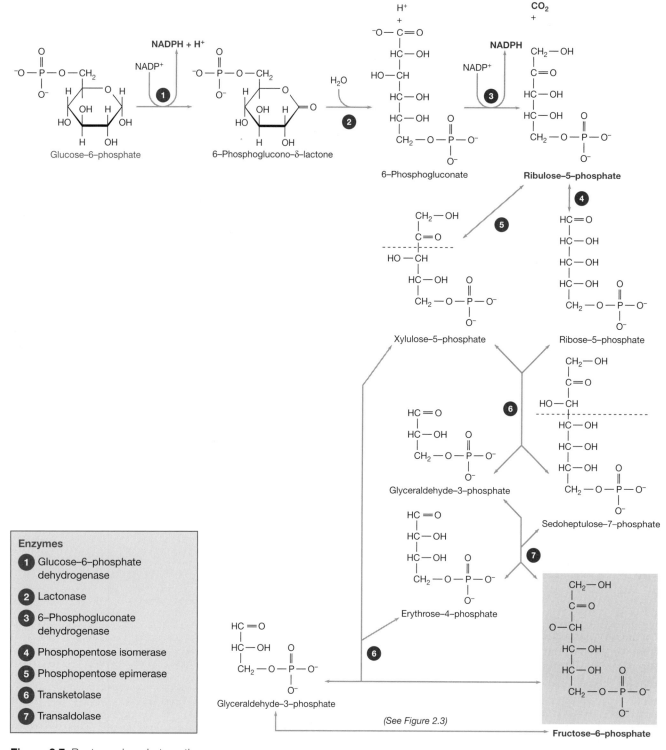

Figure 2.7 Pentose phosphate pathway.

Enzymes

1. Glucose–6–phosphate dehydrogenase
2. Lactonase
3. 6–Phosphogluconate dehydrogenase
4. Phosphopentose isomerase
5. Phosphopentose epimerase
6. Transketolase
7. Transaldolase

Interconversion of pentose phosphate and hexose phosphate

The remaining steps of the pathway are essentially rearrangements of the pentose phosphate product. The end result of these steps (which is shown diagrammatically in Box 1 of Figure 2.7) is that six pentose phosphates are con-

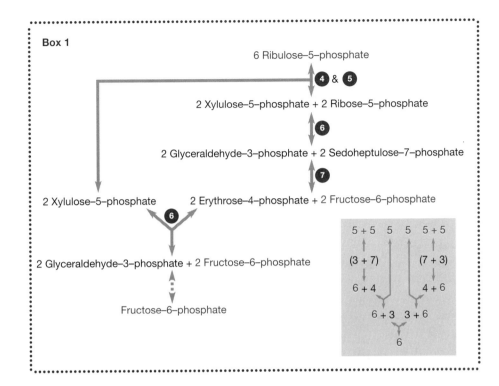

Box 1

6 Ribulose–5–phosphate

④ & ⑤

2 Xylulose–5–phosphate + 2 Ribose–5–phosphate

⑥

2 Glyceraldehyde–3–phosphate + 2 Sedoheptulose–7–phosphate

⑦

2 Erythrose–4–phosphate + 2 Fructose–6–phosphate

2 Xylulose–5–phosphate

⑥

2 Glyceraldehyde–3–phosphate + 2 Fructose–6–phosphate

Fructose–6–phosphate

```
5 + 5    5    5    5 + 5
(3 + 7)         (7 + 3)
6 + 4           4 + 6
        6 + 3  3 + 6
            6
```

Figure 2.7
Continued

verted into five fructose-6-phosphates. In order to produce the six pentoses the initial oxidative steps must be repeated six times, so that in effect one hexose is converted into six CO_2 molecules. A range of different enzymes are responsible for the rearrangement reactions. The initial pentose product is the ketose, ribulose-5-phosphate, and an isomerase is needed to convert it to ribose-5-phosphate, an aldose. The other pentose phosphate required for the rearrangements is the ketose xylulose-5-phosphate, which is formed from ribulose-5-phosphate by an epimerase. The remaining enzymes catalyse transfers of two- and three-carbon units leading to the formation of the five fructose-6-phosphates. Each removal of a two or three-carbon section (shown by the dashed lines in Figure 2.7) produces an aldose sugar-phosphate. Superficially the transketolase enzyme appears to catalyse a reaction that is rather similar to that carried out by the transaldolase or by aldolase itself, but the mechanisms involved are quite different. The transketolase has a tightly bound thiamine phosphate coenzyme, which forms a covalent link to the 2-oxo- (or keto) group during the transfer reaction. By contrast, in the aldolase reactions no coenzyme is involved, although a covalent link (Schiff's base) is formed between a lysine side chain on the enzyme and the 2-oxo group on one of the substrates.

What determines the rates of the oxidative and non-oxidative sections of the pentose phosphate pathway?

The rate at which the oxidative part of the pentose phosphate pathway operates is regulated by the requirement for NADPH, so that these steps will be most active in cells with high rates of fatty acid synthesis. Of course, it is still necessary for cells to have a supply of ribose-5-phosphate for the formation of nucleotides, but if there is no need for NADPH, the ribose phosphate can be supplied by a reversal of the rearrangement reactions shown in Box 1 of Figure 2.7.

The oxidative and non-oxidative parts of the pentose phosphate pathway are a good example of the economy and versatility of the central metabolic pathways.

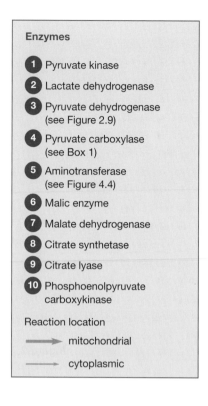

Enzymes

1. Pyruvate kinase
2. Lactate dehydrogenase
3. Pyruvate dehydrogenase (see Figure 2.9)
4. Pyruvate carboxylase (see Box 1)
5. Aminotransferase (see Figure 4.4)
6. Malic enzyme
7. Malate dehydrogenase
8. Citrate synthetase
9. Citrate lyase
10. Phosphoenolpyruvate carboxykinase

Reaction location

→ mitochondrial

→ cytoplasmic

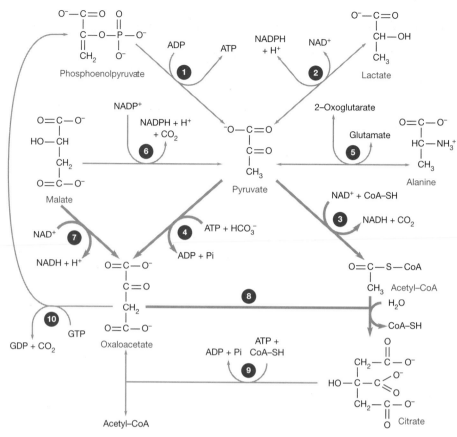

Figure 2.8

The central position of pyruvate in metabolism. Box 1 shows the role of biotin in the pyruvate carboxylase reaction. The carboxyl group of biotin forms a covalent bond with the ε-amino group of a lysine side chain in pyruvate carboxylase.

All cells need to have a supply of NADPH for biosynthetic reactions and a source of ribose-5-phosphate for the formation of nucleotides; combining the two processes avoids the need for separate pathways. However, there is no reason why the requirement for pentose phosphate should always be exactly half that for NADPH and any inequalities in the demands for these two products are taken care of by the reversible non-oxidative section of the pathway. Thus, in the absence of a need for NADPH the requirement for ribose-5-phosphate will be met from fructose-6-phosphate by the successive action of aldolase, transketolase, transaldolase and transketolase (Box 1 in Figure 2.7). On the other hand, a large demand for NADPH will result in an excess of pentose phosphate, but this is reconverted to fructose-6-phosphate (and then to glucose-6-phosphate) by the transaldolase, transketolase and aldolase reactions. To safeguard the supply of NADPH further, or in case there is a shortage of glucose-6-phosphate, the malic enzyme can also reduce $NADP^+$ to NADPH during the oxidative decarboxylation of malate to pyruvate (see Figure 2.8).

2.6 The pivotal role of pyruvate as a link between pathways

From its central position in the general overview schemes (Figures 1.1, 1.2, 1.3 and 1.12) it is clear that pyruvate occupies a key position in metabolism. This is emphasized in Figure 2.8 which indicates how pyruvate participates in a variety of reactions. Not only does pyruvate join the glycolytic pathway to the TCA cycle, but it is also linked to amino acid metabolism by the transamination reaction and to lipid metabolism by its decarboxylation to acetyl-CoA. Another important feature of the role played by pyruvate is the fact that it is produced in the cytoplasm but both its decarboxylation to acetyl-CoA and its carboxylation to oxaloacetate take place in the mitochondrial matrix. Thus, pyruvate provides the link between metabolism in the cytoplasm and the pathways that are restricted to the mitochondrial matrix. In Figure 2.8 the steps that occur in the mitochondria are shown with a heavy arrow and those in the cytoplasm with a thin arrow. This distinction between the events occurring in the mitochondria and the cytoplasm underlines the complications that arise, for example, when pyruvate is used for gluconeogenesis as described in section 2.3. Since the pyruvate carboxylase reaction occurs only in the mitochondria, it is necessary for the pyruvate to enter the matrix in order to be converted into oxaloacetate. Once formed, however, the oxaloacetate is trapped in the matrix since the mitochondrial inner membrane lacks a transporter capable of moving it out into the cytoplasm, and therefore in many species it must be converted into malate or transaminated to aspartate in order to leave the matrix (see Figure 2.11). Once in the cytoplasm it must be converted back into oxaloacetate in order to form phosphoenolpyruvate by the PEP-carboxykinase reaction. In humans there is some alleviation of this problem since PEP-carboxykinase is found in the mitochondria as well as the cytoplasm. Since gluconeogenesis occurs at a time of excess pyruvate, which will ensure a high level of mitochondrial acetyl-CoA, another potential route for the exit of the oxaloacetate from the mitochondrial matrix is through the formation of citrate which is transported out of the mitochondria when it is present in excess (see Figure 6.10). In the cytoplasm there is a separate citrate cleavage enzyme, citrate lyase, which can regenerate the oxaloacetate (see Eq. 3.3). However, this cleavage takes place at the expense of an ATP. In fact, as indicated in Chapter 3 it is probably more likely that excess acetyl groups will be transferred out of the mitochondria by carnitine, an acyl group carrier (see Figure 3.2).

The pyruvate dehydrogenase enzyme complex

In addition to the interaction of pyruvate with glycolysis, the TCA cycle intermediates and transamination, Figure 2.8 shows its conversion to acetyl-CoA. This conversion is catalysed by the pyruvate dehydrogenase enzyme complex which is responsible for a linked series of reactions involving five different cofactors. The details of this process are given in Figure 2.9. The key cofactor in the process is the vitamin B_1 coenzyme thiamine pyrophosphate (TPP) which is tightly bound to the pyruvate dehydrogenase enzyme. As shown in Figure 2.9 the five-membered thiazole ring is the active region of the cofactor. The carbon atom joining the nitrogen and sulphur atoms in the ring readily loses a proton to form a carbanion to which the pyruvate carbonyl group can add. This is rapidly followed by decarboxylation to leave the two-carbon hydroxyethyl group attached to the TPP. The next stage of the reaction is the transfer of the two-carbon unit, as acetate, to a second prosthetic group, lipoamide, which consists of lipoic acid covalently linked to a lysine side chain of the second enzyme in the

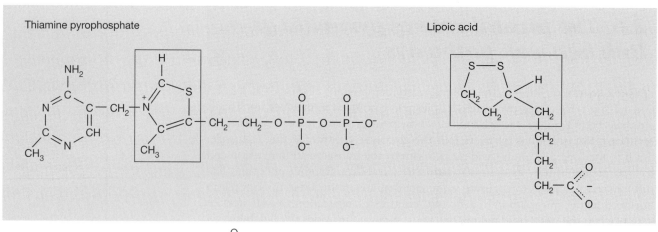

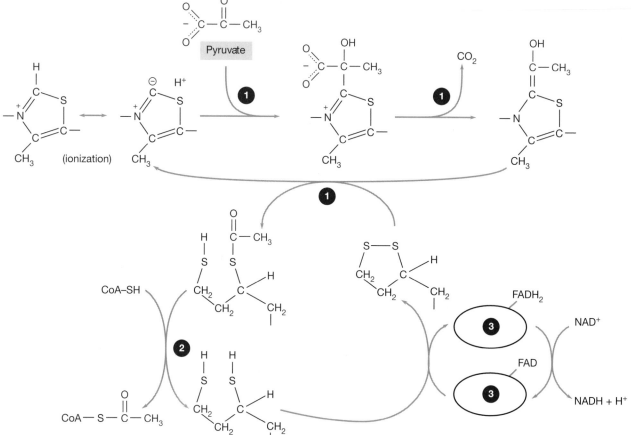

Net reaction catalysed by the pyruvate dehydrogenase complex

Pyruvate + NAD$^+$ + Coenzyme A $\longrightarrow$ Acetyl-CoA + CO$_2$ + NADH

Enzymes

1. Pyruvate dehydrogenase
2. Dihydrolipoyl transacetylase
3. Dihydrolipoyl dehydrogenase

Figure 2.9 Operation of the pyruvate dehydrogenase enzyme complex. The structures of the coenzymes thiamine pyrophosphate and lipoic acid are shown at the top and the portion of the coenzyme taking part in the reaction sequence is enclosed in a box.

complex, dihydrolipoyl transacetylase. Addition of the acetyl group breaks the disulphide bond of the lipoamide forming an acyl sulphur bond. The transacetylase then transfers the acetyl group to coenzyme A, leaving the cofactor in the dihydrolipoamide form. The third enzyme of the complex is dihydrolipoyl dehydrogenase which has a bound FAD prosthetic group and oxidizes the dihydrolipoamide back to the lipoamide form. The final stage of the reaction is the oxidation of the $FADH_2$ by external NAD^+, a reaction also catalysed by the third enzyme. The three enzymes are tightly bound together with the dihydrolipoyl transacetylase forming the core.

The pyruvate carboxylase reaction

As indicated in Figure 2.8 pyruvate is linked to the TCA cycle by the pyruvate carboxylase reaction as well as by pyruvate dehydrogenase. This process is crucial for the operation of the TCA cycle because oxidation of acetyl-CoA can only occur if oxaloacetate is available. The steps involved in the addition of the CO_2 are shown in Box 1 of Figure 2.8 which shows how the coenzyme biotin donates the carboxyl group to the methyl group of pyruvate. ATP and HCO_3^- are required to form the activated intermediate N-carboxybiotin. Biotin differs from many coenzymes because it is covalently linked to a lysine side chain on the pyruvate carboxylase enzyme by a peptide link to the ε-amino group of the lysine. It should also be noted that the enzyme is activated by acetyl-CoA, so that the rate of formation of oxaloacetate by this reaction is regulated by the availability of acetyl-CoA for citrate synthesis.

2.7 The tricarboxylic acid cycle

Functions and general characteristics of the cycle

The TCA cycle provides the final phase of the catabolism of all the major nutrients: glucose, fatty acids and the carbon skeletons of amino acids. The cycle has eight principal intermediates as shown in Figure 2.10, and it should be noted that the processes responsible for converting each intermediate into the next one are not of equal complexity. Although many of the steps can operate in either direction, the cycle only operates in a clockwise direction and with each revolution a two-carbon acetate unit is converted into two carbon dioxide molecules with the removal of four pairs of hydrogens. These hydrogens are transferred by NAD^+ or FAD to the mitochondrial respiratory chain which oxidizes them, yielding four molecules of water and pumping a total of 36 protons out of the mitochondrial matrix (10 for each NADH plus six for the $FADH_2$). In addition, succinyl-CoA yields a GTP by substrate-level phosphorylation (Box 1 in Figure 2.10). Thus, the primary function of the TCA cycle is to produce ATP by the oxidation of two-carbon units. This task is achieved efficiently since each turn of the cycle yields at least 10 nucleoside triphosphates (nine from the 36 protons pumped across the inner mitochondrial membrane plus one GTP). The acetyl-CoA units oxidized by the cycle can be produced from all three main food sources: carbohydrate, triacylglycerol and protein.

However, in addition to its role in the formation of ATP during the oxidation of two-carbon units, parts of the TCA cycle provide the crucial link between carbohydrate metabolism and the formation of both fatty acids and the carbon skeletons of the non-essential amino acids. In addition, citrate formed in the cycle helps to regulate glucose catabolism through its inhibition of the phosphofructokinase reaction. In this way unnecessary conversion of glucose into pyruvate is prevented when there are already adequate supplies of acetyl-CoA from other sources.

The location of the TCA cycle within the mitochondrial matrix is important for its operation. As illustrated in Figure 2.10 the intermediates in the cycle are all dicarboxylic or tricarboxylic acids and therefore negatively charged at neutral

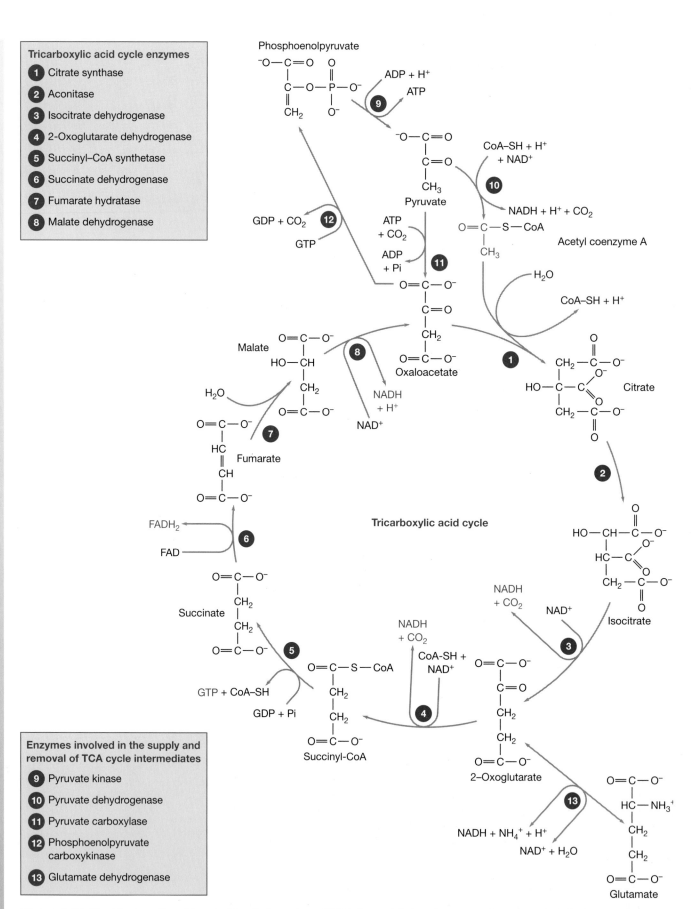

Tricarboxylic acid cycle enzymes

1. Citrate synthase
2. Aconitase
3. Isocitrate dehydrogenase
4. 2-Oxoglutarate dehydrogenase
5. Succinyl–CoA synthetase
6. Succinate dehydrogenase
7. Fumarate hydratase
8. Malate dehydrogenase

Enzymes involved in the supply and removal of TCA cycle intermediates

9. Pyruvate kinase
10. Pyruvate dehydrogenase
11. Pyruvate carboxylase
12. Phosphoenolpyruvate carboxykinase
13. Glutamate dehydrogenase

Figure 2.10 The tricarboxylic acid cycle. Box 1 shows how GTP is formed during the conversion of succinyl-CoA to succinate.

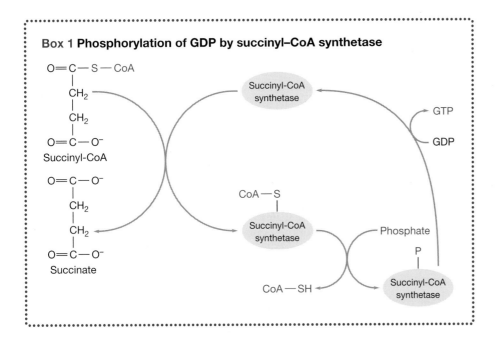

Box 1 Phosphorylation of GDP by succinyl–CoA synthetase

Figure 2.10
Continued

or alkaline pH. This serves to trap them within the matrix because of the permeability characteristics of the mitochondrial inner membrane. As we shall see in the next section many of the cycle intermediates can cross the inner membrane but they only do so in exchange for dicarboxylic acids from the cytoplasm. These exchange transporters help to maintain sufficiently high matrix concentrations of the intermediates to keep the cycle operating.

Only two of the reactions in the cycle, citrate synthesis and the oxidative decarboxylation of 2-oxoglutarate, are effectively irreversible. The oxoglutarate dehydrogenase, which is closely related to the oxidative decarboxylation of pyruvate, has several steps and requires the participation of five coenzymes: TPP, lipoic acid, coenzyme A, NAD^+ and FAD. Each individual step of this oxidative decarboxylation produces an intermediate but the small amounts formed are insufficient to permit reversal of the reaction sequence. Even though the other major reactions of the cycle are reversible, the inclusion of two unidirectional processes is sufficient to ensure that the entire cycle can only operate in one direction.

Reactions of the tricarboxylic acid cycle

Viewed in terms of its role as a vehicle for the oxidation of acetate units, the TCA cycle begins with the citrate synthase reaction which forms citrate by condensation of acetyl-CoA with oxaloacetate. In order to ensure that there is no accumulation of acetyl-CoA within the mitochondrial matrix, the formation of oxaloacetate from pyruvate by the pyruvate carboxylase reaction is stimulated by acetyl-CoA. This pathway for the formation of oxaloacetate is particularly important in the most metabolically versatile tissues such as liver and kidney. An alternative source of oxaloacetate is provided by the dicarboxylic acids, aspartate and glutamate, through a combination of transamination and deamination (see Figure 4.4a), but this generates ammonium ions which must be converted to the non-toxic waste product, urea.

The second step in the cycle, which is catalysed by aconitase, is the conversion of citrate to isocitrate. This process, which occurs in several stages, is often portrayed as two steps, dehydration to *cis*-aconitate followed by hydration to yield isocitrate. However, it seems likely that most of the substrate never leaves the aconitase enzyme until conversion to isocitrate has occurred. Isocitrate dehydrogenase is responsible for the third reaction of the cycle, the oxidative decarboxylation of isocitrate to yield 2-oxoglutarate and reduce NAD^+ to NADH. The coenzyme reduction precedes the decarboxylation so that a six-carbon intermediate, oxalosuccinate, is formed prior to the release of the carbon dioxide, but it remains bound to the active site of the isocitrate dehydrogenase and never occurs free in the mitochondrial matrix.

The second decarboxylation step in the TCA cycle is the sequence of steps that are almost identical to those in the oxidative decarboxylation of pyruvate (Figure 2.9) which convert 2-oxoglutarate to succinyl-CoA. The fact that the product of this process is succinyl-CoA rather than succinate enables additional energy to be conserved by the formation of GTP. Box 1 of Figure 2.10 shows that this is accomplished by transfer of the CoA to the succinyl-CoA synthetase enzyme followed by the phosphorolysis of the bond between the enzyme and CoA, forming an enzyme phosphate which then phosphorylates GDP. The nucleoside diphosphate kinase present in the mitochondrial matrix enables the phosphate to be transferred to ADP (see Eq. 1.5).

The additional nucleoside triphosphate formed from succinyl-CoA compensates for the lower level of energy conservation in the succinic dehydrogenase reaction. This enzyme is located on the matrix side of the mitochondrial inner membrane and transfers electrons directly to FAD rather than using NADH as an intermediary (see Figure 1.11). As a consequence only six protons are pumped out of the matrix in the succinate to fumarate step, yielding one less ATP. The addition of water across the fumarate double bond by fumarate hydratase to form L-malate sets the stage for the final oxidative step of the cycle, the malate dehydrogenase reaction in which NAD^+ is reduced during the oxidation of malate to oxaloacetate.

Supply and removal of tricarboxylic acid cycle intermediates

When he proposed the TCA cycle in 1938, H. A. Krebs conceived it as a catabolic process in which one of the intermediates was in effect acting 'catalytically' to promote the oxidation of pyruvate (or as became clear later, of acetyl-CoA). Although this is an unconventional use of the term catalyst, it is clear that oxaloacetate (or any of the other four-carbon intermediates in the cycle) is regenerated as each two-carbon acetate unit is oxidized during a single revolution of the cycle. Another reason why it is useful to think of the cycle intermediates as acting catalytically is that the maximum rate at which the cycle can operate will depend on the concentration of the intermediates in the mitochondrial matrix. As shown in Figure 2.10 the supply of cycle intermediates can be increased by the carboxylation of pyruvate to form oxaloacetate or by the oxidative deamination of glutamate. Any such increase in the total amount of the TCA cycle constituents will increase the maximum rate at which the cycle can operate, and the increased levels of the intermediates will persist unless they are removed by a side reaction, such as the formation of phosphoenolpyruvate or glutamate. As we shall see in Chapter 4, the supply of cycle intermediates can also be increased by the breakdown of amino acid carbon skeletons, or depleted by the use of the intermediates to synthesize the carbon skeletons of non-essential amino acids.

It should be emphasized that the supply of additional TCA cycle intermediates does not result in their oxidation through the cycle but merely increases the capacity of the cycle to oxidize acetyl-CoA. Thus Figure 2.11(a) and (b) emphasizes the point made in Figure 2.8 that after transamination to pyruvate the carbon skeleton of the amino acid alanine may enter the cycle in two ways: as a substrate by conversion to acetyl-CoA (Figure 2.11a) or as a 'catalyst' by conversion to oxaloacetate (Figure 2.11b).

In order to be oxidized by the TCA cycle intermediates such as 2-oxoglutarate or oxaloacetate must first be converted into phosphoenolpyruvate and then through pyruvate to acetyl-CoA. This is illustrated by comparing Figure 2.11(c) with Figure 2.11(d). Aspartic acid can be converted into oxaloacetate by transamination with 2-oxoglutarate (see Figure 2.12 for details), but in order to be oxidized by the TCA cycle it must be converted to acetyl-CoA.

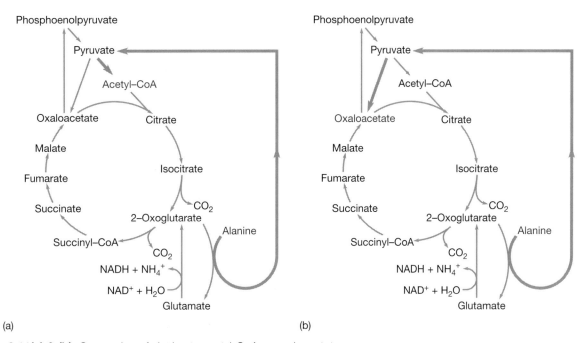

(a) (b)

Figure 2.11(a) & (b) Conversion of alanine to acetyl-CoA or oxaloacetate.

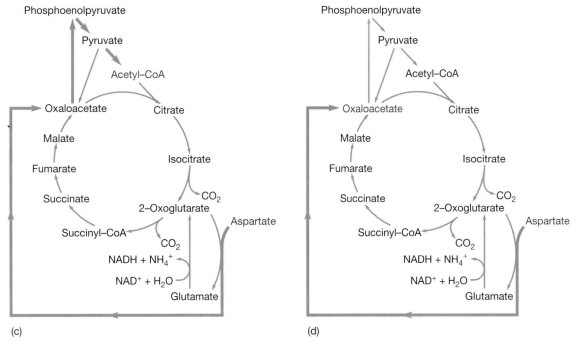

(c) (d)

Figure 2.11(c) & (d) Conversion of aspartate to acetyl-CoA or oxaloacetate.

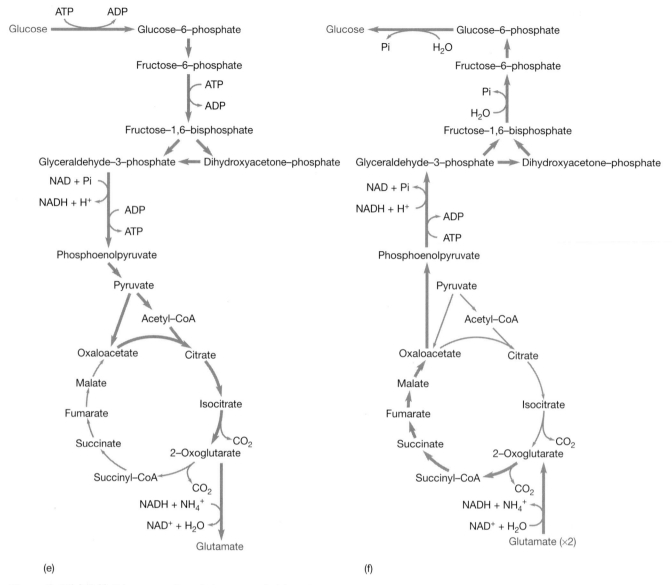

Figure 2.11(e) & (f) Interconversion of glucose and glutamate.

It should also be noted that because TCA cycle intermediates form the carbon skeletons of some non-essential amino acids, the reactions of the cycle are often used in the interconversion of glucose and amino acids. Figure 2.11(e) shows how glucose is converted into glutamate. Alternatively, the conversion of two glutamate molecules into phosphoenolpyruvate (Figure 2.11f) can yield one glucose molecule.

2.8 Reoxidation of cytoplasmic NADH

The fact that cytoplasmic NADH does not equilibrate with the NADH in the mitochondrial matrix is one of the factors that makes it possible for the cell to carry out oxidative and biosynthetic processes at the same time. However, it does mean that some other mechanism is required to oxidize the hydrogens from the cytoplasmic NADH formed during glycolysis. Figure 2.12 shows that there are two schemes.

(a) Malate–aspartate shuttle

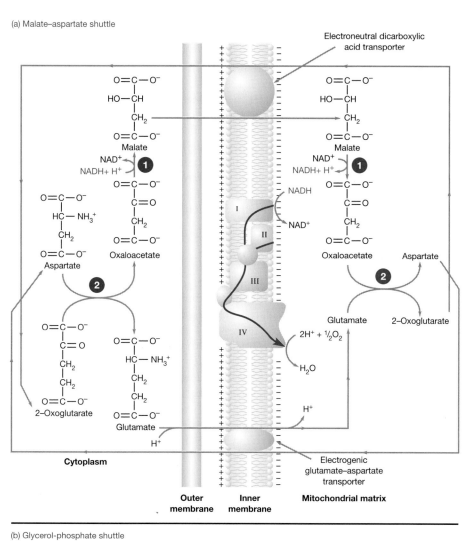

Enzymes

1 Malate dehydrogenase

2 Transaminase

(b) Glycerol-phosphate shuttle

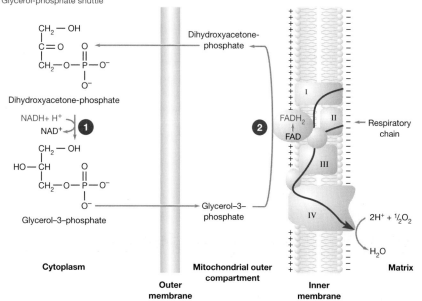

Enzymes

1 NAD–linked glycerophosphate dehydrogenase

2 FAD–linked glycerophosphate dehydrogenase

Figure 2.12

Mechanisms for the mitochondrial reoxidation of cytoplasmic NADH by the malate–aspartate and glycerol-phosphate shuttles. The constituents of the respiratory chain are described in Figure 1.11.

The glycerol-phosphate shuttle

The glycerol-phosphate shuttle makes use of the glycerophosphate dehydrogenase reaction in the cytoplasm to regenerate the NAD$^+$ from NADH by reduction of dihydroxyacetone-phosphate (see Figure 2.12b). The glycerol-3-phosphate produced diffuses across the mitochondrial outer membrane where it encounters a different glycerol-phosphate dehydrogenase which reduces FAD rather than NAD$^+$. This enzyme is on the outer face of the inner mitochondrial membrane where it can pass the electron from FADH$_2$ to coenzyme Q (see Figure 1.11). The dihydroxyacetone-phosphate produced by this glycerophosphate dehydrogenase then diffuses back to the cytoplasm where the process can be repeated. Since the glycerophosphate shuttle feeds the electrons into the respiratory chain at the coenzyme Q level, less ATP will be formed than if NADH were oxidized in the mitochondrial matrix.

The malate–aspartate shuttle

The mechanism shown in Figure 2.12(a) does transfer the hydrogens from cytoplasmic NADH into the mitochondrial matrix, but there is still a price to pay in energy terms. In this scheme malate dehydrogenase reduces oxaloacetate in the cytoplasm to malate, which is transported across the mitochondrial inner membrane by a dicarboxylic acid transporter that exchanges the malate for 2-oxoglutarate. (It should be noted that the inner membrane is impermeable to oxaloacetate which is not a substrate for this transporter so that it does not cross the inner membrane.) In the matrix the malate enters the TCA cycle where it is oxidized back to oxaloacetate, producing NADH which is reoxidized to NAD$^+$ by the respiratory chain in the usual way. In order to complete this cycle the oxaloacetate must be exported to the cytoplasm and the 2-oxoglutarate recovered. This part of the scheme makes use of the high glutamate concentration in the mitochondrial matrix to transaminate oxaloacetate into aspartate and regenerate the 2-oxoglutarate. The inner membrane also has a transporter capable of exchanging an intramitochondrial aspartate for a cytoplasmic glutamate. However, in order to operate against the high intramitochondrial glutamate concentration this exchange is electrogenic, that is the cytoplasmic glutamate enters the matrix together with a proton (so that it has no net charge) in exchange for a negatively charged aspartate. As a consequence this exchange occurs at the expense of a reduction in the proton motive force which means that the hydrogens which originated from the glyceraldehyde-3-phosphate dehydrogenase reaction in the cytoplasm still do not generate as much ATP as they would if the reaction had occurred in the mitochondrial matrix. Once out in the cytoplasm the aspartate is transaminated back to oxaloacetate and the amino group is transferred to the 2-oxoglutarate originally released from the mitochondrial matrix regenerating the cytoplasmic glutamate.

2.9 The relative importance of the various carbohydrate pathways

At one time a great deal of effort in biochemical research was devoted to trying to discover what proportion of carbohydrate followed the pentose phosphate pathway rather than glycolysis plus the TCA cycle. In fact, this was the wrong question to ask, since the relative importance of the two pathways depends on the demands for their respective products. Superficially both possibilities provide routes for the complete oxidation of a molecule of glucose with approximately the same yield of energy conserved as reduced nucleotide: 12 NADPH molecules per glucose-6-phosphate by the pentose phosphate pathway as opposed to 10 NADHs and two $FADH_2$ plus two GTPs in the combination of glycolysis and the TCA cycle. Thus, the only difference in energy conservation appeared to be the two substrate-level phosphorylation steps in glycolysis. This comparison ignored the fact established later that the ratio of reduced to oxidized nucleotide in the cytoplasm is very much greater for $NADP^+$ than for NAD^+. In part this is due to the absence of effective shuttle pathways for the NADPH hydrogens like those for NADH shown in Figure 2.12. Mitochondria also have a proton-dependent transhydrogenase which is responsible for the reduction of $NADP^+$ by NADH at the expense of an influx of two protons. Thus, some of the proton motive force generated by the respiratory chain is used to maintain a much higher reduced-to-oxidized ratio for $NADP^+$ which in turn means that NADPH is more effective as a reducing agent. With this information we are now in a position to answer the question: which route will be responsible for glucose oxidation? Glycolysis and the TCA cycle will be the predominant route because NAD^+ is more prevalent than $NADP^+$; the pentose phosphate pathway will begin to operate when there is a demand for NADPH for biosynthetic processes such as fatty acid synthesis or the production of ribonucleotides (but even then the malic enzyme (see Figure 2.8) can also help to meet the demand).

Comparable arguments can be advanced to answer questions about the relative importance of glycolysis and the other potential sources of acetyl-CoA. For most human populations carbohydrates provide the main source of energy in the diet. However, as we shall see in Chapter 4, the body maintains a strict nitrogen balance so that the high protein diets consumed by carnivores and some groups of humans will ensure that, for these individuals, the carbon skeletons of amino acids will provide a major source of acetyl-CoA. For some groups of people living in the arctic climates fat is the major source of energy, and hence of acetyl-CoA. Fat has the highest calorie content per unit weight of the three major types of food which makes it the most efficient food for those requiring a high calorie intake. However most individuals in developed countries consume more calories than they need to satisfy their energy requirements, and under these conditions the glucose-containing carbohydrates have the advantage that their catabolism is much more rigorously controlled than that of the other two main dietary constituents. Dietary fats will largely be converted into storage triacylglycerol, if they are not needed to fuel the TCA cycle. Unless there is a shortage of glucose or glycogen, the carbon skeletons of amino acids will have the same fate. By contrast, the conversion of excess glucose into fatty acids via acetyl-CoA will be strictly limited by the control of phosphofructokinase activity, and once the glycogen stores are filled, further metabolism of glucose will be inhibited by the accumulation of glucose-6-phosphate, which in turn will inhibit the phosphorylation of glucose by hexokinase. Ultimately this leads to a rise in blood glucose which inhibits the desire for food through its effect on the brain.

2.10 What can we conclude about the nutritional importance of carbohydrates from a knowledge of carbohydrate metabolism?

From the brief outline of the main features of carbohydrate metabolism in this chapter it should be clear that glucose can supply the cell with energy and can be converted into the other carbohydrates needed by the cell. At the same time it should also be obvious that in order to be useful dietary carbohydrates must be convertible into glucose or one of the other hexoses that can enter the glycolytic pathway: galactose, fructose or mannose. Thus starch is usable because it can be broken down into maltose, and then to glucose (see Figure 2.2), but cellulose, which is also a polymer of glucose, is unavailable to mammals because they lack the enzymes to split the β-1,4 linkages between the glucose units. Paradoxically, cellulose is a valuable constituent in the human diet because it is not broken down. As a consequence it adds bulk to the contents of the large intestine where some of it is metabolized by the microorganisms that live there.

A second point to be emphasized is that starch which yields glucose, or the milk sugar lactose which provides glucose plus galactose, are better sources of carbohydrate than sucrose which yields fructose as well as glucose. This is because the fructose bypasses the control point of glycolysis in the liver, thereby overloading the system with acetyl-CoA and stimulating the formation of triacylglycerol, as we shall see in the next chapter.

A final point to keep in mind while considering the next two chapters is the fact that through the central metabolic pathways glucose can supply the basic building block for fatty acid synthesis, acetyl-CoA, as well as the carbon skeletons of the non-essential amino acids. This is illustrated in Figure 2.11(e) which indicates the route by which glucose can form acetyl-CoA or glutamate. Figure 2.11(f) shows that the reverse, glucose formation from glutamate, is also possible. Furthermore by diverting the phosphoenolpyruvate to pyruvate and then acetyl-CoA it is clear that glutamate can also supply the starting material for fatty acid synthesis. By contrast, acetyl-CoA itself is not able to form the TCA cycle intermediates, and therefore is unable to form either glucose or glutamate.

EXERCISES

1. Distinguish between glycolysis and gluconeogenesis.

2. What are the control points in the glycolytic pathway?

3. How does glycogen synthesis differ from glycogen degradation?

4. Why is it more efficient to recycle lactate into glycogen than into glucose?

5. What controls are necessary to prevent wasteful recycling during gluconeogenesis?

6. What are the functions of the pentose phosphate pathway?

7. Show how two pyruvate molecules can contribute five of the six citrate carbons.

8. Why does the tricarboxylic acid cycle operate in only one direction?

9. Distinguish between the two ways that cytoplasmic NADH can be oxidized by mitochondria.

10. Why is the metabolism of sucrose more likely to lead to the formation of excess acetyl-CoA than the metabolism of lactose?

Further reading

Dow, J., Lindsay, G. & Morrison, J. (1996) *Biochemistry, Molecules, Cells and the Body*, Addison-Wesley, Chapter 8.

Gahmberg, C.G. & Tolvanen, M. (1996) Why mammalian cell surface proteins are glycoproteins, *Trends in Biochemical Sciences* **21**, 308–311.

Pilkis, S.J. & Granner, D.K. (1992) Molecular physiology of the regulation of hepatic gluconeogenesis and glycolysis, *Annual Review of Physiology* **54**, 885–909.

Pilkis, S.J., Claus, T.H., Kurland, L.J. & Lange, A.J. (1995) 6-Phosphofructo-2-kinase/fructose-2,6-bisphosphatase: a metabolic signalling enzyme, *Annual Review of Biochemistry* **64**, 799–835.

Salway, J.G. (1994) *Metabolism at a Glance*, Blackwell Scientific.

Stryer, L. (1995) *Biochemistry*, 4th edition, W.H. Freeman, Chapters 18, 19, 20 & 22.

Tzagoloff, A. (1982) *Mitochondria*, Plenum.

Wood, T. (1985) *The Pentose Phosphate Pathway*, Academic Press.

Lipid metabolism

Triacylglycerol is the most efficient form in which energy-supplying substrates can be stored in the body. Phospholipids, glycolipids and cholesterol are important constituents of the membranes that separate cells from their environment as well as forming many intracellular organelles.

3.1 Introduction

In terms of their contribution to metabolism the principal role of lipids is to provide energy-supplying substrates for a wide variety of cells. However, lipids are also essential for the structure of membranes. Consequently, the supply of lipids as building blocks for cell constituents is a major function of lipid metabolism since membranes provide the interface between each cell and its neighbours as well as the surrounding environment. Lipids are important because they form the phospholipid and glycolipid bilayer in membranes and serve as constituents of the membrane lipoproteins. Membrane lipids, such as phosphatidyl inositol and other phospholipids, also mediate many of the responses that a cell makes to signals from outside. Other lipids, such as the fat-soluble vitamins, serve as specialized cofactors which play an important part in some metabolic processes.

In this chapter we will be concerned with those aspects of lipid metabolism that operate in a variety of different cells. This includes the oxidation of fatty acids in the mitochondria and their biosynthesis in the cytoplasm. The formation of phospholipids, glycolipids and cholesterol for membrane biosynthesis and the provision of the lipid components of lipoproteins will also be considered. Finally the production of some specialized lipids such as steroid hormones formed from cholesterol and derivatives of the fat-soluble vitamins will be dealt with briefly. Figure 3.1 gives an overview of lipid metabolism.

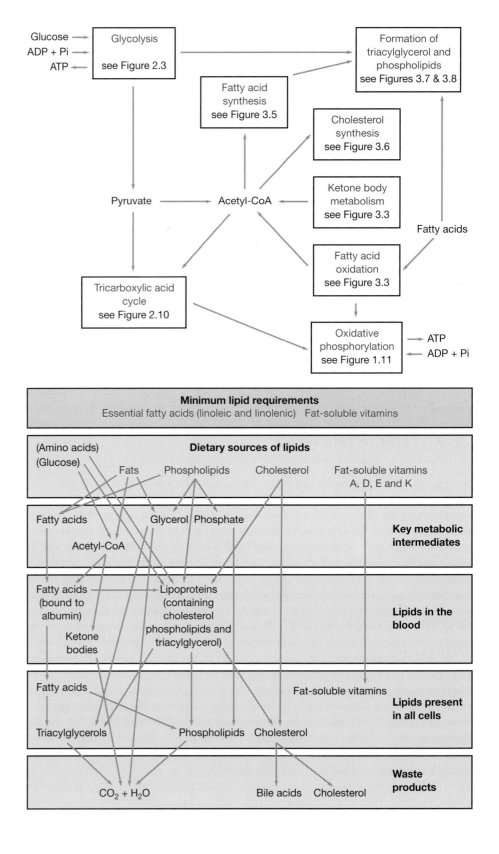

Figure 3.1
Overview of lipid metabolism.

3.2 Importance of lipids for membrane structure and energy storage

Lipids are normally characterized by their insolubility in water which is a property of the long-chain fatty acids. However, the crucial feature of most biologically important lipids is that they also have hydrophilic regions which make them at least sparingly soluble in the aqueous environment of the cell, and give many of them the capacity to form bilayers or spherical micelles when they are present in water. The fact that fatty acids vary in length and degree of saturation means that changes in fatty acid composition can alter the characteristics of the storage molecules and membrane constituents of which they form a part. For example, in mammals, droplets of triacylglycerol are the normal storage form of lipid in the adipose tissue, and in order to be liquid at body temperature approximately 50% of the long-chain fatty acids contain at least one double bond. In membranes it is important that a high level of fluidity be maintained and the greater the proportion of unsaturated and short-chain fatty acids in the phospholipids that make up the bilayer, the greater the fluidity of the membrane at any given temperature.

Another aspect of the contribution that lipids make to biological membranes is through the variety of different types of lipid constituents that are present. Thus even with a fixed proportion of unsaturated and short-chain fatty acids the fluidity of the membrane can be increased by the addition of cholesterol or decreased by a larger proportion of glycolipids.

The triacylglycerols are particularly efficient as storage molecules because they are highly reduced and lack the large amount of oxygen present in carbohydrates. Because triacylglycerol lacks the hydroxyl groups present in glycogen, it does not bind water and can be stored in droplets which are almost completely free of water. These factors maximize the amount of stored carbon per unit volume. Humans store sufficient triacylglycerol to supply energy for about three weeks whereas the glycogen stores only contain enough energy for about 24 hours.

3.3 Fatty acid activation and oxidation in the mitochondrial matrix

Fatty acid activation

Long-chain fatty acids are supplied to most cells from the blood where they are present at a concentration of 0.3–2.0 mM largely bound to the circulating albumin. Because of their insolubility in water the bound fatty acids are in equilibrium with a very low free fatty acid concentration in the blood ($\sim 10^{-6}$ M). Nevertheless they enter the cell down a concentration gradient via a carrier. Within the cell the free fatty acids are again bound to specific proteins. In order to enter the metabolic pathways the fatty acids are activated by conversion to fatty acyl-CoA at the expense of both terminal phosphates of ATP (Eqs 3.1 and 3.2).

$$R\text{–}COO^- + ATP \longleftrightarrow R\text{–}CO\text{–}AMP + \text{pyrophosphate} \tag{3.1}$$

$$R\text{–}CO\text{–}AMP + CoA\text{–}SH \longleftrightarrow R\text{–}CO\text{–}S\text{–}CoA + AMP \tag{3.2}$$

Although the sum of these two reactions is reversible in principle, hydrolysis of the pyrophosphate to inorganic phosphate ensures that they only operate in the direction of fatty acyl-CoA synthesis.

Fatty acid oxidation

The oxidation of fatty acids has been shown to occur within the matrix of the mitochondria, so that it is necessary for the activated fatty acids to cross the mitochondrial inner membrane. Acyl-CoA cannot cross the membrane and Figure 3.2 shows how carnitine acts to transfer the acyl group from CoA in the cytoplasm to a separate pool of CoA in the mitochondrial matrix. In fact most of the CoA in the cell is located inside the mitochondria so that activation of fatty acids in the cytoplasm to form acyl-CoA is rapidly followed by transfer to the much larger pool of carnitine in the cytoplasm. Separate carnitine:fatty acid transferase enzymes for short-chain and long-chain acyl-CoA molecules are present on each side of the mitochondrial inner membrane, to add and remove the acyl group from the carnitine. Transfer of the acyl-carnitine across the membrane into the matrix by the translocase is linked to the exit of free carnitine. Carnitine is found in most cells but is synthesized mainly in the liver by the methylation and hydroxylation of a lysine side chain in a protein.

Once inside the mitochondrial matrix the long-chain fatty acyl-CoA molecules are progressively converted into acetyl-CoA by the β-oxidation scheme shown in Figure 3.3. Two separate oxidative steps occur in each sequential removal of an

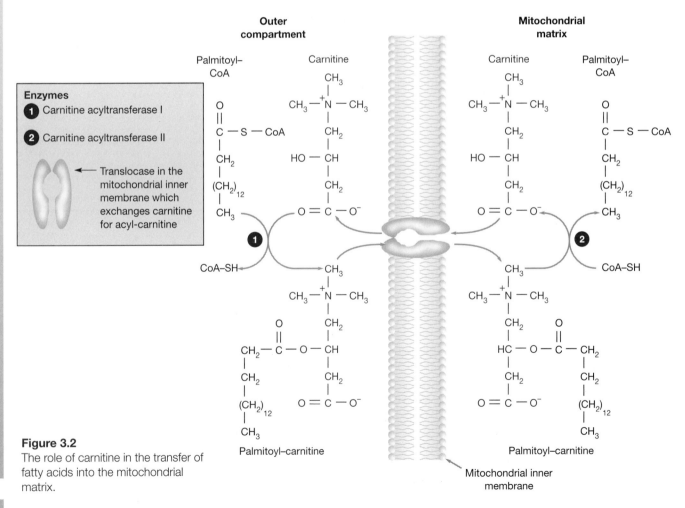

Figure 3.2
The role of carnitine in the transfer of fatty acids into the mitochondrial matrix.

acetyl-CoA unit: the first is by an FAD-linked acyl-CoA dehydrogenase on the mito-chondrial inner membrane, and following the addition of water to the double bond a second oxidative step reduces NAD$^+$ in the matrix. As a consequence of the proton translocation ratios for FADH$_2$ and NADH oxidation by the respiratory chain (see section 1.8) we can calculate that the release of each acetyl-CoA will be associated with the formation of four ATPs (1.5 from FADH$_2$ + 2.5 from NADH). Seven cycles of the β-oxidation scheme are required to degrade palmitoyl-CoA yielding a total of eight acetyl-CoA molecules. Thus the total potential yield of ATP from the complete oxidation of palmitate would be $7 \times 4 = 28$ ATPs plus 10 for the

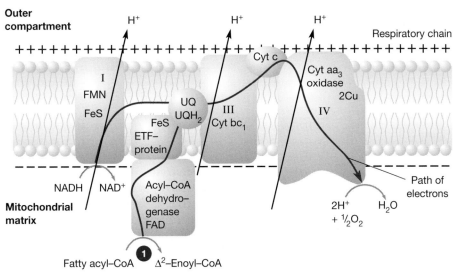

Enzymes

1 Acyl–CoA dehydrogenase

2 Enoyl–CoA hydratase

3 3–Hydroxyacyl–CoA dehydrogenase

4 Thiolase

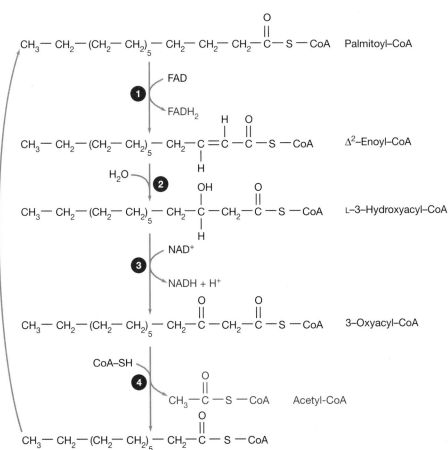

Figure 3.3

β-Oxidation of fatty acids. Box 1 shows the formation of acetyl-CoA from ketone bodies.

Box 1

Metabolism of ketone bodies

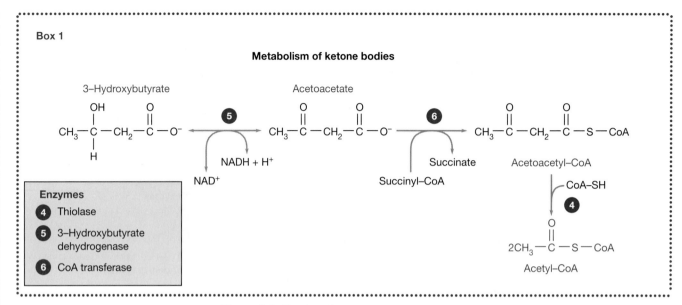

Figure 3.3 Continued

oxidation of each acetyl-CoA by the TCA cycle making 108, or a net yield of 106 after allowing for the two phosphates lost in the activation reaction. It should be noted that this ATP yield is lower than that shown in most texts as a consequence of taking account of current views on the number of protons pumped out of the mitochondrial matrix during the oxidation of $FADH_2$ and NADH.

Metabolism of ketone bodies

When the formation of acetyl-CoA by the β-oxidation of fatty acids in the liver exceeds the capacity of the TCA cycle to oxidize it, the excess is converted into ketone bodies (see Figure 6.10). Most other cells are able to convert these substrates back into acetyl-CoA within the mitochondrial matrix (see Figure 3.3 Box 1) by the transfer of coenzyme A from succinyl-CoA. However, it is important to recognize that the two major ketone bodies, 3-hydroxybutyrate and acetoacetate, are acids. As a consequence, large increases in the vascular concentrations of the ketone bodies can cause serious acidosis.

3.4 Metabolism of unsaturated fatty acids and those with an odd number of carbons

Two special cases of fatty acid oxidation need to be considered briefly: unsaturated fatty acids and those with an odd number of carbons. At first sight it would appear that unsaturated fatty acyl-CoA should offer no problem for the β-oxidation scheme since one of the intermediates is an enoyl-CoA, but the next intermediate is L-3-hydroxyacyl-CoA so that both the position and the *trans* orientation of the double bond are crucial for the β-oxidation scheme. Since naturally occurring unsaturated fatty acids have the *cis* configuration, it is necessary to have the additional steps shown in Figure 3.4 to alter the orientation or position of the double bond.

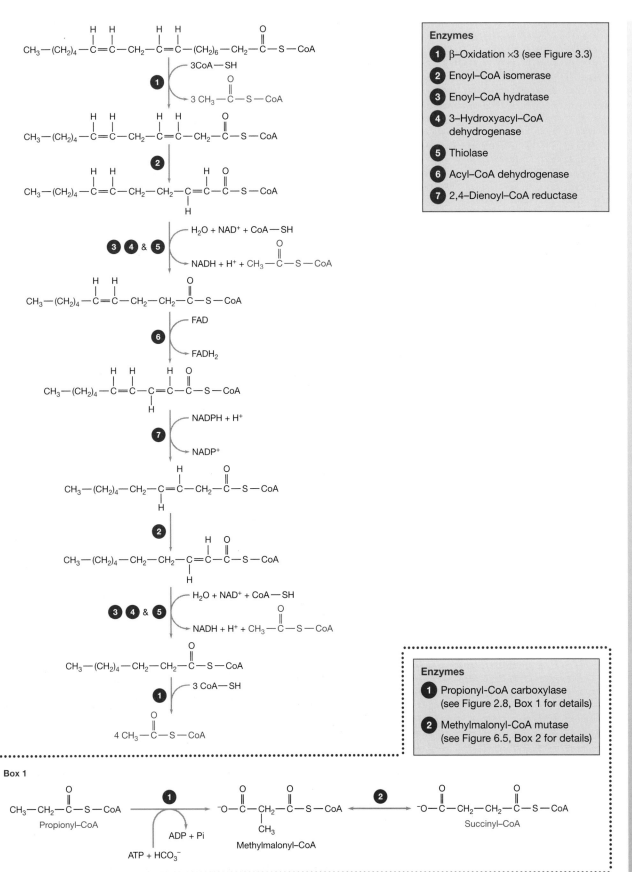

Figure 3.4 Metabolism of an unsaturated fatty acid (linoleic acid). Box 1 shows the conversion of propionyl-CoA from odd numbered fatty acids into succinyl-CoA.

Although it was emphasized earlier that acetyl-CoA from fatty acids with an even number of carbons cannot be converted into glucose, the final product of the β-oxidation scheme for fatty acids with an odd number of carbons is propionyl-CoA. Box 1 in Figure 3.4 shows that propionyl-CoA is carboxylated to methylmalonyl-CoA and then isomerized to succinyl-CoA which can enter the TCA cycle. In this way it is actually possible for the last three carbons of a fatty acid with an odd number of carbons to form glucose or the carbon skeletons of non-essential amino acids. It is also important to note that the glycerol part of triacylglycerol molecules can also yield carbohydrates and be used to form non-essential amino acids.

3.5 Transfer of acetyl-CoA to the cytoplasm and the synthesis of long-chain fatty acids

Transfer of acetyl-CoA from the mitochondrial matrix to the cytosol

Fatty acid synthesis begins with acetyl-CoA and since most of this is produced within the mitochondrial matrix it is obviously necessary for the acetyl-CoA to be transferred to the cytosol before it can be converted into fatty acids. Acetyl-CoA can leave the mitochondria as citrate formed from acetyl-CoA and oxaloacetate by the citrate synthase of the TCA cycle. Citrate, together with a proton, is transferred out of the mitochondrial matrix in exchange for malate and is split in the cytosol by the citrate lyase reaction:

$$\text{Citrate} + \text{ATP} + \text{CoA} \rightarrow \text{acetyl-CoA} + \text{ADP} + \text{Pi} + \text{oxaloacetate} \qquad (3.3)$$

This process has the advantage that the oxaloacetate produced in the cytosol will be reduced to malate which can then be converted to pyruvate by the malic enzyme (see Figure 2.8), thereby forming the NADPH needed for fatty acid synthesis (see below). However, it is now clear that the carnitine translocation system shown in Figure 3.2 is also responsible for the transfer of acetyl groups from the matrix to the cytosol. This is particularly valuable because acetyl groups leaving the mitochondria in this way can remain in the form of acetyl-carnitine in the cytoplasm until required instead of exhausting the relatively small cytoplasmic pool of coenzyme A.

Acetyl-CoA is activated for fatty acid synthesis by carboxylation

The initial step in the conversion of acetyl-CoA into fatty acids is the formation of malonyl-CoA by the acetyl-CoA carboxylase reaction:

$$\text{Acetyl-CoA} + \text{HCO}_3^- + \text{ATP} \rightarrow \text{malonyl-CoA} + \text{ADP} + \text{Pi} + \text{H}^+ \qquad (3.4)$$

The addition of a carboxyl group to acetyl-CoA requires biotin as a coenzyme (see Figure 2.8) and the ATP is used to form a carboxybiotin intermediate as in the pyruvate carboxylation reaction. Long-chain fatty acids with even numbers of carbons are formed by successive additions of malonyl-CoA units to the initial acetyl-CoA. However, as shown in Figure 3.5, both the initial acetyl group and the successive malonyl groups must first be transferred to the acyl carrier protein within the fatty acid synthetase complex.

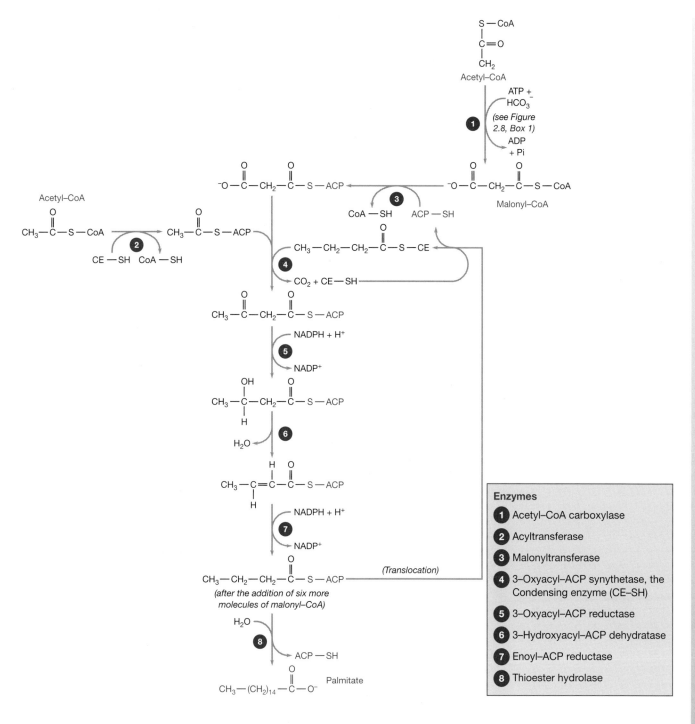

Enzymes

1 Acetyl–CoA carboxylase

2 Acyltransferase

3 Malonyltransferase

4 3–Oxyacyl–ACP synythetase, the Condensing enzyme (CE–SH)

5 3–Oxyacyl–ACP reductase

6 3–Hydroxyacyl–ACP dehydratase

7 Enoyl–ACP reductase

8 Thioester hydrolase

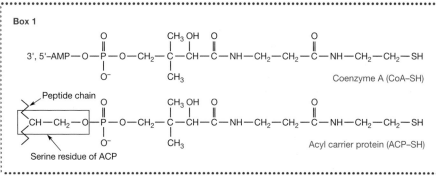

Figure 3.5
Fatty acid synthesis. Box 1 shows the structure of coenzyme A (CoA-SH) and the fatty acid attachment section of the acyl carrier protein (ACP).

The acyl carrier protein is a key feature of the fatty acid synthetase complex

Figure 3.5 shows that the fatty acids are elongated by two carbons with the addition of each malonyl-CoA. This means that the extra carbon added by the carboxylation reaction (Eq. 3.4) is lost again in the condensation reaction catalysed by 3-oxyacyl-ACP synthetase. The condensation step becomes energetically favourable because it is linked to a decarboxylation. Since fatty acid synthesis involves the successive addition of two carbon units to construct a fatty acid of 16 or 18 carbons in length it is important that the intermediates do not diffuse away from the synthetase complex. This is achieved by transfer of the growing fatty acid chain back and forth between a cysteine side chain on the condensing enzyme (CE-SH) and the –SH group of the acyl carrier protein (ACP). As in protein synthesis this arrangements prevents the escape of partially completed products. Box 1 of Figure 3.5 shows that the ACP prosthetic group, like that of coenzyme A, is derived from the B vitamin pantothenic acid.

The long flexible arm of ACP enables each two-carbon unit to be presented in turn to the 3-oxyacyl reductase, the 3-hydroxyacyl dehydratase and the enoyl reductase enzymes in the synthetase complex (Figure 3.5). The fatty acyl group is then transferred back to the condensing enzyme in order to enable the ACP to receive a new malonyl group from the malonyl transferase. Final release of the completed fatty acid, which is mainly the 16-carbon palmitate, is through the action of a thioester hydrolase which is also associated with the fatty acid synthetase complex. Mammary glands have a special thioesterase which removes completed fatty acids with eight or ten carbons.

Each cycle of the elongation process requires an ATP for the carboxylation reaction to form malonyl-CoA plus two NADPHs for the reduction reactions so that the overall equation for palmitate (C16) formation is:

$$8\text{Acetyl-CoA} + 7\text{ATP} + 14\text{NADPH} \rightarrow$$
$$\text{palmitate} + 8\text{CoA} + 7\text{ADP} + 7\text{Pi} + 14\text{NADP}^+ \quad (3.5)$$

From this equation it is possible to calculate an approximate energy cost for the synthesis of a 16-carbon fatty acid since each acetyl-CoA could yield 10 ATPs and each NADPH would yield 2.5 ATPs, making a total equivalent to 122 ATPs. When this is compared with the energy yield from the oxidation of palmitate, 106 ATPs (section 3.3), we can see that the energy cost of storing excess acetyl-CoA in the form of fatty acids is effectively 16 ATPs or one per carbon atom. The comparable calculation of the energy cost of the storage of three-carbon units in the form of glycogen (section 2.4) is four ATPs per six-carbon unit, but of course it should be noted that the extensive hydration of glycogen means that it takes up much more storage space in the cell. This explains why triacylglycerol is the main energy store in humans and other mammals.

Synthesis of unsaturated fatty acids

The melting point of triacylglycerol molecules is dependent on the length of their constituent fatty acids and the degree to which they are unsaturated. Since the predominant fatty acids in mammals are 16 or 18 carbons in length, a triacylglycerol molecule composed only of saturated fatty acids would be solid at body temperature. Mobilization of fat stores depends on the storage triacylglycerols being in liquid form, so they must contain at least one unsaturated fatty acid. The important features that phospholipids contribute to biological membranes are flexibility and fluidity. As in the case of the triacylglycerols, the presence of unsaturated fatty acids in membrane phospholipids is at least partially responsible for the fluidity of membranes.

In mammals most of the unsaturated fatty acids are 16, 18 or 20 carbons in length. The *cis* double bonds are introduced into saturated fatty acids after they have been synthesized. The desaturation process involves the introduction of molecular oxygen by microsomal oxygenase reactions. These will be considered in section 6.7 since they are particularly characteristic of the liver microsomal systems. However, it should be noted that in order to form 18- or 20-carbon fatty acids separate additions of malonyl-CoA units must be made, and this occurs separately from the fatty acid synthetase system.

Mammals cannot synthesize unsaturated fatty acids containing two or more double bonds, if the double bond occurs beyond carbon 9. As a consequence the doubly unsaturated fatty acid, linoleate, is an essential dietary constituent, especially in the young. Linolenate (often considered essential) and arachidonate, with three and four double bonds respectively, can probably be synthesized from linoleate, if there is an adequate supply. Arachidonate is important as a precursor for prostaglandins, the local hormones (see section 3.11) which can affect the cells forming them (autocrine action) or influence neighbouring cells (paracrine action).

3.6 Cholesterol biosynthesis: an alternative fate for cytoplasmic acetyl-CoA

The other major contributor to fluidity of membranes is cholesterol, which despite its complex ring structure is formed from acetyl-CoA. In addition to serving as a membrane constituent, cholesterol is also a precursor for steroid hormones and for the bile salts that are important for the digestion and absorption of lipids. Unfortunately, cholesterol also has a downside metabolically since high levels in the blood can lead to the deposition of cholesterol esters in foam cells beneath the endothelial lining of the walls of arterioles (see section 12.9). The resulting narrowing of the blood vessels seems likely to be a major cause of coronary heart disease.

Biosynthesis of cholesterol

This essential constituent of membranes is present in the diet of most people, but more than half of the body's requirement for cholesterol is satisfied by biosynthesis from acetyl-CoA. Although most cells have the capacity to form cholesterol, the pathway is most active in the liver where some of the cholesterol is used to produce bile acids (see section 6.10). Figure 3.6 shows the initial steps of the biosynthetic pathway. Three acetyl-CoA units are used to form the six-carbon mevalonate by way of acetoacetate and hydroxymethylglutaryl-CoA (HMG-CoA) in the cytoplasm. The mevalonate is then phosphorylated three times and after decarboxylation forms the two unsaturated five-carbon compounds, isopentenyl pyrophosphate and dimethylallyl pyrophosphate. Six of these five-carbon units then go on to form the 30-carbon squalene which has no ring structure (see Figure 6.11). Cyclization of squalene produces lanosterol and further reactions involving the removal of three methyl groups yield the 27-carbon cholesterol molecule shown in Box 1 of Figure 3.6.

Enzymes

1 Thiolase

2 HMG–CoA synthetase

3 HMG–CoA reductase

4 Mevalonate kinase

5 Phosphomevalonate kinase

6 Phosphomevalonate decarboxylase

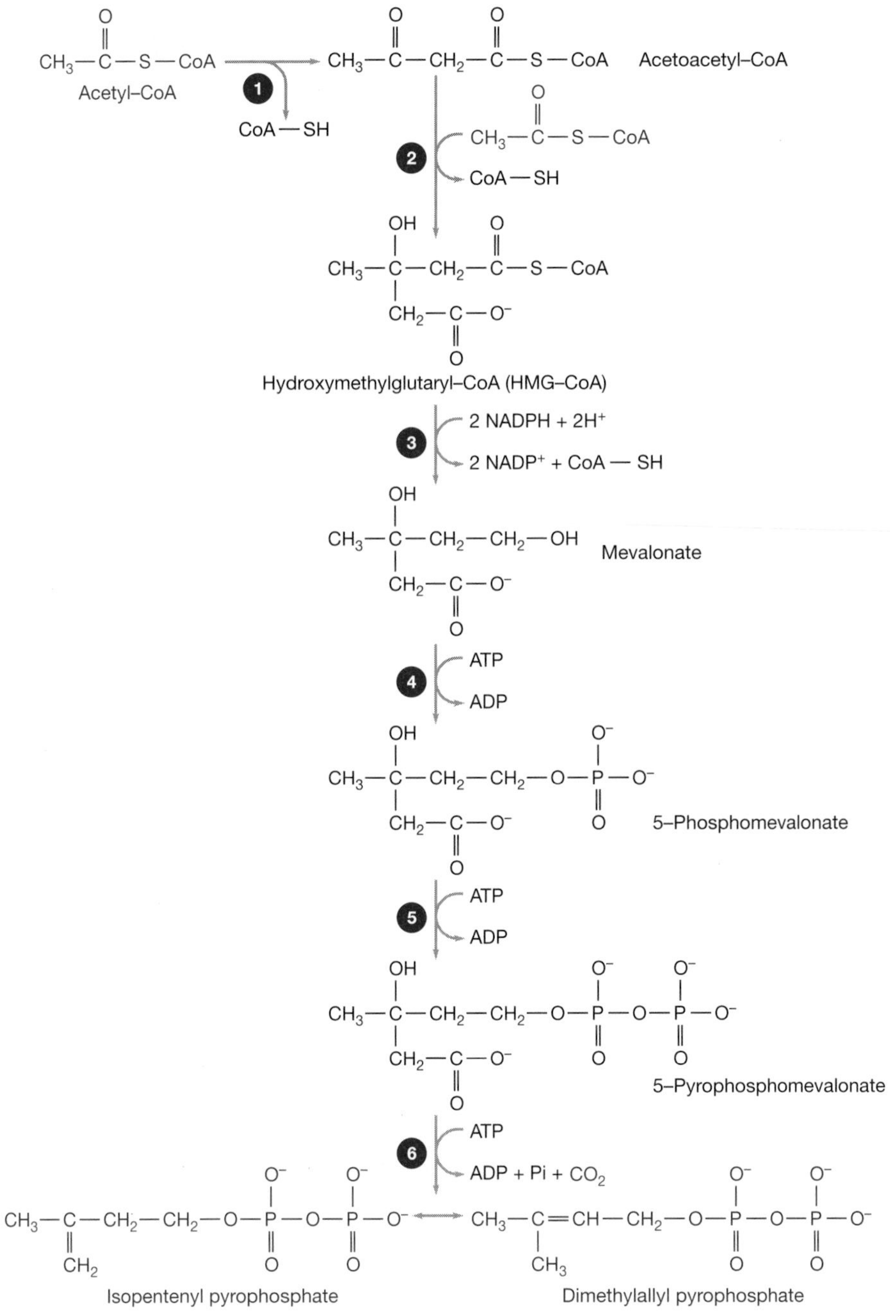

Figure 3.6

The initial steps of cholesterol biosynthesis.

Box 1 Structure of cholesterol

(see Figure 6.11 for the final stages of cholesterol synthesis)

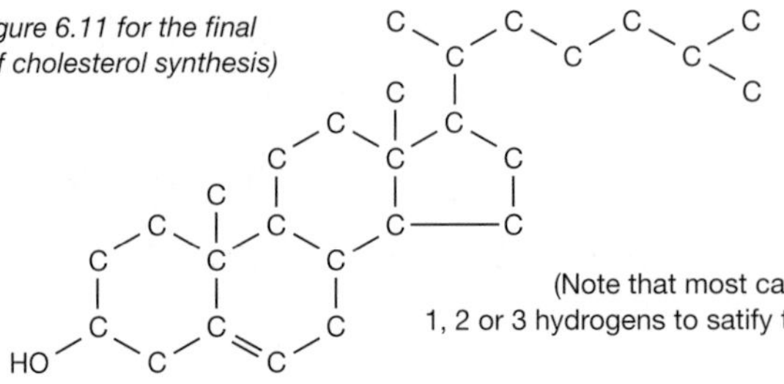

(Note that most carbons also need 1, 2 or 3 hydrogens to satify the four bonding positions)

3.7 Formation of triacylglycerols

Storage of acetyl-CoA

Fatty acids are stored in the body as triacylglycerols, and most of this storage is in specialized white adipose tissue cells dispersed around the body under the skin and in the loose connective tissue that encloses most of the internal organs. The body also contains some brown adipose tissue which is important for the production of heat, particularly in the newborn human and in hibernating animals.

It is important to recognize the fact that any form of excessive food intake can end up as triacylglycerol. Section 3.3 shows that dietary fatty acids can be converted into acetyl-CoA, but this is also true for glucose and the other hexoses, and for all of the amino acids. Once the acetyl-CoA has been formed and the requirements for biosynthetic precursors have been met, there are really only two quantitatively important alternatives for excess acetyl-CoA: oxidation or storage. As we shall see when we consider liver metabolism in Chapter 6, the oxidation of acetyl-CoA may not occur in the tissue where it is produced. Ketone bodies formed in the liver from acetyl-CoA are reconverted into acetyl-CoA in most other tissues and are then available for oxidation by the TCA cycle. When there is insufficient energy demand, the excess acetyl-CoA will leave the mitochondria and be converted into fatty acids. It was pointed out in the previous section that cholesterol biosynthesis is an alternative fate for the acetyl-CoA, but excessive cholesterol synthesis will only occur when the normal controls are defective. The body's natural tendency to convert all excess acetyl-CoA into fatty acids makes it very clear that excess food intake will tend to increase storage of the fatty acids as triacylglycerols unless the production of acetyl-CoA is balanced by increased exercise.

Synthesis of triacylglycerols

Conversion of fatty acids into triacylglycerols occurs in four steps as shown in Figure 3.7. The glycerol backbone is supplied as glycerol-3-phosphate derived from glucose via dihydroxyacetone-phosphate in the glycolytic pathway. The first two fatty acids are added to the backbone by glycerol-phosphate acyltransferase from the coenzyme A derivatives of the fatty acids. The resulting phosphatidate is a precursor for the formation of phospholipids (see Figure 3.8) as well as for triacylglycerols. In most cases the fatty acid on the second glycerol carbon of the triacylglycerol is unsaturated whereas that on carbon 1 is saturated. In order to add the third fatty acid the phosphate must be removed by hydrolysis and the diacylglycerol is then acylated by diacylglycerol acyltransferase, forming a triacylglycerol. Formation of the triacylglycerols occurs on the smooth endoplasmic reticulum membranes where the enzymes are linked together in a synthetase complex.

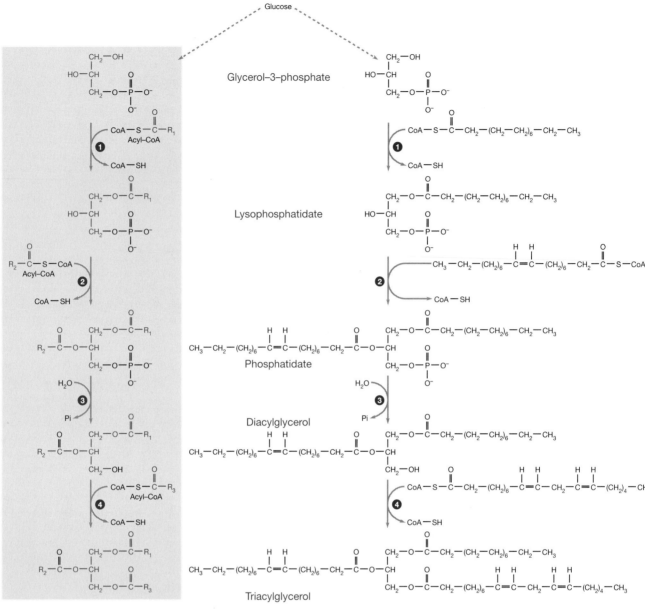

Enzymes

❶ Glycerol phosphate–1–O–acyltransferase

❷ Glycerol phosphate–2–O–acyltransferase

❸ Phosphatidate phosphohydrolase

❹ Diacylglycerol acyltransferase

Figure 3.7 Triacylglycerol synthesis. The blue panel shows the general pattern of triacylglycerol synthesis and the reaction sequence on the right gives a specific example of the formation of a triacylglycerol molecule with one saturated and two unsaturated fatty acids.

3.8 Biosynthesis of phospholipids and glycolipids

Phospholipid synthesis

The phospholipids are formed from phosphatidate in two different ways. For phosphatidyl inositol the initial step makes use of CTP to form a CDP-diacylglycerol intermediate in a reaction analogous to the production of UDP-glucose during glycogen synthesis, and hydrolysis of the pyrophosphate produced in this

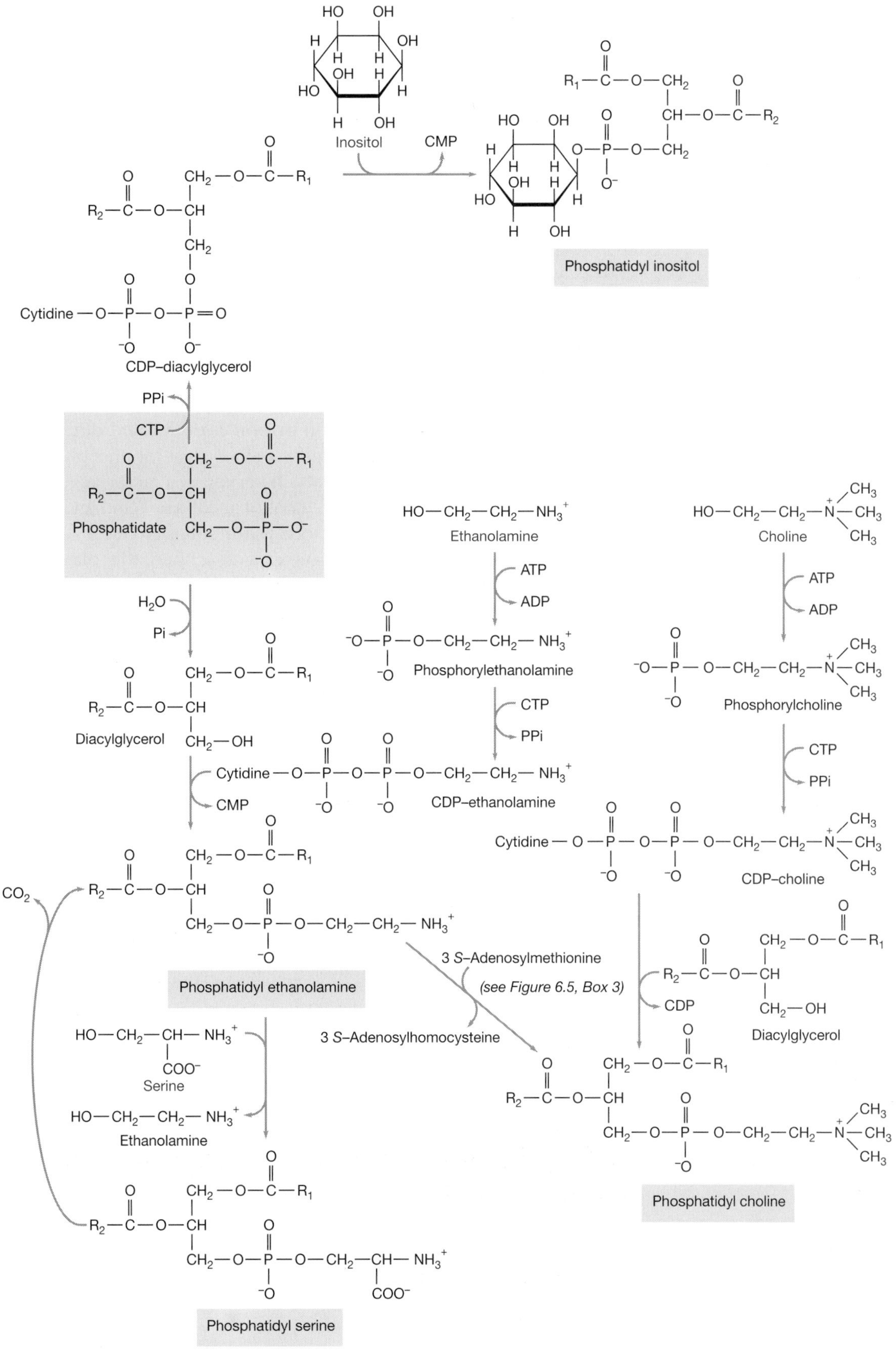

Figure 3.8 Phospholipid synthesis.

step prevents reversal. As indicated in Figure 3.8, the CDP-diacylglycerol reacts with inositol, to form the phosphatidyl inositol.

Figure 3.8 also shows that two of the other common glycerol phospholipids, phosphatidyl choline and phosphatidyl ethanolamine, are formed using a CDP derivative of the base rather than the diacylglycerol. In both cases the base is first phosphorylated by ATP and then reacts with CTP to yield the CDP derivative plus pyrophosphate. Phosphatidyl serine is formed by exchanging serine for ethanolamine and can be converted back to phosphatidyl ethanolamine by decarboxylation. Phosphatidyl choline can also be formed from phosphatidyl ethanolamine by methyl group transfer from *S*-adenosylmethionine (see Figure 6.5, Box 3, for details).

Formation of plasmalogens and other ether phospholipids

Phospholipids with an ether bond on carbon 1 are formed directly from dihydroxyacetone-phosphate rather than by way of glycerol-phosphate. The ether analogue of phosphatidyl choline, which serves as a factor aggregating blood platelets, is formed by addition of an alcohol at carbon 1 and an acetyl group at carbon 2 which serves to make it more water soluble. Other ether phospholipids have long-chain fatty acids on carbon 2, and the plasmalogens are synthesized by addition of an α,β-unsaturated alcohol on carbon 1. The pattern of synthesis for the ether phospholipids involves an initial acylation of carbon 1 of the dihydroxyacetone-phosphate, followed by exchange of the acyl group for an alcohol, reduction of the 2-oxo group, acylation and, finally, addition of the CDP-choline.

Sphingomyelin synthesis

The phosphosphingolipids are another important class of phospholipids. Sphingomyelin is the most common lipid of this type in membranes and Figure 3.9 shows how it is formed, starting with palmitoyl-CoA plus serine. The basic form of the sphingolipid is sphingosine with the amino group acylated with a long-chain fatty acid. This combination, which is called a ceramide, gives the molecule a shape similar to that of diacylglycerol. Reaction with CDP-choline adds phosphorylcholine to produce sphingomyelin.

Formation of glycolipids

Glycolipids are also formed from ceramide, but in this case sugar units provide the hydrophilic portion of the molecule. As indicated in Figure 3.9, UDP-sugars are used to add single glucose or galactose units to produce cerebrosides. Gangliosides are more complex glycolipids with an oligosaccharide linked to the *N*-acyl sphingosine by glucose. The oligosaccharide section of a ganglioside contains at least one sialic acid unit such as *N*-acetylneuraminate (see Figure 2.6a). Gangliosides are particularly important in the membranes of the central nervous system.

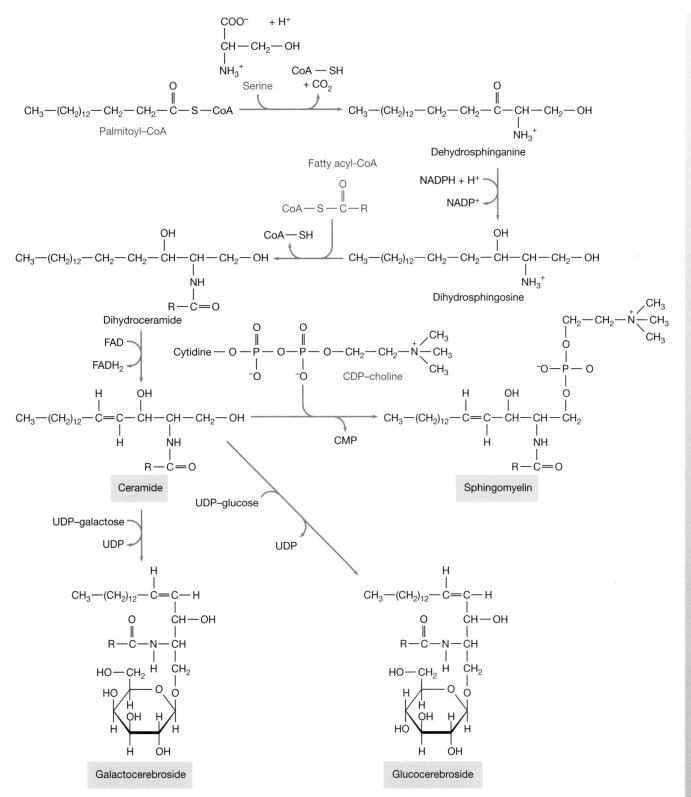

Figure 3.9 Formation of sphingomyelin, ceramide and the glycolipids, galactocerebroside and glucocerebroside.

3.9 Composition, assembly and characteristics of membranes

Membrane composition

All cells are surrounded by a plasma membrane and membranes also form compartments within the cell. The characteristics of a particular membrane reflect its composition. Those membranes that serve primarily as barriers to ions, such as the myelin sheath, have a high proportion of lipid whereas those that are metabolically active or have a large number of membrane transport proteins may be more than two-thirds protein.

Because phospholipids and glycolipids are molecules with a large hydrophobic portion and a smaller hydrophilic region, they behave in a highly predictable manner when placed in an aqueous medium by forming a bimolecular layer. This behaviour gives the maximum exposure of the hydrophilic region of the lipids to water while at the same time minimizing the interaction of the hydrophobic fatty acid chains with water. Cylindrical phospholipid molecules form bimolecular layers more easily than droplets, or micelles, because the layer allows more room for the bulky fatty acids. The fact that phospholipids and glycolipids spontaneously form bimolecular sheets means that no mechanism is necessary for the assembly of a membrane. As soon as the membrane lipids are synthesized they will immediately form a bimolecular layer.

Physical characteristics of membranes

The physical characteristics of a membrane are largely determined by the nature of the membrane lipids. If the fatty acid chains in the phospholipids were to consist entirely of saturated acyl groups the membrane would be quite rigid at body temperature. Normally one of the two fatty acids in a glycerol phospholipid is unsaturated which helps to increase membrane fluidity because it keeps the adjacent membrane lipid molecules from packing together too closely. Another constituent that increases fluidity is cholesterol. This rigid molecule is entirely lipophilic except for its single hydroxyl group. This structure enables the cholesterol molecules to slip between adjacent phospholipids, increasing the fluidity in the centre of the bilayer.

A bimolecular layer consisting entirely of membrane lipids presents an effective barrier to hydrophilic molecules and ions, although not to water. This means that movement of hydrophilic substances across a membrane requires the presence of transport proteins, or proteins that form channels or pores. Membrane proteins responsible for the transfer of polar molecules across the membrane normally have a number of sections (typically seven or more) of polypeptide which span the bilayer and these regions of the protein interact strongly with the phospholipid fatty acids and cholesterol. As indicated in the next chapter, these membrane proteins are incorporated into a newly formed bimolecular layer either by entering it as they are being synthesized by a membrane-bound ribosome, or by being delivered to the membrane by a chaperone protein which binds the polypeptide as it is being synthesized. Not all of the proteins associated with membranes are integrated into the lipid bilayer. Some of the enzymes that give a membrane its functional characteristics are bound to the polar head groups of the membrane lipids and are known as peripheral proteins. Such proteins can easily be distinguished from integral proteins because they can be dissociated from the membrane lipids by a simple buffer solution, whereas those spanning the bilayer must be extracted by a detergent.

3.10 The role of lipoproteins in the transport of triacylglycerol and cholesterol between tissues

Although triacylglycerols that are formed in one tissue, such as the liver, are transported by the blood to another, such as adipose tissue, this transfer only occurs in the form of a complex with protein. These lipoproteins can be divided into four main types: chylomicrons formed from dietary triacylglycerols in the small intestine (see Chapter 10), very low density lipoproteins (VLDL) formed by the liver (see Chapter 6), low density lipoprotein (LDL) and high density lipoprotein (HDL). The composition of the four types is summarized in Figure 3.10 which shows that LDL has the highest cholesterol content (48%) and the HDL lipoproteins, which are the smallest, are 47% protein.

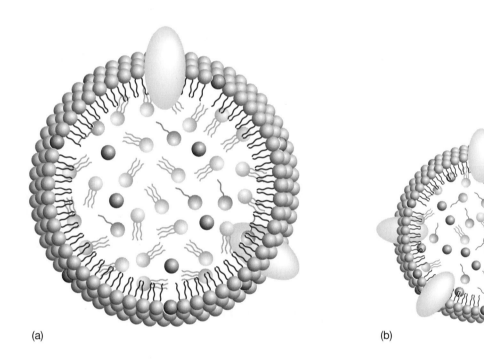

(a)   (b)

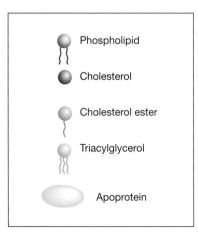

Properties of human lipoproteins	Diameter (nm)	Percentage composition				
		Protein	Cholesterol free	ester	Phospholipid	Triacylglycerol
Chylomicrons	80–200	2	1	3	9	85
VLDL	30–80	10	7	13	15	55
LDL	20–25	23	8	40	22	7
HDL	8–10	47	5	15	25	8

Figure 3.10 Composition of the main classes of lipoproteins and schematic representation of the structures of VLDL (a) and LDL (b).

Legend:
- Phospholipid
- Cholesterol
- Cholesterol ester
- Triacylglycerol
- Apoprotein

Chylomicrons

Chylomicrons are by far the largest of the lipoproteins and they also have the lowest density since they contain the least protein (about 2%). Their function is to carry dietary triacylglycerols and other dietary lipids from the intestine by way of the lymphatic system to the adipose tissue and to other extrahepatic tissues such as muscle. In these tissues the lipoprotein lipase on the surface of the endothelial cells lining the capillaries hydrolyses the triacylglycerols, allowing the fatty acids to be taken up by the tissue in which the capillaries are located. The glycerol released by the lipase is removed from the blood by the liver and this organ also deals with the remnant of the chylomicron with its increased proportion of cholesterol, cholesterol esters and phospholipids.

Very low density lipoprotein

VLDL, which also consists mainly of lipid, is responsible for the transport of the triacylglycerol formed in the liver to adipose tissue and other extrahepatic sites. Again in this case the fatty acids are released to the tissues by the endothelial lipoprotein lipase. As VLDL loses its triacylglycerol its density increases and it becomes intermediate density lipoprotein (IDL). IDL lipoproteins are either taken up by the liver or turned into the cholesterol-delivering lipoprotein, LDL.

Low density lipoprotein

The function of LDL is to transport cholesterol from the liver to peripheral tissues. Most of the cholesterol is in the form of cholesterol esters. The change from VLDL to LDL is not just a consequence of the loss of triacylglycerol, but also results in a shift in the protein composition. Apoprotein-B, which is the principal protein component in LDL, binds to a specific receptor on the cells to which it is delivering the cholesterol. This enables the LDL to enter the cell by endocytosis together with the receptor, and after fusing with a lysosome the cholesterol esters are hydrolysed so that the cholesterol can be used for membrane synthesis.

High density lipoprotein

HDL can be distinguished from the other lipoproteins by the nature of its apoproteins as well as its small size and high proportion of protein. The principal function of HDL appears to be to carry excess cholesterol, mainly in the form of cholesterol esters, away from the peripheral tissues and back to the liver.

3.11 Prostaglandins and steroid hormones

There are two main classes of hormones which are derived from lipids, the eicosanoids and the steroid hormones. As indicated in Figure 3.11, the structures of these two groups of hormones are very different. The eicosanoids, which include the prostaglandins, are formed from 20-carbon polyunsaturated fatty acids such as arachidonate. Steroid hormones are formed from cholesterol in the adrenal cortex and reproductive tissues. In addition to their structural differences

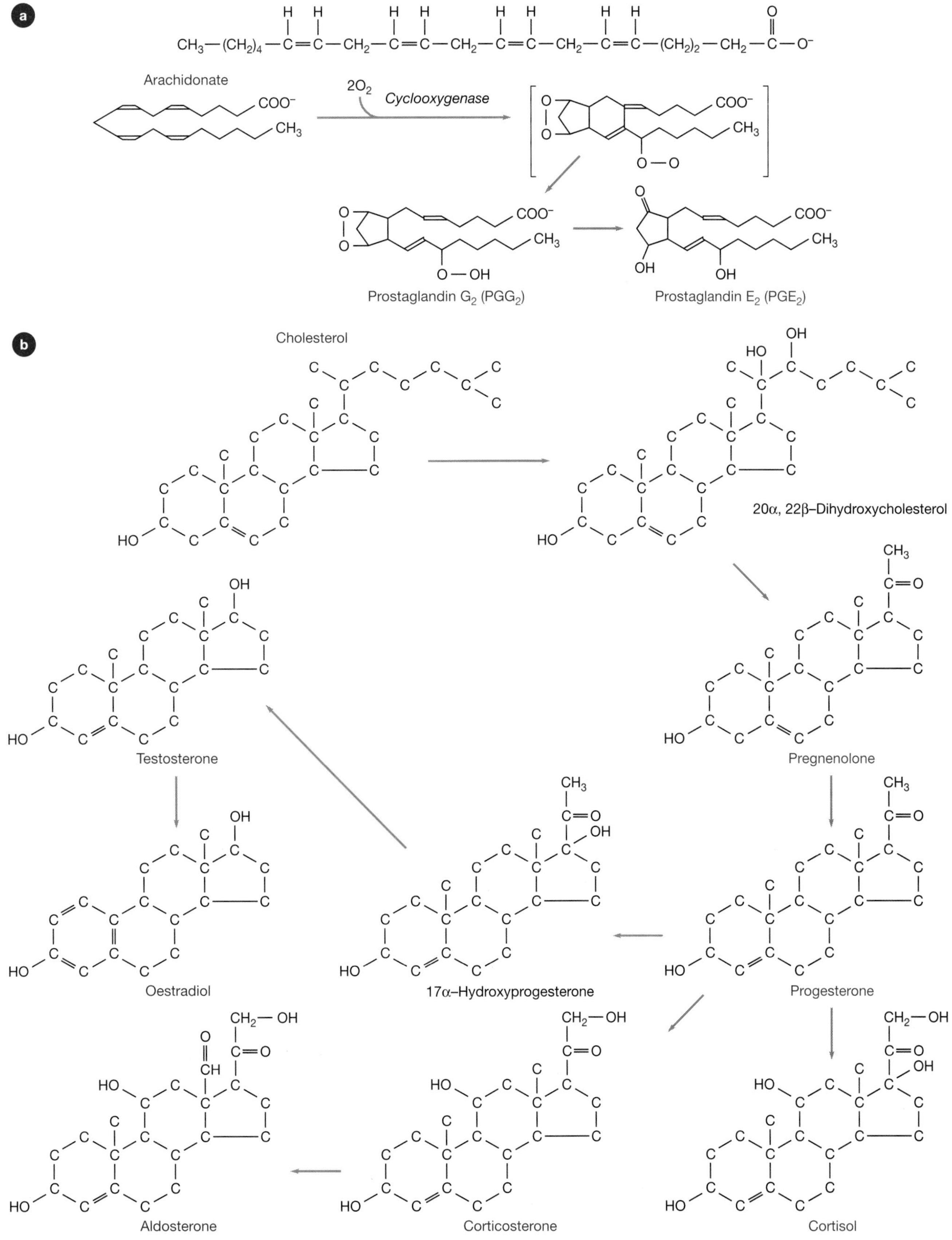

Figure 3.11 (a) Formation of prostaglandins from arachidonate. (b) General scheme for the formation of steroid hormones from cholesterol.

these two groups of hormones also differ in the way they produce their effects. The steroid hormones behave as classical hormones, that is they are formed by specialized cells, circulate through the bloodstream and cause specific effects on cells which are generally far removed from the site of hormone synthesis. The eicosanoids, on the other hand, are known as local hormones because they either produce their effects in the cells in which they are synthesized (autocrine effects) or in immediately adjacent cells (paracrine effects).

Prostaglandins

Figure 3.11(a) shows in outline how prostaglandin can be formed from arachidonate. Prostaglandins have a range of actions too broad to be described here, but one example is their stimulation of the inflammation resulting from injury or disease. This is particularly interesting from a metabolic point of view because the common anti-inflammatory drug aspirin acts to block the formation of prostaglandins by inhibiting the cyclooxygenase enzyme at the start of the synthetic pathway.

Steroid hormones

The formation of some of the steroid hormones from cholesterol is shown in outline in Figure 3.11(b). The initial stage of this process involves oxidation of the cholesterol side chain by the cytochrome P-450 monooxygenase system (see Figure 6.11, Box 1), and is followed by removal of most of the side chain to form pregnenolone, the precursor of the common hormonal steroids. There are three main groups of steroid hormones: glucocorticoids such as cortisol, mineralocorticoids such as aldosterone or corticosterone, and the male and female reproductive hormones such as testosterone and oestradiol.

3.12 Fat-soluble vitamins

There are four fat-soluble vitamins, A, D, E and K which are all essential for humans. Figure 3.12 shows their structures and although these compounds look quite different they are all derived from five-carbon isoprene units.

Retinol (vitamin A)

This compound is essential for the formation of the visual pigment rhodopsin. Although retinol does not occur in plants, many vegetables contain β-carotene which can be converted into vitamin A. Retinol is oxidized to the aldehyde retinal and bound to a protein, opsin, to form light-sensitive rhodopsin.

Cholecalciferol (vitamin D)

Cholecalciferol is formed from 7-dehydrocholesterol as a result of the action of UV light on the skin. Two hydroxylation steps, the first in the liver and the second in the kidneys, convert it into the active hormone 1,25-dihydroxycholecalciferol which is essential for calcium absorption from the small intestine and the regulation of the deposition of calcium phosphate in bone.

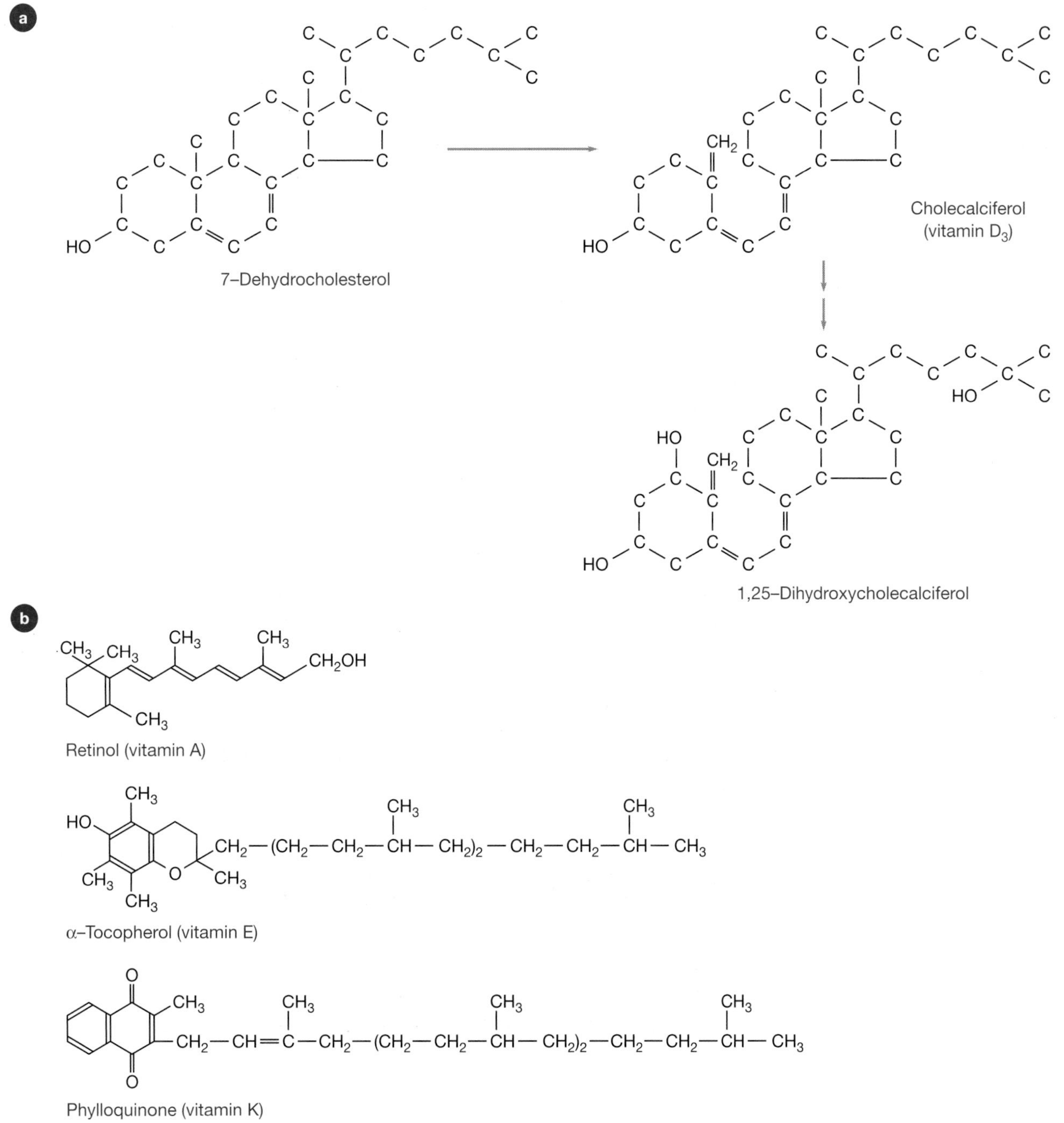

Figure 3.12 Fat-soluble vitamins. (a) Formation of cholecalciferol and its active hormonal derivative from 7-dehydrocholesterol. (b) Structures of vitamin A, vitamin E and vitamin K.

α-Tocopherol (vitamin E)

This vitamin is an important antioxidant which, like vitamin C, helps to prevent oxidative damage to membrane lipids by reacting with oxygen-free radicals. Although a deficiency of this vitamin appears to be rare, it is possible that increased intake of the vitamin may help to overcome the harmful effects of pollutants that increase the formation of oxygen-free radicals.

Phylloquinone (vitamin K)

Vitamin K is an essential cofactor for the formation of the plasma protein prothrombin, the precursor of a proteolytic enzyme which converts fibrinogen into fibrin during blood clotting (see Figure 12.6).

E X E R C I S E S

1. What advantages do triacylglycerols have as storage molecules?

2. How does the presence of unsaturated fatty acids change the characteristics of triacylglycerols and phospholipids?

3. Explain why special reactions are required to oxidize unsaturated fatty acids.

4. List the ways in which the β-oxidation pathway for fatty acids differs from the fatty acid synthetase system.

5. How can fatty acid oxidation and fatty acid synthesis occur in the same cells?

6. Explain the role of phosphatidate in the synthesis of phospholipids and triacylglycerol.

7. How does sphingomyelin differ from the glycerol phospholipids?

8. Discuss the metabolic consequences of the fact that fatty acids are degraded in the mitochondrial matrix and synthesized in the cytosol.

9. Distinguish briefly between the four main classes of lipoproteins.

10. What are the principal functions of vitamins A, D, E and K?

Further reading

Dow, J., Lindsay, G. & Morrison, J. (1996) *Biochemistry, Molecules, Cells and the Body*, Addison-Wesley, Chapter 9.

Gurr, M.I. & Harwood, J.L. (1991) *Lipid Biochemistry*, 4th edition, Chapman & Hall.

Kent, C. (1995) Eukaryotic phospholipid biosynthesis, *Annual Review of Biochemistry* **64**, 315–343.

Salway, J.G. (1994) *Metabolism at a Glance*, Blackwell Scientific.

Stryer, L. (1995) *Biochemistry*, 4th edition, W.H. Freeman, Chapters 24 & 27.

Vance, D.E. & Vance, J.E. eds (1991) *Biochemistry of Lipids, Lipoproteins, and Membranes*, Elsevier.

Nitrogen metabolism

It is the nitrogen atoms that are largely responsible for the essential roles that amino acids, nucleotides and B vitamins play as constituents of proteins, nucleic acids and coenzymes.

In an adult the dietary nitrogen intake must be balanced by an equivalent rate of nitrogen excretion.

4.1 Introduction

Nitrogen metabolism is particularly important because all cells need the three classes of nitrogen-containing cell constituents: nucleic acids, proteins and co-enzymes. Genetic information specifying the amino acid sequences of proteins is stored in the cell's DNA and expressed through RNA. In addition to their role as messenger RNA (mRNA) templates specifying the amino acid sequence in pro-teins, RNA molecules also provide crucial parts of the machinery required for protein synthesis: the transfer RNA (tRNA) and ribosomal RNA (rRNA). Key con-stituents of these nucleic acid molecules are the purine and pyrimidine bases which are heterocyclic ring compounds containing nitrogen. As pointed out in section 1.7, the triphosphate forms of the nucleotides from which RNA is made also play an indispensable role in all cells by transferring energy from the central metabolic pathways for many energy-requiring reactions and various types of work that take place within the cell. Every amino acid contains at least one nitro-gen atom, and it is these amino nitrogens which give peptide bonds the special characteristics that provide the basic features of protein folding and help to determine the overall three-dimensional shapes of individual proteins. The cat-alytic activity of enzymes is partly a consequence of the composition and three-dimensional structure of the active site, but the activity of many enzymes also depends on the third class of essential nitrogen-containing molecules: coen-zymes. Many of these compounds are derived from the B vitamins.

Because of the crucial importance of nitrogen compounds they must be con-tinually available to all cells, and for mammalian cells they are supplied in the form of amino acids and B vitamins. Although the purine and pyrimidine bases are essential they can be synthesized from amino acids. Dietary proteins can nor-mally provide all 20 amino acids but it is only necessary for the body to have eight or nine essential amino acids, since the others can be synthesized from these essential amino acids, if necessary. In fact, the body can break down some of its protein to supply amino acids for a limited period if there is a shortage of one or more essential amino acids in the diet. Despite the importance of the amino acids and the other nitrogen molecules derived from them, a fairly strict balance is maintained between nitrogen intake and excretion. This balance prevents

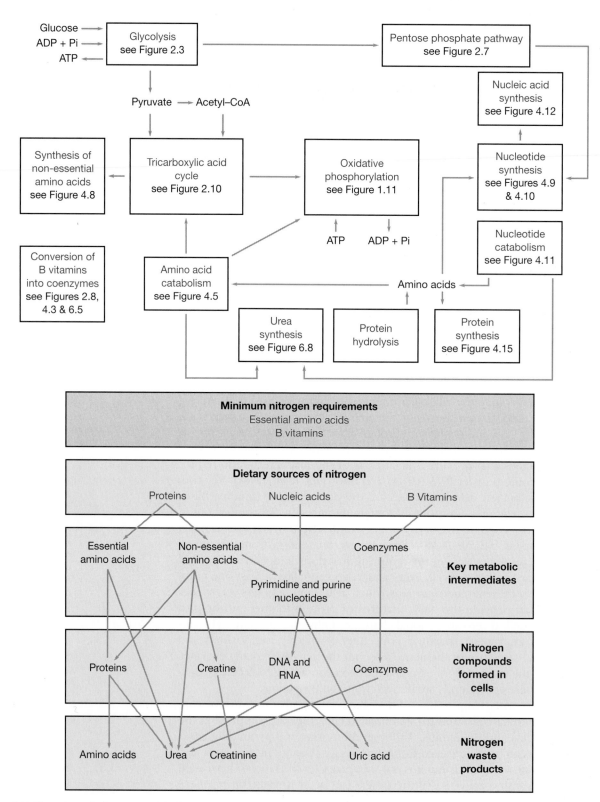

Figure 4.1 Overview of nitrogen metabolism.

excessive accumulation of nitrogen compounds The chief waste products, ammonia and urea, are formed during the breakdown of any dietary amino acids which are not needed for the synthesis of proteins or nucleic acids. Even when surplus levels of the B vitamins are available, cells cannot store most of them, so that a daily supply of most of the B vitamins is needed to maintain optimum levels of the coenzymes which are formed from them. Figure 4.1 shows a schematic summary of nitrogen metabolism.

4.2 Why are nitrogen compounds essential?

The value of the nitrogen in amino acids appears to be largely a result of the fact that it permits the amino acids to be linked together by peptide bonds. The planar nature of these bonds is important for the basic features of protein folding (both the α-helix and the β-pleated sheet) and in the formation of hydrogen bonds which help to stabilize three-dimensional structure. Some of the nitrogen-containing R-groups are also important in the active sites of many enzymes.

Why are the nitrogen-containing purines and pyrimidines essential constituents of the nucleic acids? It might be possible, but perhaps not easy, to devise a genetic code based on a set of four carbohydrate units. However, a major advantage of using the nitrogenous bases for the genetic code is that their heterocyclic rings enable them to form a stable DNA double helix, by vertical stacking of the planar rings in each strand and by forming hydrogen bonds between the bases on opposite strands. Because this pairing of the bases occurs in a highly specific way it facilitates the accurate copying of the sequence information during the replication of DNA. Base pairing is also important for the formation of RNA from DNA, and for translating the information from the mRNA to protein. This final stage of information transfer requires the rapid matching of adaptor tRNA to mRNA in order to select the correct amino acids in the sequential synthesis of proteins. The fact that bases can undergo mutation relatively easily also enables evolutionary changes to occur, and this makes it possible for organisms to adapt to changes in environmental conditions.

What is the role of nitrogen in the B vitamins and the coenzymes derived from them? These special molecules take advantage of the lone pair of electrons on the nitrogen atoms which allows them to take up an extra proton. This enables some of the coenzymes to use their nitrogens in oxidation–reduction reactions (e.g. NAD^+, FAD, see Figure 1.11). The tendency to form hydrogen bonds is important for the coenzyme involved in nitrogen transfer and decarboxylation (pyridoxal phosphate). Other vitamins have special structural features which permit group transfers (e.g. biotin, cobalamin, pantothenic acid, tetrahydrofolate and thiamine).

4.3 Nitrogen balance

In a growing individual it is obvious that there will be an increase in the total amounts of proteins, nucleic acids and other essential nitrogen compounds. However in a healthy adult with a constant body weight the total mass of nitrogen compounds remains constant, so that nitrogen excretion must balance nitrogen intake. A net nitrogen loss occurs during trauma or physical injury (see section 14.9). Small amounts of amino acids and traces of nitrogen-containing cofactors appear in the urine, but nitrogen excretion is concentrated in three main nitrogenous waste products: urea, uric acid and creatinine. This means that changes in nitrogen intake must be balanced by changes in the excretion of one or more of the major waste products. Creatinine (see Figure 6.5, Box 4) is the breakdown product of creatine in muscle and the rate at which it is formed is more closely related to the rate of muscle contraction than nitrogen intake. Uric acid is formed from purines and therefore its rate of excretion will depend on dietary purine intake and the rate of nucleic acid breakdown. Most nitrogen intake is in the form of dietary protein, and when the constituent amino acids are degraded the nitrogen released is almost exclusively converted into urea. Consequently, the main change that balances increases or decreases in nitrogen intake is an alteration in the rate at which urea is synthesized and excreted.

4.4 Essential and non-essential amino acids

Because the normal range of dietary proteins contains all 20 amino acids, it is not easy to determine which amino acids are essential for humans. Many years ago W.C.Rose and his colleagues carried out an exhaustive series of tests with volunteers who were fed a strict diet containing a mixture of amino acids in which one amino acid at a time was omitted. If the individual lost weight the missing amino acid was deemed to be essential. The results of these tests were compared with the results of similar tests on rats, and with the available information on the enzyme reactions responsible for the formation of amino acids. As a result 10 amino acids can confidently be classed as non-essential, and the metabolic pathways by which they are formed are described later in this chapter. Eight of the remaining 10 amino acids were shown by Rose's tests to be essential and the pathways for their formation do not occur in mammals. The other two, arginine and histidine, gave rather equivocal results. Histidine appeared to be essential, at least for growing mammals, but it is equally clear that mammals have the enzyme pathways necessary for the synthesis of both arginine and histidine. The probable explanation for the apparent requirement for histidine in the young is that the rate of synthesis is insufficient to meet the demand for the amino acid in the

Table 4.1 Essential and non-essential amino acids

Essential	Non-essential
*Histidine (His) H	Alanine (Ala) A
Isoleucine (Ile) I	Arginine (Arg) R
Leucine (Leu) L	Asparagine (Asn) N
Lysine (Lys) K	Aspartate (Asp) D
Methionine (Met) M	Cysteine (Cys) C
Phenylalanine (Phe) F	Glutamate (Glu) E
Threonine (Thr) T	Glutamine (Gln) Q
Tryptophan (Trp) W	Glycine (Gly) G
Valine (Val) V	Proline (Pro) P
	Serine (Ser) S
	Tyrosine (Tyr) Y

* In the young.

growing individual. In the case of arginine the rate of breakdown may exceed the rate at which the body can form it under some circumstances, but arginine is not generally considered to be essential. Table 4.1 shows the amino acids that fall into the two groups, together with their three-letter and one-letter abbreviations. The amino acid structures are shown in Figure 4.2.

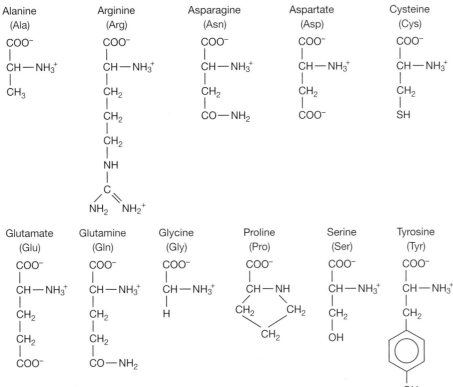

Non-essential amino acids

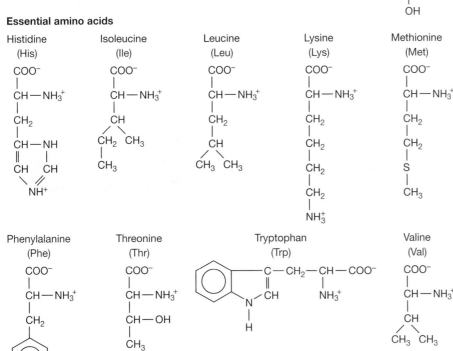

Essential amino acids

Figure 4.2
Structures of essential and non-essential amino acids.

4.5 B vitamins and the synthesis of nitrogen-containing coenzymes

The water-soluble B vitamins yield a range of coenzymes which are indispensable for many of the metabolic reactions that we have already considered in the earlier chapters (see Table 4.2). In some cases the biosynthetic pathways for the conversion of the basic vitamin structure into the coenzyme are too complicated to describe here, but Figure 4.3 shows a number of the pathways in outline.

For four of the B vitamins, biotin, folate, pyridoxine (B_6) and thiamine (B_1), the modifications required to turn the vitamin into its coenzyme are relatively modest. In order to function as a carboxyl donor biotin must be covalently linked to the ε-amino group of a lysine side chain in the enzyme it is serving (see Figure 2.8). As shown in Figure 4.3 folate has a fairly complex structure ending with glutamic acid. In order to produce the active form of the coenzyme in mammals folate is reduced to tetrahydrofolate and additional glutamate residues are added in the form of a polyglutamate peptide. Vitamin B_6 occurs both as pyridoxine and the aldehyde pyridoxal. The latter is phosphorylated to produce the coenzyme which is tightly bound to a large number of different enzymes (see for example Figure 4.4b). Conversion of vitamin B_1 into its coenzyme (Figure 2.9) merely requires the addition of pyrophosphate to the thiamine, at the expense of ATP, by a pyrophosphate transferase.

Nicotinamide and riboflavin (vitamin B_2) are essential constituents of oxidation–reduction coenzymes and Figure 4.3 shows in outline how the conversion occurs. NAD^+ and $NADP^+$ differ from the other coenzymes described above because they commonly occur in a soluble form rather than bound to an enzyme. This is also true for coenzyme A (Figure 3.5) which is formed from pantothenate, with addition of cysteine and 3'-phospho-ADP.

The most complex of the B vitamins is cobalamin (B_{12}). The coenzyme forms of B_{12} (Figure 6.5, Boxes 1–3) will be considered in Chapters 6 and 8 because they are concerned with the transfer of methyl groups in the liver and the catabolism of branched chain amino acids that takes place in muscle. Biotin and B_{12} differ from the other B vitamins in that they can be supplied by microorganisms in the large intestine. Biotin is available from plant sources as well, but B_{12} is only found in meat and meat products. B_{12} deficiencies are rare because, unlike many of the other B vitamins, cobalamin is highly conserved in the body. Nevertheless additional vitamin B_{12} is required during growth.

Table 4.2 B vitamins and related nitrogen-containing coenzymes

Vitamin	Coenzyme	Figure showing structure
Biotin	Biotin	Figure 2.8
Folates	Tetrahydrofolates	Figure 4.7
Niacin	NAD^+ and $NADP^+$	Figure 1.10
Pantothenic acid	Coenzyme A	Figure 3.5
Pyridoxine	Pyridoxal phosphate	Figure 4.4(b)
Riboflavin	FMN and FAD	Figure 4.3
Thiamine	Thiamine pyrophosphate	Figure 2.9
Vitamin B_{12}	Cobalamin	Figure 6.5

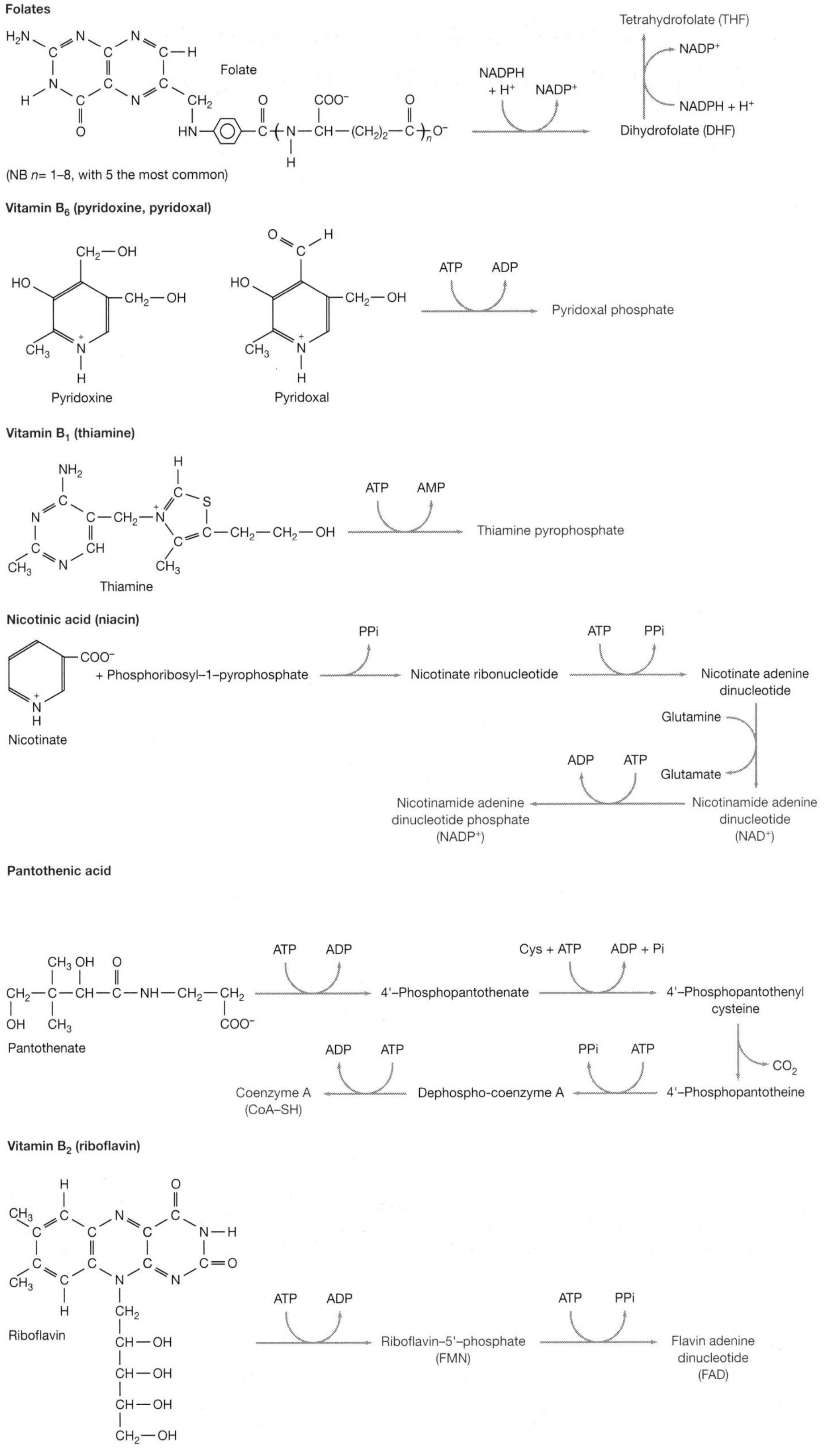
Folates
Folate
NADPH + H⁺
NADP⁺
Tetrahydrofolate (THF)
NADP⁺
NADPH + H⁺
Dihydrofolate (DHF)
(NB n= 1–8, with 5 the most common)
Vitamin B6 (pyridoxine, pyridoxal)
Pyridoxine
Pyridoxal
ATP
ADP
Pyridoxal phosphate
Vitamin B1 (thiamine)
Thiamine
ATP
AMP
Thiamine pyrophosphate
Nicotinic acid (niacin)
Nicotinate
+ Phosphoribosyl–1–pyrophosphate
PPi
Nicotinate ribonucleotide
ATP
PPi
Nicotinate adenine dinucleotide
Glutamine
Glutamate
Nicotinamide adenine dinucleotide (NAD⁺)
ADP
ATP
Nicotinamide adenine dinucleotide phosphate (NADP⁺)
Pantothenic acid
Pantothenate
ATP
ADP
4'–Phosphopantothenate
Cys + ATP
ADP + Pi
4'–Phosphopantothenyl cysteine
CO2
4'–Phosphopantotheine
PPi
ATP
Dephospho-coenzyme A
ADP
ATP
Coenzyme A (CoA–SH)
Vitamin B2 (riboflavin)
Riboflavin
ATP
ADP
Riboflavin–5'–phosphate (FMN)
ATP
PPi
Flavin adenine dinucleotide (FAD)

Figure 4.3
B vitamin structures and the steps involved in their conversion to coenzymes.

4.6 Transamination, deamination and the links between amino acid catabolism, urea synthesis and the TCA cycle

Because nitrogen excretion must balance nitrogen intake, after allowing for any increase in body mass, it is obviously necessary to have metabolic pathways that remove the nitrogen from all of the amino acids so that it can be converted into the principal nitrogen waste product, urea. The general features of amino acid breakdown are illustrated in Figures 4.4 and 4.5. Details of the catabolic pathways for individual amino acids are given in Figures 4.6, 6.4, 6.5, 6.6, 6.7, 6.9 and 8.5.

Transamination

For many amino acids the initial stage of catabolism is transamination, a process in which a group of aminotransferase enzymes are responsible for converting the α-amino acids into 2-oxo acids. By this means the α-amino groups are transferred to either oxaloacetate or 2-oxoglutarate forming aspartate or glutamate, respectively (Figure 4.4a). Figure 4.4(b) shows in detail how the vitamin B_6 coenzyme

Enzymes

1. Aminotransferase
2. Glutamate dehydrogenase
3. Glutamine synthetase
4. Glutaminase
5. Carbamoyl-phosphate synthetase

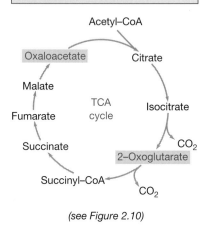

(see Figure 2.10)

Figure 4.4(a)
The combination of deamination plus transamination: links from these processes to glutamine synthesis, urea synthesis and the tricarboxylic acid (TCA) cycle.

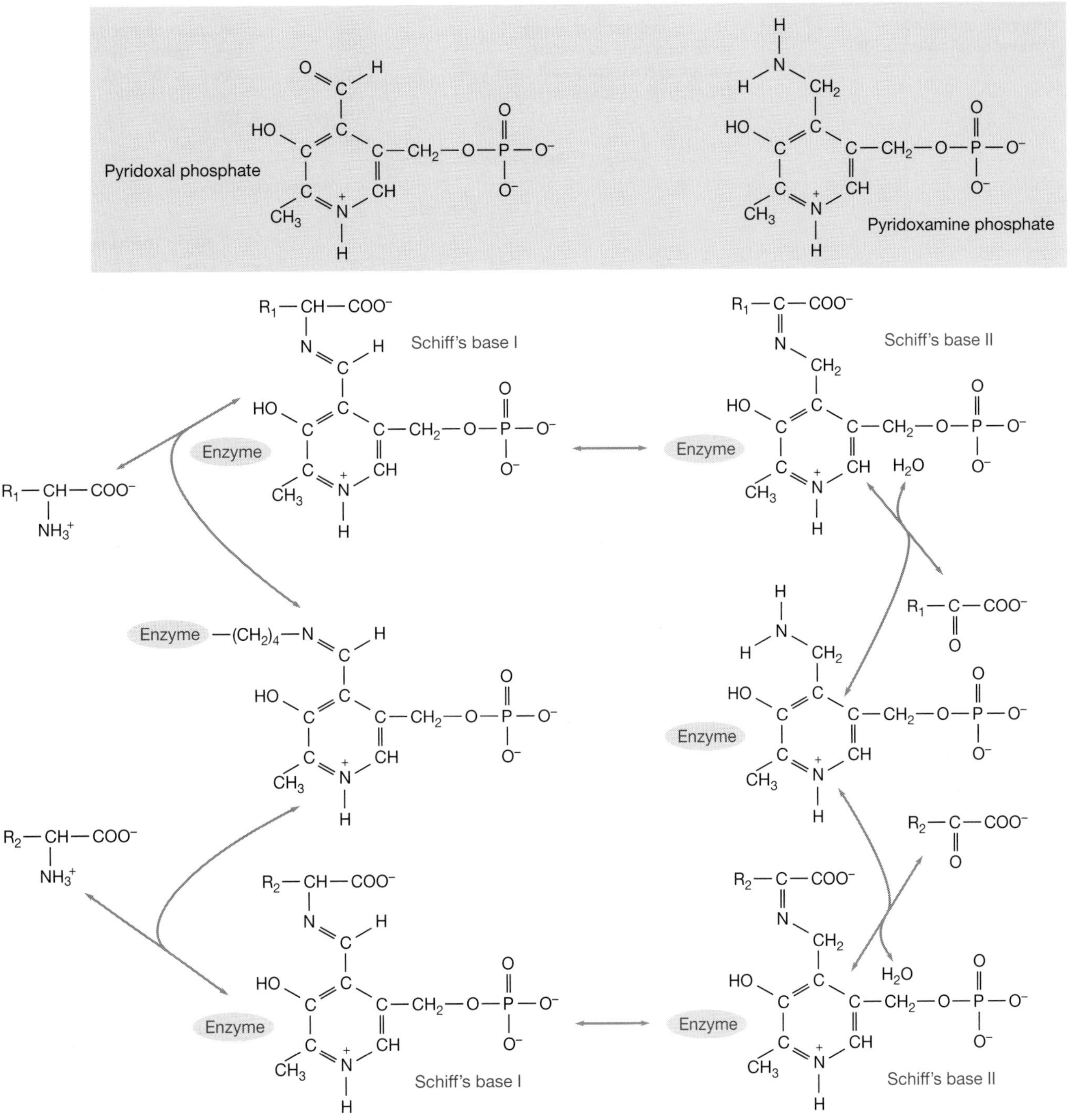

Overall reaction

$$R_1\text{—}\underset{\displaystyle NH_3^+}{\underset{|}{CH}}\text{—}COO^- + R_2\text{—}CO\text{—}COO^- \longleftrightarrow R_1\text{—}CO\text{—}COO^- + R_2\text{—}\underset{\displaystyle NH_3^+}{\underset{|}{CH}}\text{—}COO^-$$

Figure 4.4(b) Detailed steps of the transamination reaction.

pyridoxal phosphate acts to transform an α-amino acid into a 2-oxo acid. In order to act as a coenzyme pyridoxine must first be converted to pyridoxal phosphate (PLP) (see the box at the top of Figure 4.4b) and it is then linked covalently to a lysine side chain in the catalytic site of the aminotransferase enzyme forming a Schiff's base. This link to the ε-N of lysine is displaced by the amino acid sub-

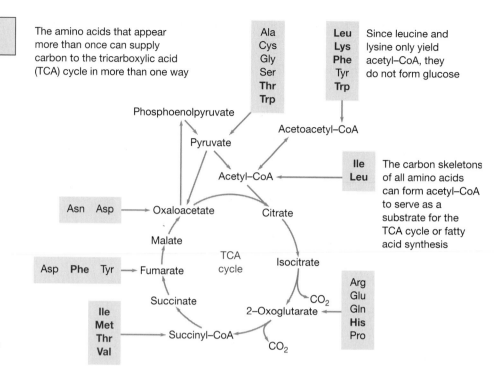

Figure 4.5
General patterns of amino acid catabolism showing the fate of the carbon skeletons.

strate for the transamination reaction so that the α-amino group forms a Schiff's base with the PLP. Despite losing the covalent link to lysine the PLP remains tightly bound to the active site of the enzyme, and in the second step of the reaction the double bond of Schiff's base I switches to the other side of the nitrogen forming Schiff's base II. Addition of water across the double bond releases the 2-oxo form of the former amino acid and leaves the amino group attached to the coenzyme which has now become pyridoxamine phosphate, still tightly bound to the enzyme. The 2-oxo acid now diffuses away to be replaced by another 2-oxo acid which enters the active site and forms a Schiff's base II with the pyridoxamine phosphate. The double bond then changes to the pyridoxine side of the nitrogen (Schiff's base I) and, as a result, the α-amino acid corresponding to the second 2-oxo acid is released with renewal of the Schiff's base between the lysine side chain and PLP which completes the cycle.

For five of the amino acids, arginine, lysine, proline, threonine and tryptophan, there is no aminotransferase, and, in fact, the major route of degradation for half of the amino acids involves conversion to a different amino acid or removal of the amino group by a reaction other than transamination. Nevertheless, the aminotransferase enzymes play an important part in the removal of amino nitrogen, particularly because they are responsible for transferring amino nitrogen to form glutamate and aspartate. These two amino acids supply nitrogen directly for urea synthesis; alternatively glutamate can serve as the substrate for glutamine synthesis (see Figure 4.4a). Furthermore, as we shall see in section 4.8, the aminotransferases play a crucial role in the biosynthesis of non-essential amino acids (see Figure 4.8).

Urea synthesis

Figure 4.4(a) also shows how the two amino acids formed by the transamination reactions, glutamate and aspartate, participate in urea synthesis. Glutamate must be deaminated by glutamate dehydrogenase to provide the ammonia for the synthesis of the carbamoyl-phosphate for the synthesis of citrulline from ornithine in the mitochondrial matrix. Aspartate, on the other hand, participates directly in urea synthesis, being responsible for the conversion of citrulline to arginine in the cytoplasm. However, it must be stressed that the full sequence of the urea synthesis reactions can only take place in the liver (see Figure 6.8). The formation of citrulline from ornithine can occur in the intestine, but in other tissues the only quantitatively important aspects of nitrogen removal are transamination and deamination. Since a great deal of amino acid catabolism takes place outside the liver, it is clear that some mechanism must exist to transfer the nitrogen to the liver. At first sight it might seem that glutamate or aspartate could take part in this transfer because of their key role in transamination. However, this does not occur. Despite the fact that most cells have relatively high intracellular concentrations of these two acidic amino acids the concentrations in the blood are low. Instead, intra-organ transfer of nitrogen to the liver relies on the production of two neutral amino acids, alanine and glutamine, by the peripheral tissues. Alanine is formed from pyruvate by alanine aminotransferase, which is present in the cytoplasm of most cells. Glutamine, on the other hand, must be formed from glutamate by glutamine synthetase which adds ammonia at the expense of the hydrolysis of ATP:

$$\text{Glutamate} + NH_4^+ + ATP \rightarrow \text{glutamine} + ADP + Pi \qquad (4.1)$$

The synthesis of glutamine raises an interesting problem since in most tissues the oxidative deamination of glutamate will be the main source of the ammonia, and yet the synthesis of glutamine is essential to protect the cell from excessive ammonia levels. The answer probably lies in the localization of both the deamination and most of the glutamine synthesis within the mitochondrial matrix where the glutamate concentration is maintained at a high level by uptake from the cytosol. Mitochondria also accumulate NH_4^+ from the cytoplasm, a process that is driven by the membrane potential (negative inside) across the mitochondrial inner membrane.

How does the cell form nitrogen compounds by the addition of ammonia?

The conversion of 2-oxoglutarate to glutamate and of glutamate to glutamine illustrate two of the techniques used by cells to protect against rising ammonia concentrations by incorporating nitrogen into a non-toxic compound. In both cases the expenditure of energy is necessary, but the two mechanisms are very different.

The conversion of 2-oxoglutarate into glutamate by glutamate dehydrogenase is a reductive amination which can occur with either NADH or NADPH as the reducing agent. However, the reaction is freely reversible so that it can occur in either direction depending on the ratios of reactants and products. Thus, although the amination requires NH_4^+, it does not depend exclusively on the NH_4^+ concentration. Glutamine synthesis, on the other hand, is linked to the hydrolysis of ATP and under normal conditions the reverse reaction requires a separate enzyme, glutaminase. Since the cell normally maintains a high ATP/ADP ratio the rate of formation of glutamine by glutamine synthetase is largely dependent on the concentration of ammonia and this has the effect of protecting the cell from dangerously high levels of ammonia.

The other way that NH_4^+ can be incorporated into a cell constituent is by the formation of carbamoyl-phosphate. There are two enzymes that can form this useful biosynthetic intermediate and the difference between the reactions that they catalyse underlines the importance of mitochondrial/cytoplasmic compartmentation in restricting the areas of the cell that are exposed to NH_4^+.

Carbamoyl-phosphate synthesis for the conversion of ornithine to citrulline occurs in the mitochondrial matrix and involves the addition of NH_4^+ at the expense of two ATPs. Carbamoyl-phosphate for pyrimidine synthesis also requires two ATPs but is formed in the cytoplasm with the ammonia first being incorporated into glutamine and then donated by glutamine to the enzyme responsible for carbamoyl-phosphate synthesis.

A third technique for NH_4^+ addition is to form glutamate by amination of 2-oxoglutarate and then transfer the $-NH_3^+$ by transamination to oxaloacetate, forming aspartate. Aspartate can then donate its nitrogen, yielding fumarate. When this mechanism is used in biosynthesis an ATP is split to give ADP plus phosphate, as in purine biosynthesis, or to give AMP plus a pyrophosphate, as in the urea cycle.

4.7 *General pattern of amino acid catabolism*

It is important to recognize that all 20 of the amino acids are metabolized by humans and other mammals. If this were not so it would be necessary for any non-metabolized amino acid occurring in the diet to be excreted. Although trace amounts of amino acids do appear in the urine there is no evidence that particular amino acids are systematically excreted rather than broken down.

The combination of deamination with or without transamination provides the general pattern for nitrogen removal from some of the amino acids (see Figure 4.6). However, with 20 different amino acid structures it is not surprising to find that there are important differences in detail for individual amino acids. In addition to the oxidative deamination of glutamate by glutamate dehydrogenase, a number of other amino acids can be deaminated directly without transferring the amino group to 2-oxoglutarate. For serine and threonine the major catabolic pathway is deamination by the removal and readdition of water through the action of serine–threonine dehydratase:

$$CH_2 - CH - COO^- \rightarrow CH_2 = C - COO^- \rightarrow CH_3 - CO - COO^- + NH_4^+ \quad (4.2)$$

$$\underset{OH}{|} \quad \underset{NH_3^+}{|} \qquad \qquad \underset{NH_3^+}{|} \qquad \qquad + H_2O$$

Serine $\qquad \qquad \qquad \qquad \qquad \qquad \qquad \qquad \qquad$ Pyruvate

In the case of threonine the product is 2-ketobutyrate rather than pyruvate. In order to enter the central metabolic pathways this product is converted to propionyl-CoA by an oxidative decarboxylation reaction scheme, analogous to that for pyruvate. The propionyl-CoA then forms succinyl-CoA by the pathway shown in Figure 3.4, Box 1, with a biotin-dependent carboxylation followed by the vitamin B_{12}-dependent methylmalonyl-CoA mutase (see Figure 6.5).

Three other amino acids, histidine, glycine and methionine, can lose their α-amino groups through deamination reactions. Histidine–ammonia lyase releases the α-amino group from histidine as NH_4^+ and initiates a pathway which eventually yields glutamate after the removal of a formimino group by tetrahydrofolate (see Figure 6.7). The tetrahydrofolate coenzyme also takes part in the interconversion of serine and glycine (see Figure 4.7) and is responsible for the breakdown of glycine by removing a $-CH_2-$ group to leave NH_4^+ and carbon dioxide (Figure 4.6). After methionine donates its terminal methyl group in the form of *S*-adenosylmethionine, the resulting homocysteine can combine with serine to form cystathionine. The action of cystathionine γ-lyase releases NH_4^+ and cysteine (see Figure 6.5).

There is a further group of three amino acids, arginine, glutamine and proline, that are deaminated by glutamate dehydrogenase after being converted to glutamate. Arginine is first converted to ornithine by the urea cycle enzyme arginase (see Figure 6.8), and then the terminal amino group of ornithine is removed by ornithine–oxoacid aminotransferase to yield the γ-semialdehyde of glutamate (see Figure 6.7). This intermediate is also produced by the oxidation of proline by proline dehydrogenase, and the glutamate γ-semialdehyde is further oxidized to glutamate. The conversion of glutamine to glutamate releases the amide nitrogen as NH_4^+. The formation of glutamate is used in quite a different way to remove the terminal amino group from lysine (see Figure 6.6). In this case 2-oxoglutarate reacts with the ε-amino group in the presence of NADPH as a reducing agent and the resulting compound is hydrolysed with NAD^+ as an oxidizing agent to yield glutamate and the semialdehyde of 2-aminoadipate. A reductive deamination is responsible for removal of the R-group nitrogen from tryptophan after a series of reactions has opened its five-membered ring by a dioxygenase reaction and removed the α-carbon and the α-amino group as alanine (see Figure 6.6a).

The alanine from the tryptophan side chain, alanine itself and the remaining nine amino acids shown in Figure 4.5 all lose their α-amino groups by transamination. The arginine R-group contains three nitrogens; two are lost as urea by the action of arginase in the liver, while the third one (as the δ-amino group of ornithine) is also removed by transamination.

The catabolism of isoleucine, leucine and valine is shown in Figure 8.5. Isoleucine and valine lose their amino groups by transamination producing derivatives of valeric acid. Both amino acids are ultimately converted to succinyl-CoA by way of the branched chain compound methylmalonyl-CoA. This is also the fate of the carbon skeleton of methionine, but this amino acid loses its amino group by deamination of the derivative cystathionine (see Figure 6.5). As indicated in Figure 6.9, phenylalanine and tyrosine are degraded by a common pathway, since the first step in the catabolism of phenylalanine is its hydroxylation to form tyrosine. The amino group is removed from tyrosine by transamination.

Metabolism of the carbon skeletons

Following removal of the nitrogens (and the sulphur in the case of methionine or cysteine) most of the carbon atoms from the amino acid carbon skeletons are degraded to acetyl-CoA, pyruvate or one of the TCA cycle intermediates (see Figure 4.5). Two amino acids, leucine and lysine, can only form acetyl-CoA so that their carbon skeletons are not capable of conversion into glucose, but all the others can form glucose in tissues capable of gluconeogenesis. However, since all of the TCA cycle intermediates can be converted into pyruvate by way of the oxaloacetate to phosphoenolpyruvate step and pyruvate can be decarboxylated to acetyl-CoA, this means that all amino acids are capable of supplying the cell with energy, or providing the two-carbon building blocks for fatty acid synthesis.

It is important to recognize the dietary significance of the fact that all amino acid carbon skeletons can form acetyl-CoA. As a consequence, an exclusively protein diet will provide cells with both the acetyl-CoA and the oxaloacetate necessary to enable the TCA cycle to keep the cell supplied with ATP, and it will also yield glucose for those tissues that depend on it. However, in the human diet protein is usually associated with a large intake of glucose in the form of starch. The maintenance of nitrogen balance means that in an adult the amino acids taken in as dietary protein must be balanced by an equivalent amount of amino acid degradation, and therefore excessive protein intake will lead to the production of pyruvate and acetyl-CoA in a largely uncontrolled way. If the protein is

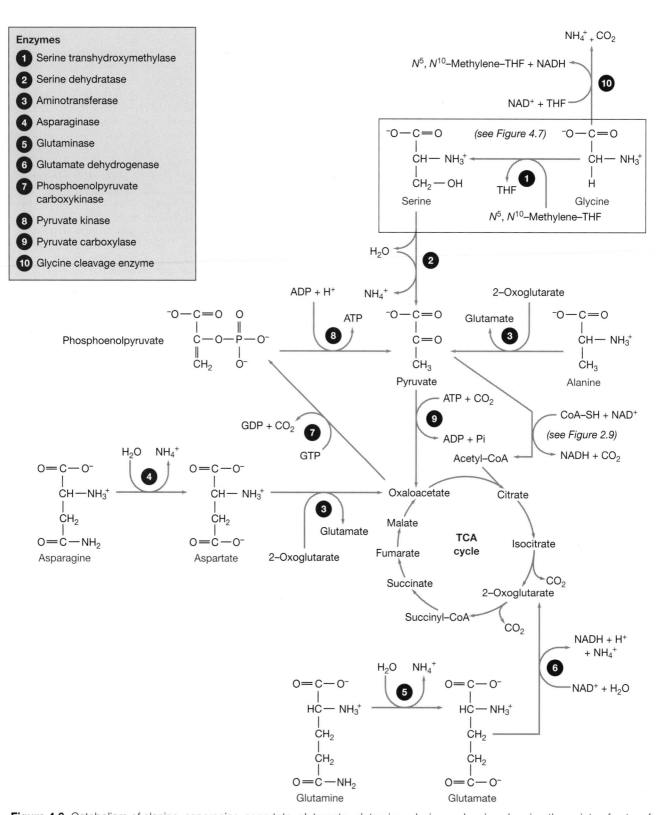

Figure 4.6 Catabolism of alanine, asparagine, aspartate, glutamate, glutamine, glycine and serine showing the points of entry of the carbon skeletons into the tricarboxylic acid (TCA) cycle. THF, tetrahydrofolate.

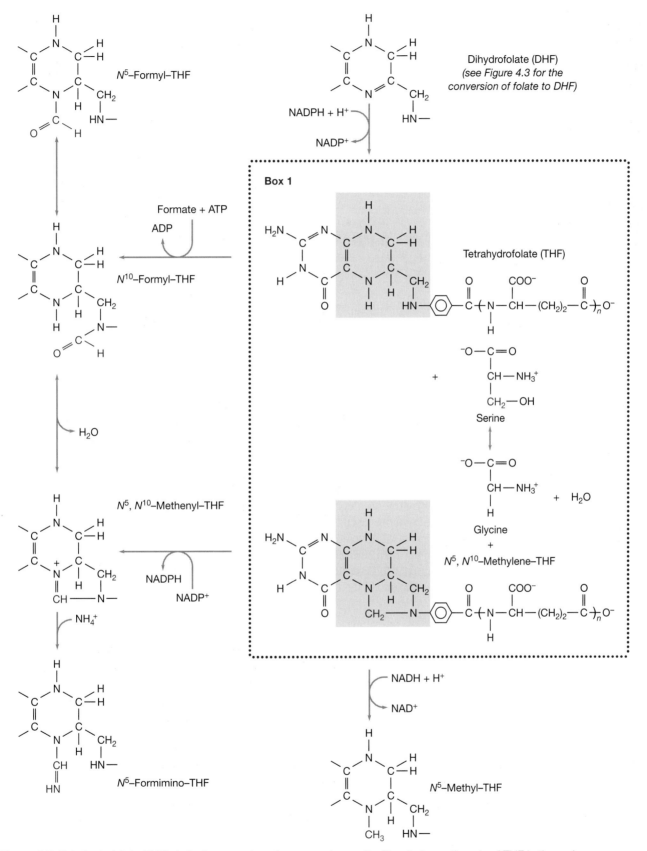

Figure 4.7 Tetrahydrofolate (THF) derivatives can transfer one-carbon units. Box 1 shows the role of THF in the serine hydroxymethyltransferase reaction. The steps responsible for the formation of other derivatives of the THF region enclosed in the small blue boxes are also shown.

associated with dietary glucose, this will ensure that the amino acids are not used for gluconeogenesis, and therefore any amino acid breakdown products in excess of those required for the formation of ATP by the TCA cycle will be converted into fatty acids. Thus, it is ineffective to attempt to reduce fat intake by substituting protein for fat in a mixed diet. A reduction in the precursors for fatty acid synthesis can only be achieved by reducing the total amount of fat *and* protein. Furthermore, even a reduction in fat and protein intake is ineffective if replaced by an increase in carbohydrate, since the extra carbohydrate intake will prevent the oxidation of fat and protein unless the increased carbohydrate intake is balanced by an increased demand for energy, through exercise or the need to keep warm.

4.8 Synthesis of non-essential amino acids

Nine of the eleven non-essential amino acids are formed from pyruvate or the TCA cycle intermediates, 2-oxoglutarate or oxaloacetate (Figure 4.8). Three amino acids, alanine, glutamate and aspartate, are formed directly from these intermediates by the addition of nitrogen. Glutamate is formed by the reductive amination of 2-oxoglutarate through the action of glutamate dehydrogenase (see Figure 4.8) and the other two are formed from pyruvate and oxaloacetate by transamina-tion, usually with glutamate. The two amides, glutamine and asparagine, are formed by ATP-dependent addition of ammonia to the terminal carboxyl groups of glutamate and aspartate (see Eq. 4.1). Proline, the imino acid, is also formed from glutamate, by reduction to glutamate semialdehyde, followed by dehydration to form the five-membered ring (see Figure 4.8). Ornithine is also formed from glutam-ate semialdehyde by transamination, and this is then converted into arginine in the liver by the urea cycle (see Figure 6.8). Serine and cysteine are formed from pyruvate by more circuitous routes (see Figure 4.8). The remaining two non-essential amino acids, glycine and tyrosine, are formed by special reactions. Glycine can be formed from serine by the tetrahydrofolate-dependent removal of a single carbon (Figure 4.7). Tyrosine is produced by hydroxylation of the essential amino acid phenylalanine (see Figure 6.9 for the details).

4.9 Purines and pyrimidines

It is obvious that the nucleotides, particularly ATP and GTP which have purine bases, play an essential part in metabolism. In addition, every cell needs a steady supply of purine and pyrimidine ribonucleotides in order to synthesize the RNA molecules required for protein synthesis. Smaller but equally essential amounts of the deoxyribonucleotides are needed by a cell whenever it divides and for making crucial repairs of defects that may arise in the cell's DNA. Such defects would cause potentially harmful mutations if left uncorrected. In order to preserve the genetic information stored in DNA and to reproduce the base sequence faithfully in the mRNA it is obviously essential that the structure of the purine and pyrimidine bases is maintained in an accurate and unaltered form.

There are three potential sources of purine and pyrimidine bases: absorption from the diet, biosynthesis and salvage following the breakdown of existing nucleotides and nucleic acids. The pentose sugar present in the nucleotides and

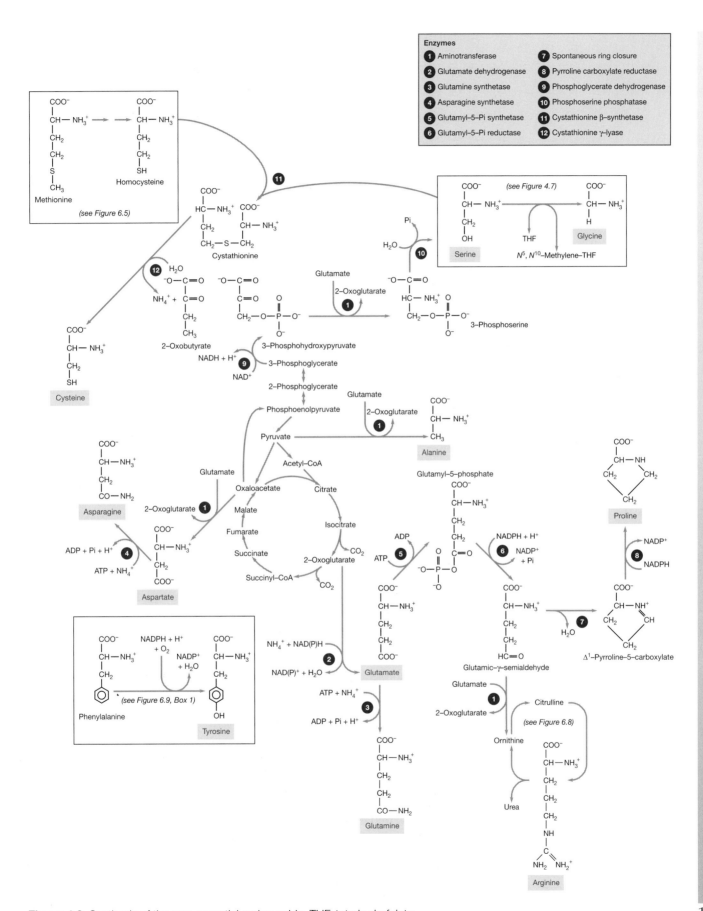

Figure 4.8 Synthesis of the non-essential amino acids. THF, tetrahydrofolate.

nucleic acids is obtained from the pentose phosphate pathway, and therefore is available in virtually all cells. The final component of the nucleotides is the phosphate which must be obtained from the diet, although once absorbed by the small intestine it is strongly conserved by reabsorption in the kidneys so that the available phosphate is effectively recycled. Maintenance of calcium and phosphate levels in the blood by the operation of transport processes in the kidney and intestine is vital in order to prevent loss of calcium from the bones and teeth.

Purine and pyrimidine absorption

All food contains at least small amounts of nucleic acids so that it would be possible to supply much of the body's requirement for purines and pyrimidines from the diet. As described in detail in Chapter 10, the initial stage of the digestion of dietary nucleic acids occurs through the action of pancreatic ribonuclease. This releases 3'-mononucleotides which are dephosphorylated by brush-border phosphatases on the surface of the absorptive cells lining the small intestine. As a result of the actions of these enzymes the apical surface of the intestinal cells is presented with a mixture of purine and pyrimidine nucleosides. All of these nucleosides, except adenosine, cytidine and their deoxyribose forms, are actively absorbed from the lumen of the intestine. Once inside the epithelial cells the nucleosides are split by phosphorolysis to yield the free bases plus pentose phosphate. Adenosine is deaminated to inosine by an enzyme on the surface of the epithelial cells prior to absorption and phosphorolysis of the nucleoside. Cytidine, on the other hand, is hardly absorbed at all. Thus, as a consequence of the digestion and absorption of nucleic acids, the enterocytes acquire relatively large amounts of the purines hypoxanthine and guanine and the pyrimidine uracil plus small amounts of thymine.

The purines are largely converted into the waste product uric acid which effectively deprives them of any value as a source of bases for nucleotide synthesis. Much of the thymine is converted into uracil, so that uracil is virtually the only pyrimidine that enters the bloodstream unchanged. In mammals uracil is generally degraded to β-alanine in the liver, rather than converted into UMP. Thus the dietary nucleic acids are of little nutritional value as potential precursors of new nucleotides or nucleic acids. Only the ribose phosphate is recovered in quantitatively significant amounts. However, as pointed out below in the section on purine catabolism, the formation of uric acid does make a valuable contribution since it is a powerful antioxidant helping to protect the body from free radicals. The normal concentration of uric acid in the human is about 0.3 mM and this is increased substantially by the metabolism of dietary purines in the small intestine.

As pointed out at the start of this chapter the purine and pyrimidine bases are central to the genetic material and its expression in all cells. As a consequence it is not surprising to find that virtually all cells have the metabolic pathways required to form the nucleotides containing the purines, adenine and guanine, and the pyrimidines, cytosine, uracil and thymine. There are two pathways, one for formation of the purines and the other for the pyrimidines, and in both pathways the pentose phosphate is added in the form of the activated intermediate, 5-phosphoribosyl-1-pyrophosphate. The two pathways are considered in detail below and they illustrate the function of a number of the nitrogen-containing coenzymes derived from the B vitamins.

Pyrimidine biosynthesis

This is the simpler of the two pathways, as the product is a single six-membered ring formed from the two starting materials, aspartate and carbamoyl-phosphate.

The steps are shown in Figure 4.9. Ring closure is followed by NAD^+-dependent oxidation to form orotic acid, and the addition of the sugar phosphate with the liberation and subsequent hydrolysis of pyrophosphate. The latter step ensures that the formation of the nucleotide orotidine is an effectively irreversible step. Finally, release of CO_2 yields the uracil-containing constituent 5'-UMP. As mentioned above the nitrogen-donor for the carbamoyl-phosphate used in the synthesis of the pyrimidines is glutamine, and the same source provides the additional nitrogen needed for the conversion of UTP to CTP. The third pyrimidine nucleotide contains thymine, but since this is only present in DNA it can only be synthesized from the 2'-deoxyribonucleotide 5'-deoxy-UMP. Reduction of the sugar is accomplished by an NADPH-dependent process in which the hydrogens are transferred by a disulphide-containing protein called thioredoxin. The methyl group which converts uracil into thymine is derived from serine by way of the folic acid coenzyme N^5-N^{10}-methylene-tetrahydrofolate.

Control of the pathway for pyrimidine synthesis occurs mainly by regulation of the enzyme aspartate transcarbamylase which is responsible for the first committed step, the formation of carbamoyl aspartate. This enzyme is inhibited by the final ribonucleotide product CTP, and it is stimulated by ATP. These regulatory effects help to maintain a balance between the concentrations of purine and pyrimidine nucleotides, since an excess of pyrimidines would be reflected in a higher CTP concentration, whereas an excess of purines would result in a higher ATP/CTP ratio.

Synthesis of purines

This pathway follows a different pattern from that for pyrimidine biosynthesis, as shown in Figure 4.10, since the sugar phosphate forms the starting material. The two rings forming the purine nucleus contain a total of four nitrogens and five carbons which are added sequentially to the sugar phosphate backbone. Glutamine provides the first nitrogen, and this is followed by glycine which provides two carbons and the second nitrogen. After that the atoms are added singly. One carbon comes from CO_2 by a carboxylation reaction and the other two from N^{10}-formyl-tetrahydrofolate. The remaining two nitrogens come from glutamine and aspartate. Closure of the six-membered ring yields the first purine nucleotide, inosinic acid. At this point the pathway divides, with aspartate providing the additional nitrogen for AMP synthesis and glutamine donating the nitrogen for the conversion to GMP. The branch in the pathway at the level of inosinic acid makes it possible for the synthesis of the two purine nucleotides to be regulated independently. Each mononucleotide inhibits its own formation from inosinic acid, and both mononucleotides inhibit the whole pathway at the first step where glutamine adds the first nitrogen to the sugar phosphate.

Salvage pathway for purines and pyrimidines

The purine bases, adenine, guanine and hypoxanthine, can also be converted into nucleotides directly by two salvage enzymes that make it possible to reuse purines released from the degradation of nucleic acids. These enzymes effectively use 5-phosphoribosyl-1-pyrophosphate to add ribose-5-phosphate to the free purines with the release and subsequent hydrolysis of pyrophosphate. Two separate enzymes are involved. Adenine phosphoribosyl transferase is responsible for the formation of AMP:

$$\text{Adenine} + \text{5-phosphoribosyl-1-pyrophosphate} \rightarrow \text{AMP} + \text{PPi} \qquad (4.3)$$

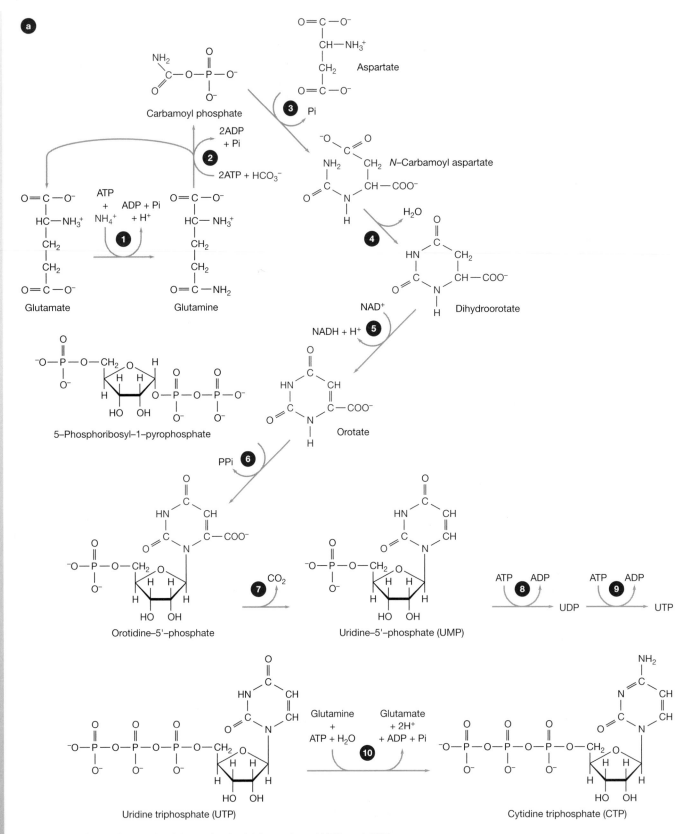

Figure 4.9 Pyrimidine nucleotide synthesis: (a) formation of UTP and CTP.

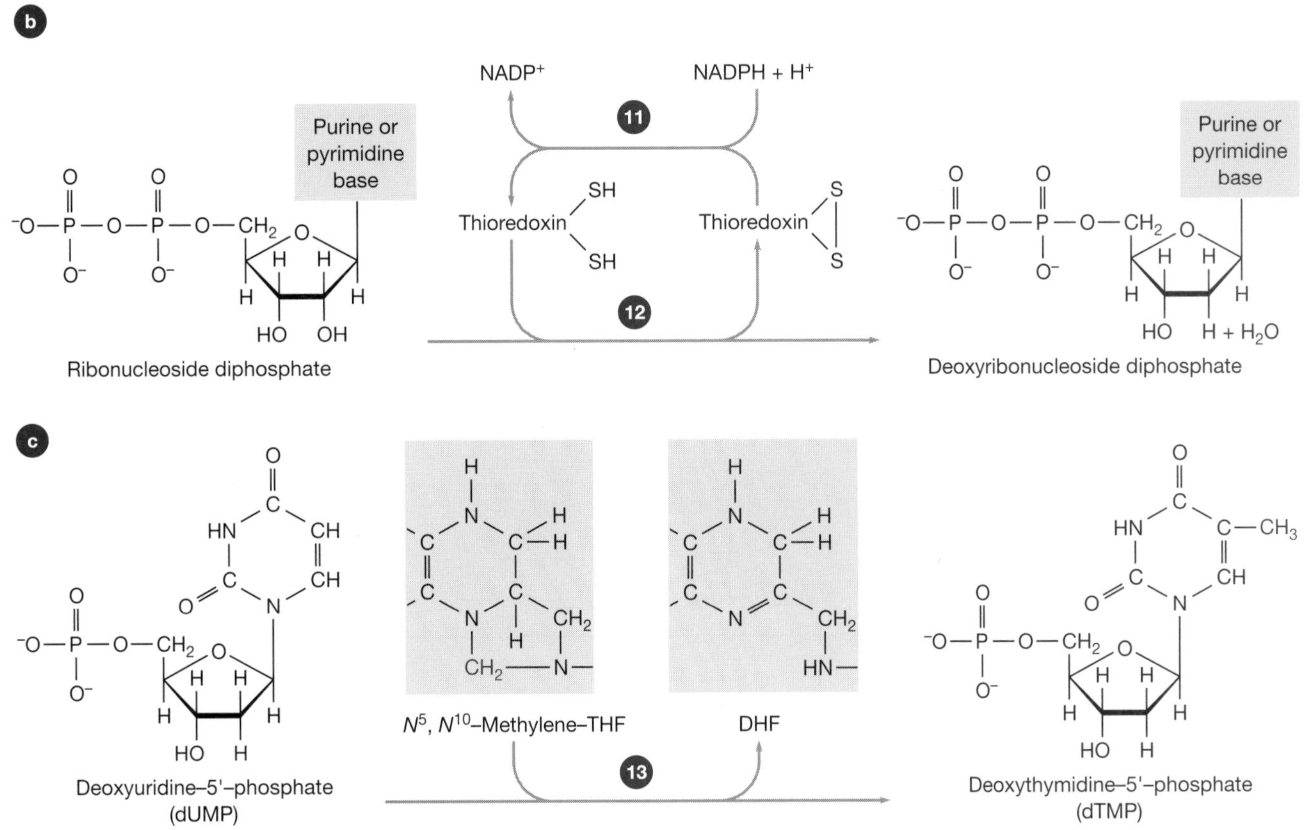

Figure 4.9 Pyrimidine nucleotide synthesis: (b) deoxynucleotide synthesis; (c) conversion of dUMP to dTMP. THF, tetrahydrofolate; DHF, dihydrofolate.

Hypoxanthine–guanine phosphoribosyl transferase can form either IMP or GMP:

$$\text{Hypoxanthine} + \text{5-phosphoribosyl-1-pyrophosphate} \rightarrow \text{IMP} + \text{PPi} \qquad (4.4)$$

$$\text{Guanine} + \text{5-phosphoribosyl-1-pyrophosphate} \rightarrow \text{GMP} + \text{PPi} \qquad (4.5)$$

The operation of the salvage pathways is only likely to be effective in those cells where the enzyme xanthine oxidase is absent. As shown in the next section this enzyme converts purines to the waste product, uric acid. Some salvage of the pyrimidine bases cytosine and uracil does occur but it is quantitatively less important than the salvage of purine bases.

Purine nucleotides can be converted into second messengers

As indicated at the end of Chapter 1 (Figure 1.13), hormones and other external effectors combine with specific receptors on the cell membrane, and in order to exert their influence within the cell they often stimulate the synthesis of a second messenger which operates in the cytoplasm. The purine nucleoside triphosphates, ATP and GTP, are the substrates for two of the most important intracellular messengers 3′,5′-cyclic AMP and 3′,5′-cyclic GMP. As Eq. 4.6 shows, the cyclic nucleotides are formed with the elimination of pyrophosphate which is immediately hydrolysed:

Enzymes

1 Glutamine synthetase
2 Carbamoyl phosphate synthetase II
3 Aspartate transcarbamylase
4 Dihydroorotase
5 Dihydroorotase dehydrogenase
6 Orotate phosphoribosyl transferase
7 Orotidylate decarboxylase
8 UMP kinase
9 Nucleoside diphosphate kinase
10 CTP synthetase
11 Thioredoxin reductase
12 Ribonucleotide reductase
13 Thymidylate synthetase

113

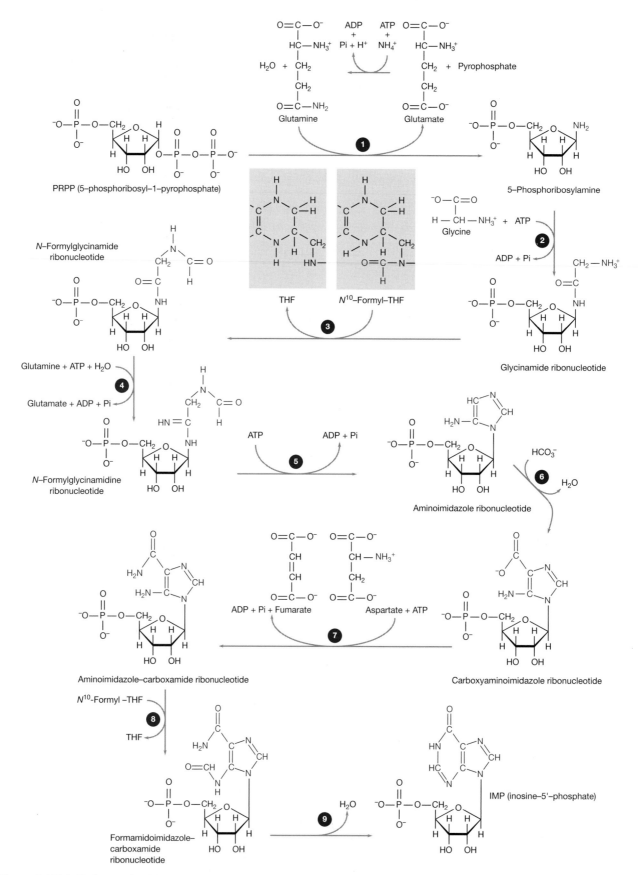

Figure 4.10(a) Purine nucleotide synthesis. The formation of inosine-5'-phosphate (IMP).

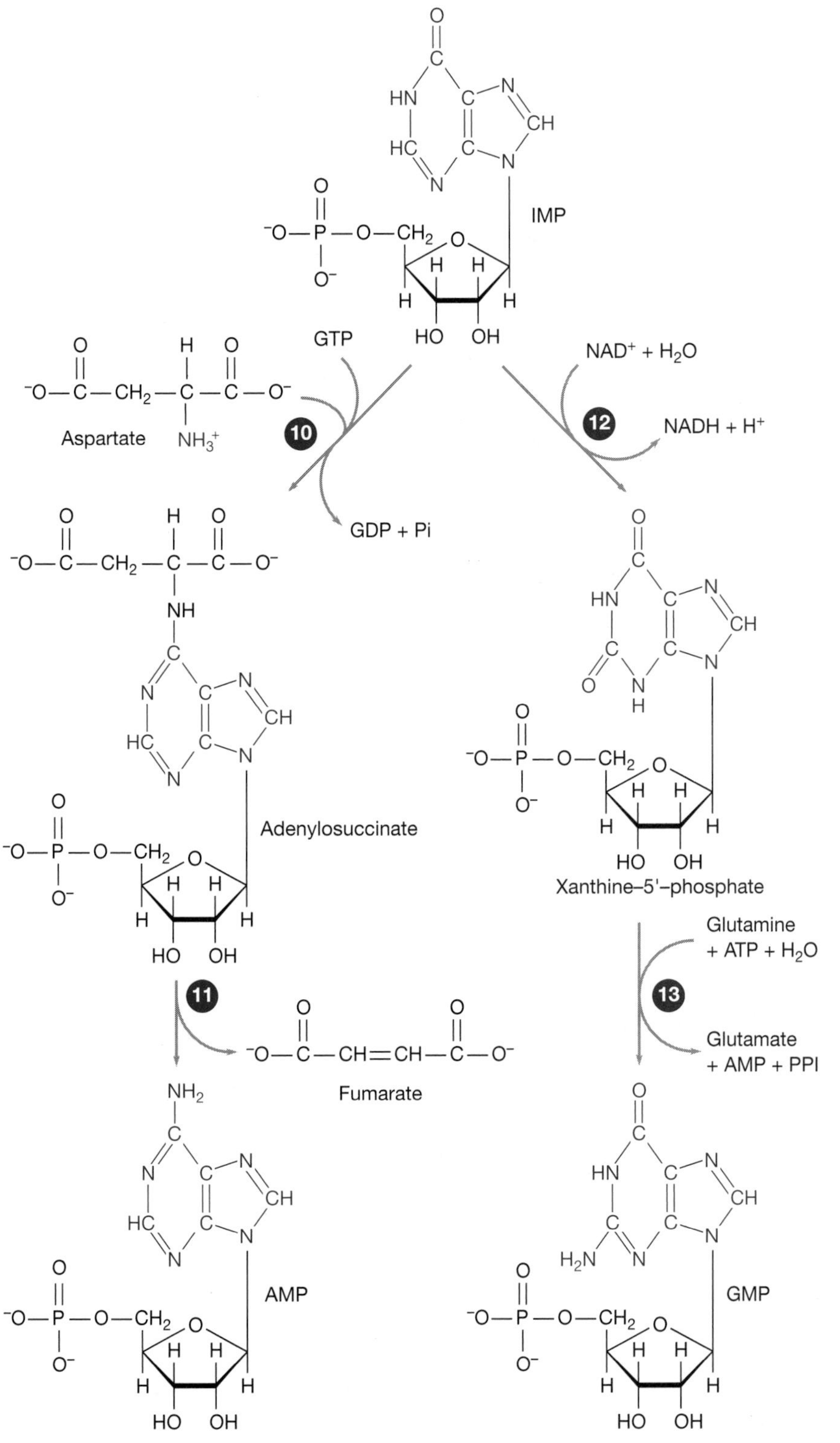

Enzymes

1. PRPP amidotransferase
2. Glycinamide ribonucleotide synthetase
3. Glycinamide ribonucleotide transformylase
4. Formylglycinamidine ribonucleotide synthetase
5. Aminoimidazole ribonucleotide synthetase
6. Aminoimidazole ribonucleotide carboxylase
7. Aminoimidazole–carboxamide ribonucleotide synthetase
8. Aminoimidazole–carboxamide ribonucleotide transformylase
9. IMP cyclohydrolase
10. Adenylosuccinate synthetase
11. Adenylosuccinate lyase
12. IMP dehydrogenase
13. GMP synthetase

Figure 4.10(b)
The conversion of IMP into AMP and GMP.

$$\text{ATP} \rightarrow 3',5'\text{-cyclic AMP} + \text{pyrophosphate} \qquad (4.6)$$

Adenyl cyclase is responsible for the formation of 3',5'-cyclic AMP and for it to be effective as an internal messenger it must be continually degraded so that its cytoplasmic concentration reflects the magnitude and duration of the external stimulus (see Figure 1.13). The widely distributed phosphodiesterase enzyme is responsible for the hydrolysis of both cyclic nucleotides.

Recently another purine derivative, cyclic ADP-ribose, has been shown to act as a second messenger in a number of different types of cells such as heart muscle, smooth muscle and in both types of secretory cells in the pancreas. This compound appears to be particularly important in controlling Ca^{2+} release from intracellular organelles. It is formed by the cyclic ADP-ribose synthetase enzyme from NAD^+:

$$NAD^+ \rightarrow cyclic\ ADP\text{-}ribose + nicotinamide \tag{4.7}$$

As with the other cyclic nucleotides, hydrolysis to ADP-ribose is essential for its role as a messenger and this is accomplished by cyclic ADP-ribose hydrolyase which appears to be closely associated with the synthetase.

Purine and pyrimidine catabolism

The pathways for the catabolism of the purines and pyrimidines are shown in Figure 4.11. The pattern of breakdown is very different for the two types of bases. In the case of the pyrimidines the ring is reduced and then opened, and with the exception of β-alanine the nitrogen is removed by deamination and transamination as ammonia, which must ultimately be converted into urea. However, in the case of the purines only the amino nitrogen outside the ring is removed as ammonia. The purine ring itself is oxidized to uric acid by xanthine oxidase and excreted. Humans and other primates lack the enzyme, found in lower mammals, to convert the urate to allantoin, but recent studies have shown that this conversion can occur non-enzymatically by interaction with oxygen free radicals (see Figure 4.11b). In this way the relatively high urate concentration in the blood helps to protect the body against the potentially damaging effects of free radicals. This action of urate provides an alternative to the combined actions of the enzymes superoxide dismutase and catalase.

4.10 Nucleic acid synthesis

The synthesis of nucleic acids is an essential feature of the metabolism in all cells. When a cell divides, it passes on its genetic information to both the daughter cells, and before this can occur the cell's DNA must be replicated. Furthermore, the protein constituents of the cell must also be duplicated and this requires RNA synthesis to supply both the machinery for protein synthesis, in the form of ribosomes and tRNA molecules, and the mRNA template by which the sequence information is transferred from the DNA to the site of protein synthesis on the ribosomes.

From a metabolic point of view nucleic acid synthesis is an uncomplicated process as shown schematically in Figure 4.12(a). The molecules are formed sequentially with each nucleotide unit added as a triphosphate to the 3'-hydroxyl of the preceding nucleotide with the release and subsequent hydrolysis of a pyrophosphate molecule. The particular nucleotide to be added in each case is determined by pairing with the base on a complementary strand. This ensures that the base sequence is accurately transmitted to the newly synthesized molecule.

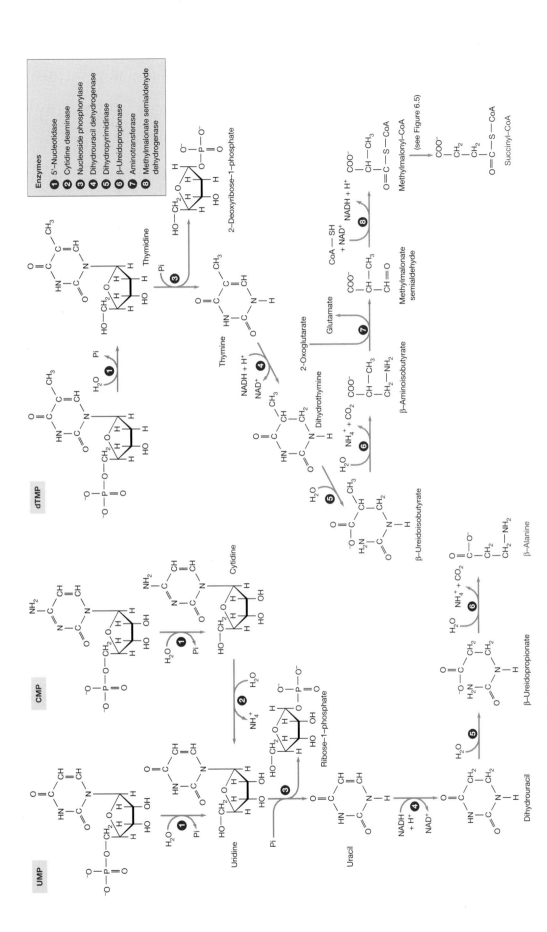

Figure 4.11(a) Pyrimidine nucleotide degradation.

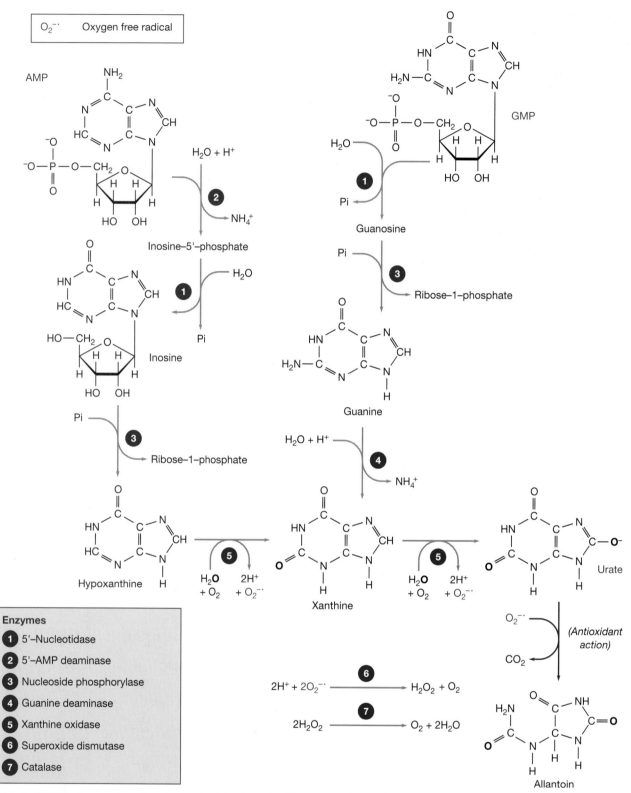

Figure 4.11(b) Conversion of purine nucleotides to urate. The oxygen free radicals produced can be destroyed enzymatically or by the non-enzymatic conversion of urate to allantoin.

DNA synthesis

For DNA synthesis the basic mechanism of nucleic acid synthesis poses a problem since the two complementary strands of the DNA double helix are antiparallel. To duplicate DNA it is necessary to separate the two strands and synthesize a new strand complementary to each. Autoradiographic evidence has shown that the two DNA strands are formed at the same time as the replicating fork moves along the DNA molecule. This pattern of DNA replication means that only one strand can be synthesized in the accepted 5'→3' direction, and that the other apparently will have to be formed by adding the 3' end of a nucleotide to the 5' end of the strand. However, the latter process does not occur and instead, as shown in Figure 4.12(b), the second strand is replicated in short (Okazaki) segments by separate DNA polymerase III molecules working in the standard 5'→3' direction. The gaps between the short sections are filled in by DNA polymerase I and then joined by a ligase enzyme. In addition to the polymerase enzymes, Figure 4.12(b) shows that DNA replication requires a number of other enzymes to unwind the double helix, to stabilize the single DNA strands and to form an RNA primer for the synthesis of the lagging strand.

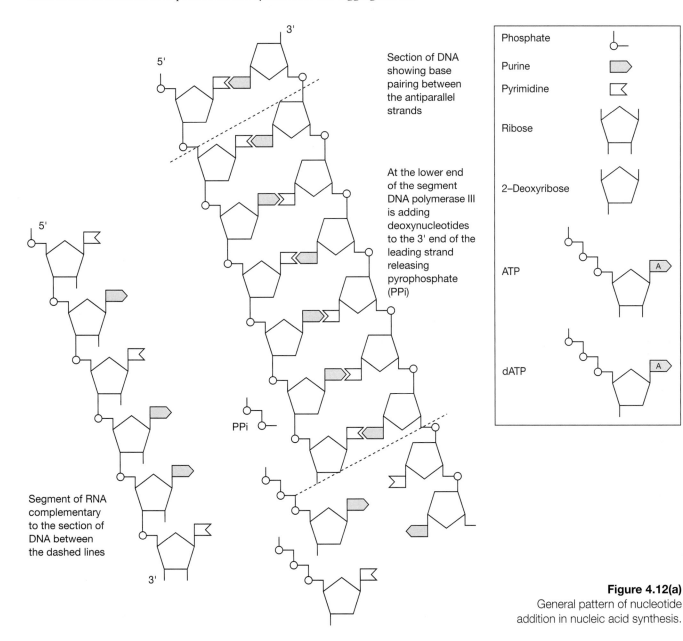

Section of DNA showing base pairing between the antiparallel strands

At the lower end of the segment DNA polymerase III is adding deoxynucleotides to the 3' end of the leading strand releasing pyrophosphate (PPi)

Segment of RNA complementary to the section of DNA between the dashed lines

Phosphate

Purine

Pyrimidine

Ribose

2–Deoxyribose

ATP

dATP

Figure 4.12(a)
General pattern of nucleotide addition in nucleic acid synthesis.

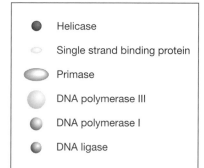

●	Helicase
○	Single strand binding protein
⬭	Primase
○	DNA polymerase III
●	DNA polymerase I
●	DNA ligase

Materials required for DNA replication
- dATP, dCTP, dGTP and dTTP
- Mg^{2+}
- RNA primer

Enzymes and their functions
- dnaB protein – initiates unwinding of DNA.
- Helicase – unwinds the DNA double helix.
- Single strand binding protein – stabilizes unwound DNA.
- Primase – forms RNA primers for the lagging strand.
- DNA gyrase – introduces negative supercoils.
- DNA polymerase III – synthesizes the DNA strand.
- DNA polymerase I – hydrolyses the RNA primers and fills the gaps between the Okazaki fragments of the lagging strand.
- DNA ligase – joins the ends of the Okazaki fragments.

3'
5'
Leading strand

5'
3'

Okazaki fragments

Lagging strand
3'
5'

RNA primer

Figure 4.12(b)
Requirements for DNA replication in prokaryotes.

RNA synthesis

RNA synthesis, on the other hand, avoids these complications because RNA is formed as a single strand complementary to one of the strands in its DNA template (see Figures 4.12a and 4.13). Since RNA synthesis takes place in the 5'→ 3' direction, it is the 3' → 5' strand of the DNA that is complementary to the newly formed RNA molecule. In order to form an RNA strand complementary to one of the DNA strands, it is necessary for the RNA polymerase to separate the two DNA strands at the point of replication. Because RNA is single stranded it lacks the three-dimensional form of DNA and once it is formed it is vulnerable to hydrolysis by ribonuclease which is widely distributed in all cells. This problem is overcome in different ways for the three main types of RNA. rRNA does have complementary regions so that it can form double-stranded loops even though it is a single-stranded molecule. rRNA is also closely associated with the ribosomal proteins. The short tRNA molecules (about 80 bases long) also have regions

Materials required for RNA synthesis

- ATP, CTP, GTP and UTP
- Mg^{2+}
- DNA template

Classes of RNA and their functions

- Messenger RNA (mRNA)   Transfers the sequence information from DNA to the site of protein synthesis on ribosomes.

- Ribosomal RNA (rRNA)   Long single-stranded RNA molecules that form the major components of ribosomes. Eukaryotic ribosomes have four rRNA molecules; three in the large subunit and one in the small subunit.

- Transfer RNA (tRNA)   There are 20+ tRNA molecules containing 73–93 bases many of which are methylated; the molecules are L-shaped and have two double-stranded segments. Each tRNA carries a specific amino acid from its activating enzyme to the ribosome. The tRNA matches its anticodon to the codon on the mRNA placing the amino acid in the correct sequence.

Enzymes required for RNA synthesis

RNA polymerase I   –   Nucleolar enzyme responsible for the synthesis of 3 rRNAs
RNA polymerase II   –   Synthesises mRNA and heterogenous nuclear RNA (hnRNA).
RNA polymerase III   –   Synthesises tRNA molecules and the fourth rRNA

Mechanism of RNA synthesis

- RNA is formed in a 5' to 3' direction by successive addition of nucleoside triphosphates matched to the coding strand of the DNA template with the release of pyrophosphate.
- A 7-methyl-GTP cap is added to the 5' end of the mRNA and in most cases a polyadenylate tail is also added to the 3' end.
- The mRNA transcripts leave the nucleus after extensive processing to remove introns from the initial transcript.

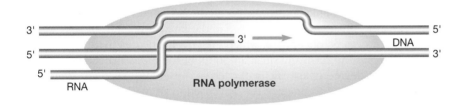

The RNA polymerase unwinds a 17 base section of the DNA in order to copy the sequence of a single strand into mRNA

Figure 4.13
RNA synthesis in eukaryotes.

of base pairing and many of the bases in these molecules are enzymatically modified. By contrast mRNA provides the template for the amino acid sequence of proteins so that it does not normally have complementary regions and must be protected from hydrolysis by association with proteins or ribosomes. When the mRNA that is to be used in protein synthesis is formed in the nucleus it is associated with proteins until it moves into the cytoplasm and becomes bound to ribosomes. The RNA formed in the nucleus that is not protected in this way is rapidly degraded within the nucleus. The production of mRNA involves the addition of a 7-methyl-guanosine cap at the 5' end and a polyadenylate tail at the 3' end. Before leaving the nucleus mRNA is processed to remove intervening sequences (introns) before the final product (exon) is released from the nucleus to be translated by the ribosomes.

4.11 Protein synthesis

Protein synthesis interacts with metabolism in three main ways: it requires a supply of all 20 amino acids, it is a major consumer of energy both for formation of the RNA used in the process and more directly because of the ATP and GTP required for conversion of the amino acids into polypeptide chains, and it is responsible for producing the appropriate levels of the enzymes which operate the metabolic pathways. In simple prokaryotic cells protein synthesis provides the mechanism through which genetic information is expressed. For humans and other higher animals the situation is more complex, since all cells in the body have the same genetic information, but differentiation and specialization of function dictate both qualitative and quantitative differences between the proteins present in the cells in the various organs of the body. Even within a particular organ there are often important differences in protein composition in different cell types. Furthermore, in the higher eukaryotes a gene may be expressed, but the protein produced may not become an active enzyme until it has been activated, modified or converted from some precursor form.

Amino acid activation

In common with the synthesis of other macromolecules, protein synthesis needs the constituent amino acids to be active before they can form a protein. Since the amino acid sequence in a protein is specified by the base sequence of the mRNA, the amino acids must be attached to an adaptor (a tRNA molecule) to decode the message. To avoid errors in the amino acid sequence it is essential that the attachment of the amino acids to the appropriate tRNA should be as accurate as possible. The amino acyltransferase enzymes are each responsible for the activation of a specific amino acid and for linking it to the correct tRNA molecule as shown in Figure 4.14. The pyrophosphate molecule released in the first step of this process is immediately split to inorganic phosphate, which effectively ensures that the reaction is irreversible despite the relatively small amounts of the individual amino acyltransferases. The high degree of specificity of each of these enzymes for a given amino acid provides reasonable accuracy of the first reaction above, but an additional safeguard is needed since there is little difference in structure among the various amino acid molecules. Further protection against errors is provided by the fact that the activating enzymes can function as aminoacyl-tRNA hydrolyases so that the rate of transfer of the activated amino acid to the tRNA must be more rapid than the rate of hydrolysis to give a significant yield of aminoacyl-tRNA. Since the enzyme-bound aminoacyl-AMP reacts more slowly with an incorrect tRNA molecule than with the correct one, the hydrolytic activity of the enzyme acts as a proof-reading device.

Chain initiation

In order to initiate protein synthesis it is necessary to bring together four molecules: the mRNA, the small subunit of the ribosome, the first aminoacyl-tRNA (tRNA^{Met}) and a GTP. Furthermore, it is essential that the first aminoacyl-tRNA, which is a methionine bound to the special tRNA^{Met}, is lined up with the start codon (AUG) on the mRNA in order to fix the reading frame. The organization of these initial steps is managed by a group of proteins known as initiation factors. The probable sequence of events is shown diagrammatically in Figure 4.15(a). When the main group of initiation factors dissociates from the small subunit of the ribosome with the hydrolysis of GTP and the blocking factor (eIF6) is released, the large subunit can bind to the small subunit, forming a functioning ribosome to complete the synthesis of the protein.

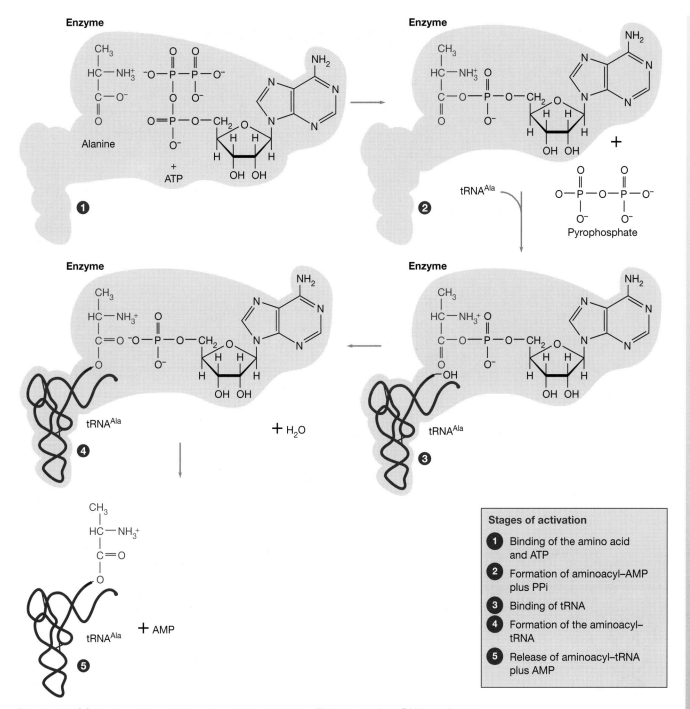

Stages of activation

1. Binding of the amino acid and ATP

2. Formation of aminoacyl–AMP plus PPi

3. Binding of tRNA

4. Formation of the aminoacyl–tRNA

5. Release of aminoacyl–tRNA plus AMP

Figure 4.14(a) Amino acid activation: formation of alanine-tRNA by alanine-tRNA synthetase.

Chain elongation

At the conclusion of the initiation process the first aminoacyl-tRNA is bound to the peptidyl site (P-site) on the ribosome, leaving the acceptor site (A-site) free to bind the second aminoacyl-tRNA which must match the second codon of the message. The binding of each new aminoacyl-tRNA molecule requires an elongation factor as well as a GTP which is then split to GDP plus phosphate. Once the A-site is occupied by the new aminoacyl-tRNA molecule, the stage is set for formation of the peptide bond through action of the peptidyl transferase enzyme on the large ribosomal subunit. It is important to recognize that no additional input

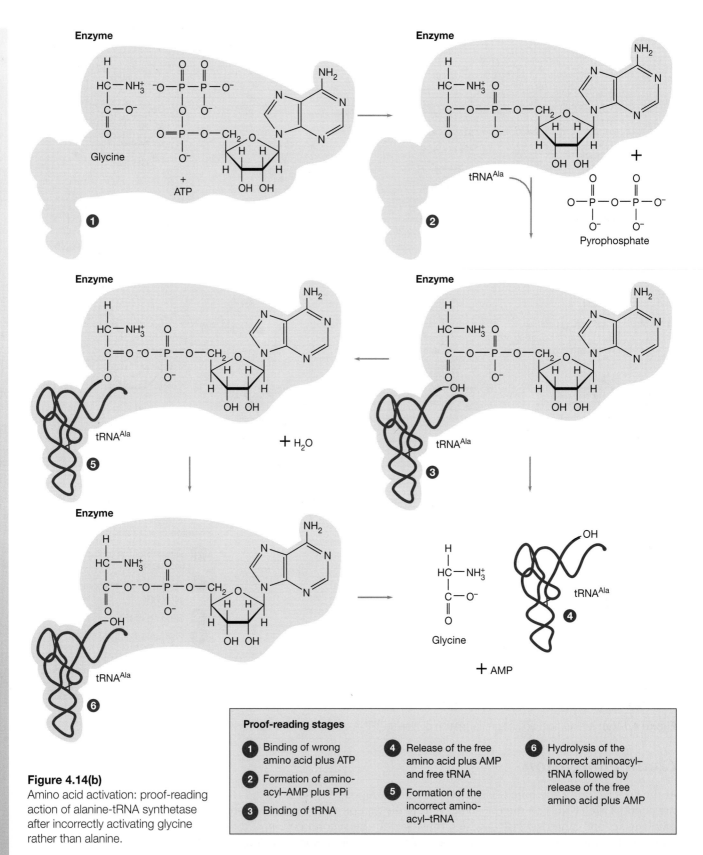

Figure 4.14(b)
Amino acid activation: proof-reading action of alanine-tRNA synthetase after incorrectly activating glycine rather than alanine.

Proof-reading stages

1. Binding of wrong amino acid plus ATP
2. Formation of amino-acyl–AMP plus PPi
3. Binding of tRNA
4. Release of the free amino acid plus AMP and free tRNA
5. Formation of the incorrect amino-acyl–tRNA
6. Hydrolysis of the incorrect aminoacyl–tRNA followed by release of the free amino acid plus AMP

of energy is required to synthesize the peptide bond, since its formation is associated with the splitting of the bond between the amino acid and the tRNA on the P-site. The final stage of elongation is the translocation of the complex of mRNA

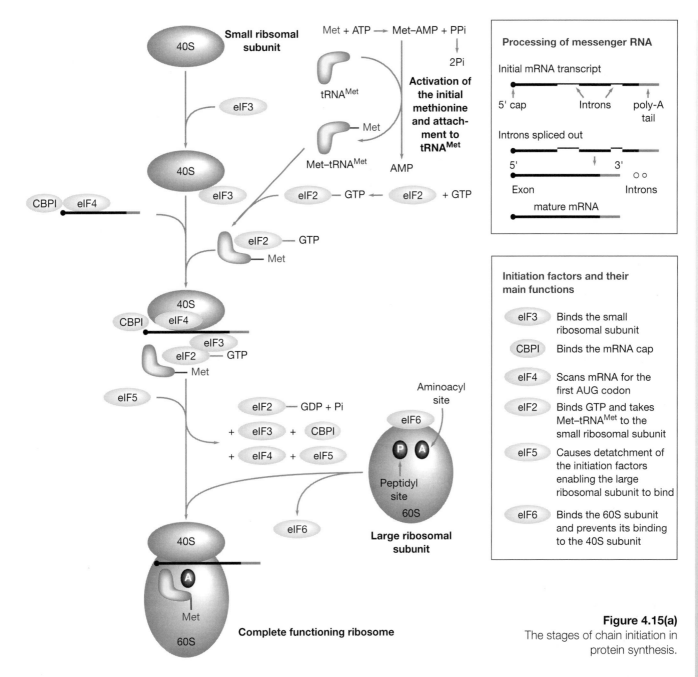

Figure 4.15(a)
The stages of chain initiation in protein synthesis.

and the peptidyl-tRNA from the A-site to the P-site. This process also requires a protein factor (eEF2) and is associated with the hydrolysis of a second GTP to GDP and phosphate. Figure 4.15(b) summarizes these events.

Chain termination

A total of 61 out of the 64 possible triplet codons specify particular amino acids. The remaining three (UAA, UGA and UAG) are stop codons. These codons have no matching tRNA molecules and are recognized instead by a single releasing factor. The binding of this protein alters the specificity of the peptidyl transferase so that it becomes a hydrolase and releases the completed polypeptide from the last tRNA. Chain termination also results in the hydrolysis of a GTP (see Figure 4.15b).

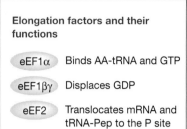

Elongation factors and their functions

eEF1α   Binds AA-tRNA and GTP

eEF1βγ   Displaces GDP

eEF2   Translocates mRNA and tRNA-Pep to the P site

Elongation steps

1 Binding of aminoacyl–tRNA to the A site
2 Dissociation of eEF1α and hydrolysis of GTP
3 Peptide bond synthesis
4 Translocation from A to P site
5 Displacement of spent tRNA
6 Regeneration of eEF1α–GTP

Termination of translation

1 Binding of releasing factor to the A site in recognition of a termination codon
2 Hydrolysis of the polypeptide–tRNA link by the peptidyl synthetase in the presence of eRF–GTP, hydrolysis of GTP and dissociation of the completed protein, ribosome, mRNA, tRNA, etc.

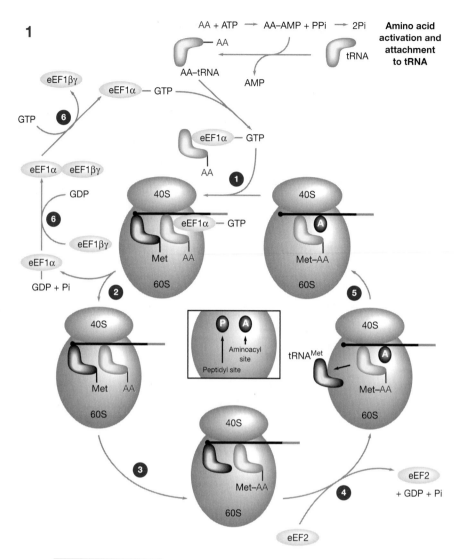

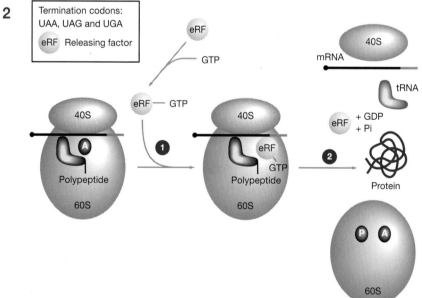

Figure 4.15(b)
Stages of translation in protein synthesis: 1, chain elongation; 2, termination.

Post-translational modifications of newly formed proteins

As a polypeptide is being formed it will have a tendency to fold up, but it is now clear that in most cases this folding is heavily constrained by a class of proteins known as molecular chaperones. Figure 4.16(a) shows two possible models for the operation of chaperone proteins. At the top of the figure an oligomeric chaperone is shown preventing a protein from folding until synthesis is complete. By binding to the polypeptide during synthesis incorrect folding is prevented; this type of chaperone can also ensure that the several separate polypeptides which make up an oligomeric protein are assembled correctly into their final form.

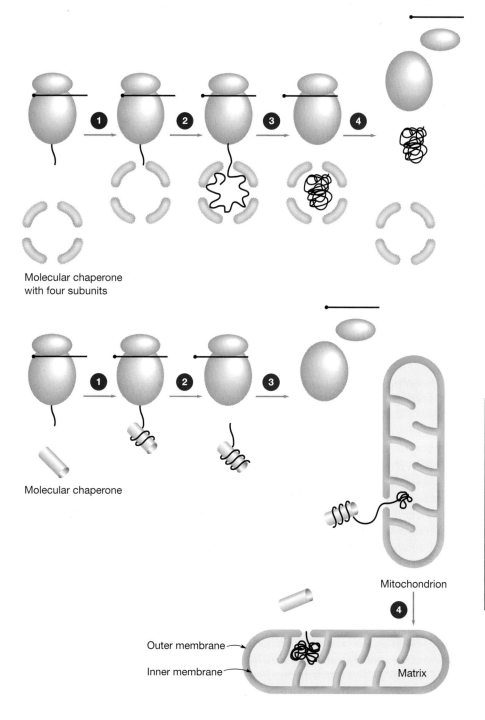

Molecular chaperone with four subunits

1. Binding of the molecular chaperone to the N-terminus of the polypeptide
2. Completion of translation with the protein bound to the chaperone
3. Folding of the protein after synthesis has been completed
4. Release of the folded protein

Molecular chaperone

1. Binding of the polypeptide to the molecular chaperone during synthesis
2. Completion of the unfolded protein
3. Transfer of the protein on the chaperone to a pore in the outer and inner membranes of the mitochondrion
4. Detatchment of the protein from the chaperone and completion of folding in the matrix

Mitochondrion

Outer membrane

Inner membrane

Matrix

Figure 4.16(a)
Two possible roles for molecular chaperones in protein folding.

Steps in the post-translational modification of a protein

1 Binding of the signal sequence to the signal recognition particle (SRP)

2 Docking of the ribosome and SRP on endoplasmic reticulum (ER) receptors

3 Completion of protein synthesis and folding within the ER

4 Removal of the signal sequence by the signal peptidase.

5 Introduction of an oligosaccharide into the ER from the cytoplasm

6 Attachment of the oligosaccharide to the protein

7 Release of the glycoprotein from the ER in a membrane vesicle

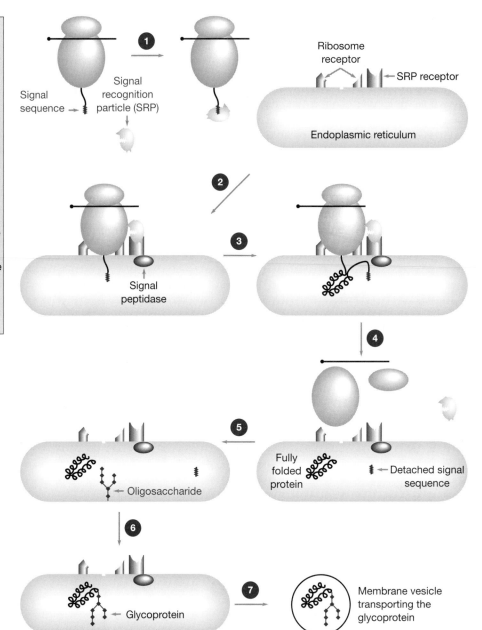

Figure 4.16(b)
Post-translational modification of a protein in the endoplasmic reticulum.

Molecular chaperones are also likely to be involved in the transport of proteins across organelle membranes (for example into mitochondria) or in the refolding or removal of damaged proteins. In fact it now appears that proteins only fold up without the help of the molecular chaperones in a few specialized locations such as the mitochondrial matrix or, as indicated below, within the lumen of the endoplasmic reticulum. The lower panel of Figure 4.16(a) shows schematically how another sort of molecular chaperone may preserve a newly synthesized mitochondrial protein in an unfolded state and deliver it to a pore through both mitochondrial membranes so that the protein can fold up within the matrix.

Many proteins are modified after they are formed. Such modification may involve the removal of part of the peptide chain or the addition of other components such as polysaccharide chains. The nature of such post-translational modifications and the ultimate destination of the protein will determine the immediate fate of the newly formed polypeptide. Those proteins that are to be secreted and membrane proteins to which carbohydrate groups will be added have signal sequences at the N-terminal end that enable the ribosomes to bind to the endoplasmic reticulum so that the newly formed peptide is passed through a pore into the lumen of the endoplasmic reticulum. This binding is accomplished with the aid of a signal recognition particle which binds to its own receptor on the endoplasmic reticulum and guides the ribosome to its receptor. The ribosome then completes the synthesis of the protein and the signal sequence on the N-terminus is removed by a signal peptidase. These events are shown diagrammatically in Figure 4.16(b). Within the vesicles of endoplasmic reticulum the proteins may be modified by the addition of carbohydrates, as indicated in Figure 4.16(b) and finally endoplasmic reticulum vesicles can carry the completed protein to the Golgi complex where the added carbohydrate may be modified or extended. Proteins that are targeted to specific sites in the cell or destined for secretion are also transported around the cell in Golgi vesicles. These processes will be considered in detail with particular pancreatic proteins as examples in Chapter 9.

4.12 General features of the catabolism of nucleic acids and proteins

It was pointed out in Chapter 1 that, with the exception of the DNA, there is constant recycling of the nucleic acids and proteins in all cells. If the cell mass remains constant, the proteins and nucleic acids will need to be broken down at the same overall rate that they are being formed. This catabolism has two general characteristics: it occurs by hydrolytic processes that are distinct from the mechanisms of biosynthesis, and the rates of catabolism vary widely for individual proteins and nucleic acids.

Nucleic acid degradation

Nucleic acids are hydrolysed by ribonuclease into 3'-nucleotides which are degraded to nucleosides by the action of a phosphatase. The nucleosides are converted to ribose-1-phosphate and free bases by phosphorolysis (see Figure 4.11). Individual RNA molecules vary widely in their susceptibility to hydrolysis. This can be demonstrated by measuring the half-life of particular RNA molecules, which reveals that most mRNA molecules have a very short half-life whereas rRNA and tRNA are much more stable. However, it has also been shown that within the nucleus there is a class of RNA with an even shorter half-life than that of mRNA. This 'heterogeneous nuclear RNA' may represent copies of non-coding regions of the DNA, but in any case it underlines the fact that RNA molecules that are not protected from hydrolysis will be degraded at once. It appears that RNA must be associated with protein to protect it from the ribonuclease, and the differences in half-life between different mRNA molecules may be controlled by binding to specific proteins which help to determine the half-life of the message.

Protein degradation

Proteins are also degraded by hydrolysis, and half-lives vary from a few hours in the case of RNA polymerase to weeks or months in the case of some structural proteins. So far as enzymes are concerned it appears that the more active enzymes have a shorter half-life. However, since changes in enzyme activity because of altered conditions bring rapid adjustments in enzyme levels, the control over protein degradation may be quite complex. Protein degradation is also an important feature of apoptosis, programmed cell death. Apoptosis involves the production of special proteins and when the normal controls for this process are disturbed as a result of somatic mutations, the growth of tumours occurs.

Some protein hydrolysis occurs in the lysosomes where a low pH is required. As a consequence this form of protein degradation requires the expenditure of a considerable amount of ATP in order to maintain the high H^+ concentration within the lysosomes. Protein hydrolysis also takes place in the general cytoplasm as the result of the action of proteosomes. These particles, which are about half the size of the small subunit of a ribosome, provide a multisubunit protease which is ATP-dependent. In order to identify a particular cytoplasmic protein for hydrolysis it must be targeted by a small globular protein, ubiquitin, which directs the protein to the proteosome.

E X E R C I S E S

1. What are the major classes of nitrogen compounds that are essential for cells?

2. What is meant by the term 'nitrogen balance'?

3. Which coenzymes are derived from nicotinic acid, pantothenic acid and riboflavin?

4. What determines whether an amino acid is deemed to be 'essential'?

5. Distinguish between the roles of glutamate and glutamine in amino acid catabolism.

6. Name the two amino acids that cannot be converted into glucose and explain why this is true.

7. Name the amino acids that are key starting materials for the purine and pyrimidine biosynthetic pathways and list the sources of the remaining nitrogens in each case.

8. Describe the basis of the purine salvage pathways.

9. Describe the basic features of nucleotide addition in the synthesis of nucleic acids.

10. List the ways in which energy is supplied for protein synthesis.

11. What properties of the aminoacyl-tRNA synthetases help to reduce the possibility of errors in protein synthesis?

12. What are the roles of the signal sequence and the signal recognition particle in protein synthesis?

Further reading

Arnez, J.G. & Moras, D. (1997) Structural and functional considerations of the aminoacylation reaction, *Trends in Biochemical Sciences* **22**, 211–216.

Bender, D.A. (1985) *Amino Acid Metabolism*, 2nd edition, Wiley.

Coux, O., Tanaka, K. & Goldberg, A.L. (1996) Structure and functions of the 20S and 26S proteasomes. *Annual Review of Biochemistry* **65**, 801–847.

Doherty, F.J. & Mayer, R.J. (1992) *Intracellular Protein Degradation*, Oxford University Press.

Dow, J., Lindsay, G. & Morrison, J. (1996) *Biochemistry, Molecules, Cells and the Body*, Addison-Wesley, Chapters 4, 5 & 10.

Hannun, Y.A. & Obeid, L.M. (1995) Ceramide: an intracellular signal for apoptosis, *Trends in Biochemical Sciences* **20**, 73–77.

Hilt, W. & Wolf, D.H. (1996) Proteasomes: destruction as a programme, *Trends in Biochemical Sciences* **21**, 96–101.

Kornberg, R.D. *et al.* (1996) The RNA polymerase II transcriptional machinery, *Trends in Biochemical Sciences* **21**, 325–356.

Lithgow, T., Cuezva, J.M. & Silver, P.A. (1997) Highways for protein delivery to the mitochondria, *Trends in Biochemical Sciences* **22**, 110–113.

Lupas, A., Flanagan, J.M., Tamura, T. & Baumeister, W. (1997) Self-compartmentalizing proteases, *Trends in Biochemical Sciences* **22**, 399–404.

Netzer, W.J. & Hartl, F.U. (1998) Protein folding in the cytosol: chaperonin-dependent and -independent mechanisms, *Trends in Biochemical Sciences* **23**, 68–73.

Neupert, W. (1997) Protein import into mitochondria. *Annual Review of Biochemistry* **66**, 863–917.

Randall, L.L. & Hardy, S.J.S. (1995) High selectivity with low specificity: how SecB has solved the paradox of chaperone binding, *Trends in Biochemical Sciences* **20**, 65–69.

Reeder, R.H. & Lang, W.H. (1997) Terminating transcription in eucaryotes: lessons learned from RNA polymerase I, *Trends in Biochemical Sciences* **22**, 473–477.

Richardson, A., Landry, S.J. & Georgopoulos, C. (1998) The ins and outs of a molecular chaperone machine, *Trends in Biochemical Sciences* **23**, 138–143.

Roeder, R.G. (1996) The role of general initiation factors in transcription by RNA polymerase II, *Trends in Biochemical Sciences* **21**, 327–335.

Stansfield, I., Jones, K.M. & Tuite, M.F. (1995) The end in sight: terminating translation in eukaryotes, *Trends in Biochemical Sciences* **20**, 489–491.

Stryer, L. (1995) *Biochemistry*, 4th edition, W.H. Freeman, Chapters 25, 28, 29, 31, 33, 34 & 35.

Suzuki, C.K., Rep, M., van Dijl, J.M., Suda, K., Grivell, L.A. & Schatz, G. (1997) ATP-dependent proteases that also chaperone protein biogenesis, *Trends in Biochemical Sciences* **22**, 118–123.

Varshavsky, A. (1997) The ubiquitin system, *Trends in Biochemical Sciences* **22**, 383–387.

Different organs have specialized areas of metabolism

What do different organs contribute to the body's metabolism?

The body has four basic requirements which are supported by metabolism: energy supply, substrates for the synthesis of cell constituents, protection and control.

Individual organs are adapted to perform specialized functions for the body as a whole, but each function is usually supported by more than one tissue.

The purpose of the second part of this book is to examine in detail the specialized functions of eight human tissues and to consider the ways in which these functions are supported by metabolism. However, before we begin to consider the individual organs in detail, it is useful to identify the basic metabolic requirements of the body as a whole and to indicate which tissues are chiefly responsible for supplying each of these needs. The third part of the book deals with the integration of the eight tissues and shows how the normal balance between them is altered by feeding, starvation, trauma and severe exercise. In order to provide the background for Part 3, we will consider briefly in this chapter how metabolism in the eight tissues is integrated and how these interactions are affected by the consumption of food and by the initiation of exercise. The chapter concludes with a summary of the major metabolic roles of the eight tissues.

5.1 What are an individual's basic metabolic requirements?

Every cell in the body requires a supply of substrates in order to provide it with the energy it needs to remain viable. As we have seen in Part 1, a variety of substrates can be used to generate the ATP necessary to meet the cell's energy demands. Provided that the cell has mitochondria and an adequate supply of oxygen, ATP can be generated by any substrate that can support oxidative phosphorylation. Thus, as summarized in Figure 5.1, carbohydrates, fatty acids, ketone bodies or amino acids are all capable of satisfying the demand for this type of energy-supplying substrate. If either oxygen or mitochondria are absent (e.g. in rapidly contracting muscle or red blood cells) only a glycolytic substrate will suffice, and this means that it is essential for the body to maintain the blood glucose concentration close to the normal level.

The rapid turnover of cell constituents that occurs in most cells means that all 20 amino acids plus phosphate and adequate levels of substrates for the central metabolic pathways in Figure 5.1 must be available to support the biosynthesis of cell constituents. Although less obvious, it is equally essential for the body to maintain adequate supplies of inorganic cations such as sodium, potas-

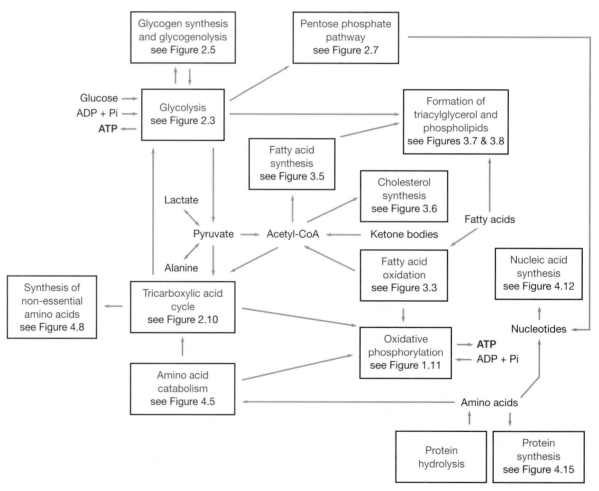

Figure 5.1 Summary of the central metabolic pathways shown in Figure 1.12. The box representing each pathway identifies the figure in which the detailed steps are given.

sium, calcium, magnesium, iron and zinc as well as the vitamin derivatives that make up coenzymes.

Protection from the hostile environment is another fundamental requirement for the organism as a whole. At a gross level protection is provided by the muscles under the control of the central nervous system (CNS). On a smaller scale protection is provided by the barrier function of the skin and internal epithelial layers, but these are not adequate to guard against physical damage, infection or the uptake of poisonous substances. Furthermore, the body must be able to protect itself from the accumulation of noxious waste products, such as ammonia or carbon dioxide which are constantly produced by substrate oxidation and the recycling of cell constituents.

The other crucial requirement, namely the control and integration necessary to make the body function as a unit, is more difficult to define. In part this involves the physical linking of different muscles and organs to the CNS by the peripheral nerves, the integration of the information from these sensory neurones and the coordination of impulses sent down the motor neurones by areas in the brain. But the actions of a wide range of chemical messengers, or hormones, is also essential to allow the body to respond to changes in conditions in an organized and integrated manner.

5.2 Groups of tissues combine to meet the body's requirements

In order to satisfy the four main bodily requirements – nutrient supply, excretion of waste products, protection and integration – particular tissues have become specialized to perform a given function for the body as a whole. However, as we shall see in this part of the book, cooperation between two or more organs normally occurs to satisfy a particular requirement. In part this provides a safety factor, avoiding reliance on a single organ, but it also allows a more balanced response to changes in conditions. Figure 5.2 gives a logo for each of the eight tissues covered in Part 2, and indicates the major function and the main metabolic processes of each tissue. This figure also indicates which tissues support the four main requirements of the body.

The supply of glucose for the body as a whole provides a good example of the interactions between tissues. Basically glucose supply is a function of the liver where the plasma membrane glucose transporter (GLUT 2) has a K_m (Michaelis constant, which is the substrate concentration for half-maximal velocity) well above the normal plasma level of 5 mM, so that the glucose concentration in the liver cytoplasm reflects that in the blood. Because glucose is phosphorylated in the liver by glucokinase with a K_m of 5 mM, the liver only removes glucose from the blood when the concentration is high; the presence of glucose-6-phosphatase enables the liver to replenish plasma glucose from its glycogen stores or by gluconeogenesis when the level falls below 5 mM. This regulation of blood glucose concentration is an example of the liver's role in metabolite homeostasis.

There are also elaborate hormonal control mechanisms which modify the basic glucose supply function of the liver. Since the pancreas has the GLUT 2 transporter, it can monitor the blood glucose levels, and respond by secreting insulin if the level is above normal or glucagon if it is too low. Insulin promotes the storage of glucose as liver glycogen whereas glucagon increases the phosphorolysis of glycogen to yield glucose-phosphate as well as stimulating gluconeogenesis. The secretion of pancreatic hormones brings two other tissues into the regulation of

TISSUE	PRINCIPAL FUNCTIONS				METABOLISM
	Nutrient supply	Excretion	Protection	Integration	
 Adipose tissue	✓✓				Storage of TAG; controlled release of fatty acids
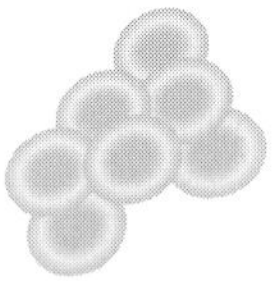 Blood			✓✓	✓	Transport of nutrients, gases and ions; antibody synthesis; formation and removal of blood clots
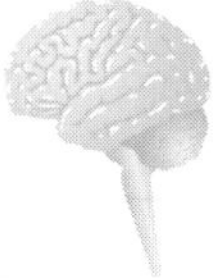 Central nervous system (CNS)			✓	✓✓	Integration and control; synthesis of chemical messengers
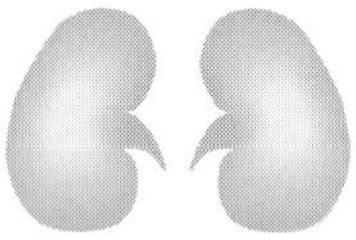 Kidneys		✓✓	✓		Waste product excretion; gluconeogenesis. Maintenance of blood pressure, volume and pH
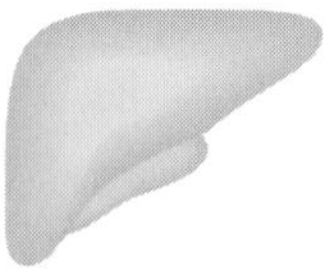 Liver	✓✓	✓	✓		Nutrient homeostasis; storage of glycogen; synthesis of TAG, ketone bodies, cholesterol, bile salts, albumin and urea
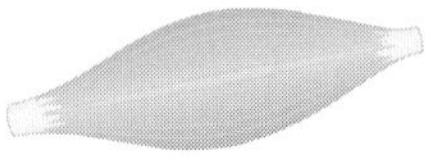 Muscle	✓		✓✓		Movement; branched chain amino acid catabolism; glutamine synthesis
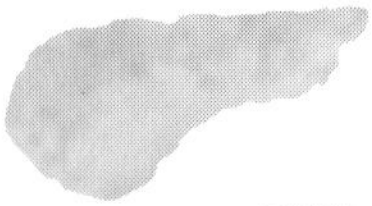 Pancreas	✓			✓✓	Synthesis of digestive enzymes and hormones
 Small intestine	✓✓		✓		Absorption of nutrients; synthesis of TAG and release of chylomicrons; conversion of glucose to lactate and glutamine to alanine

Figure 5.2 The principal functions and metabolic processes of the eight tissues in Part 2. The most important function of each tissue is indicated by ✓✓. TAG, triacylglycerol.

blood glucose. Insulin mobilizes the low K_m (GLUT 4) glucose transporters in muscle and adipose tissue which increase the rate at which glucose is removed from the blood. A further layer of control involves the CNS which stimulates muscle contraction and also permits the body to anticipate a potential increase in the requirement for glucose. Stress or excitement causes the CNS to stimulate the secretion of adrenaline and noradrenaline by the adrenal medulla. These hormones act, respectively, to stimulate the release of glucose by the liver and fatty acids by the hormone-sensitive lipase in adipose tissue. When the anticipated activity begins there will be a large increase in the demand for energy-supplying substrates. Muscle responds to adrenaline by an increase in the phosphorolysis of glycogen, which also reduces the demand for blood glucose by muscle. The increased release of fatty acids, which is caused by the effect of noradrenaline on the rate of lipolysis in adipose tissue, also helps to reduce glucose utilization by muscle because fatty acids become the major energy-supplying substrate. Thus, noradrenaline protects the glucose supply for the CNS and red blood cells.

The supply of fatty acids and ketone bodies also involves the collaboration of several tissues. The principal stores of fatty acids are in the form of triacylglycerol in adipose tissue and the extent to which the constituent fatty acids can enter the circulation depends on the rate at which they are released by the hormone-sensitive lipase as a result of stimulation by adrenaline or noradrenaline. Free fatty acids circulate in the plasma bound to albumin, where they are in equilibrium with a low concentration of unbound fatty acid. Triacylglycerol formed from fatty acids synthesized in the liver is released as a lipoprotein (VLDL) to carry newly formed fatty acids to other tissues. The fate of the fatty acids which are released from the VLDL by lipoprotein lipase in adipose tissue depends on the insulin concentration. High levels of insulin, secreted as a result of a high blood glucose, stimulate the storage of fatty acids as triacylglycerol in adipose tissue When the glucose concentration is reduced, the insulin level will be low and the secretion of noradrenaline will stimulate fatty acid release from the adipose tissue. As indicated above, the higher levels of circulating fatty acids inhibit glucose utilization by muscle since the fatty acids are oxidized instead. As the level of circulating fatty acids reaching the liver increases in response to a decline in blood glucose the liver converts the fatty acids into ketone bodies. These substrates have the advantage that they can be used by all tissues except the red blood cells so the rise in ketone body concentration has a further glucose-sparing effect. However, it is important to recognize that high levels of ketone bodies can cause acidosis.

Figure 5.3 summarizes the interactions of the eight tissues in the supply and utilization of substrates for energy supply in a resting individual. Only the major energy-supplying substrates in a fed individual are shown, and it should be emphasized that all 20 of the amino acids have the potential to supply energy for most cells. Also if the release of fatty acids from adipose tissue exceeds the rate at which they are utilized ketone bodies will be produced by the liver.

Provision of a physiological mixture of all 20 amino acids in the appropriate proportions required for protein synthesis in all the cells in the body requires the participation of skeletal muscle and the small intestine as well as the liver. The liver and the small intestine act together to adjust the plasma concentrations of the non-essential amino acids. When there is a drop in concentration of any of the essential amino acids it is important that the plasma level should be restored, but this requires the net degradation of protein, since these amino acids cannot be synthesized. The net loss of protein occurs chiefly in muscle, with the relative concentrations of the 20 amino acids adjusted subsequently by passage through the small intestine and the liver. A comparable mechanism exists to maintain the circulating concentrations of calcium and phosphate. Large quantities of these ions are present as a calcium phosphate salt in bone, but if there is a shortage of either ion, bone is resorbed to make up the deficiency.

There are no storage forms of the vitamin derivatives that make up the co-enzymes that play a vital role in metabolism. Consequently, the intake of most of the vitamins must occur on a regular basis to maintain the coenzyme content within the body. The kidneys play an important role in maintaining the concentrations of many of the soluble constituents of blood plasma such as inorganic anions and cations, amino acids and minor components such as the vitamins. In order to provide an exit route for water and other waste products, the blood passes through a filter at the top end of each kidney tubule. This filtration removes cells and proteins, but allows the water and low molecular weight solutes to pass into the tubule. The cells lining the tubule are endowed with specific transporters for reclaiming the constituents that are valuable for the body. In order to maintain the blood volume most of the water is also reabsorbed, but by regulating the reabsorption of water and ions such as sodium, potassium and phosphate, the kidneys can control the concentrations of these constituents in the blood.

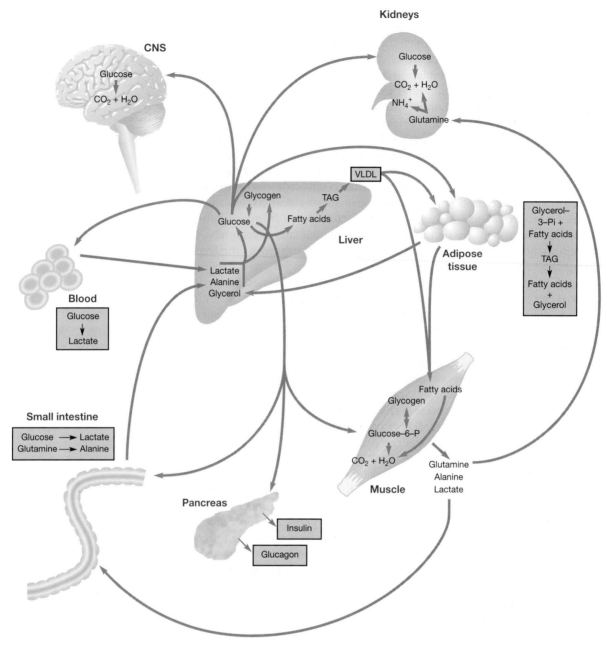

Figure 5.3 The sources and utilization of energy-supplying substrates. TAG, triacylglycerol.

Protection against the hostile environment is clearly supported by an individual's ability to move, but it is also aided by the barrier function of the skin and the epithelial layers of the digestive tract and the lungs. However, significant protective roles are also played by the liver and the kidneys, and a number of important protective roles are provided by the blood. The circulatory system operates four different types of protection. Perhaps the most obvious is the blood-clotting mechanism which prevents the loss of blood on injury, and is also responsible for removing the clot once the repair to the circulatory system is complete. A second basic level of protection is provided by bacteriocidal enzymes, such as lysozyme, and phagocytes which engulf bacteria, cell debris and foreign particles which they encounter in the blood and the extracellular fluid. The most sophisticated form of protection is the immune response to pathogenic bacteria, viruses and other foreign antigens. This process, like the clotting mechanism, requires activation;

and for an unknown antigen a significant lag period must elapse before the immune response is effective. A fourth level of protection available in the blood is a consequence of circulating antioxidant molecules that detoxify dangerous free radicals present in the blood.

A major feature of the protection provided by the liver and the kidneys is the detoxification and elimination of ammonia released during the metabolism of amino acids. By converting ammonia to urea, the liver converts it into a non-toxic compound that is not reabsorbed by the kidneys. Ammonia is also excreted directly by the kidneys in order to reduce the acidity of the blood and the urine. The liver and kidneys combine to provide a different sort of protection against foreign substances known as xenobiotics. Many of these compounds are relatively insoluble, particularly if they are polycyclic hydrocarbons. The liver contains hydroxylation systems which can increase the solubility of hydrocarbons and provide sites for their conjugation with even more strongly hydrophilic groups. In order to enter the blood, compounds must be absorbed by transport systems in the digestive tract or the lungs and in many cases the hydroxylation process changes the structure sufficiently to prevent reabsorption by the transport proteins in the kidney tubules. An alternative disposal system for the xenobiotics is provided by the liver which can excrete the compounds into the bile. In this case modification of the structure, usually by conjugation with a hydrophilic group, is also important to allow biliary secretion and prevent reabsorption in the small intestine.

The capacity of the body to operate as an integrated unit is largely achieved by the sensory and motor neurones linking all parts of the body to the higher centres in the brain. It has recently become clear that much of the specificity associated with these nerve pathways is due to variations in the structure and characteristics of the receptors for the neurotransmitters secreted by the nerve endings in the synapses and at the target tissue. Integration of the metabolic processes in the various tissues of the body is achieved by chemical messengers or hormones secreted in response to changes in conditions. The classical hormones secreted by the adrenal cortex, the pancreas, the pituitary and other endocrine glands enter the blood and produce their responses by combining with specific receptors on the tissues they regulate. As pointed out in section 1.11, the combination of hormone and receptor can trigger the formation of intracellular messengers which are capable of influencing a variety of enzymes in different ways. In Chapter 14 we shall consider in detail a number of examples of the ways in which this type of control can produce integrated effects on the metabolism of particular tissues. There is also a second group of chemical messengers (e.g. NO) which are released by certain cells and produce their effects locally, rather than travelling through the general circulation.

5.3 Tissues concerned with the supply of nutrients

Feeding radically alters the balance between those tissues responsible for providing energy-supplying substrates and the building blocks for the synthesis of cell constituents. This is because the liver and adipose tissues have to deal with a large influx of glucose, amino acids, triacylglycerol and cholesterol. Furthermore, the energy-consuming tissues, such as brain, muscle and the kidneys, can take the substrates they require directly from the blood instead of relying on supplies from other tissues. The interactions between tissues during feeding are summarized in Figure 5.4. A comparison of Figures 5.3 and 5.4 illustrates the principal changes in the relationships between tissues during feeding.

The absorption of nutrients by the small intestine requires the cooperation of the liver and pancreas. Digestive enzymes secreted by the pancreas are responsible for the hydrolysis of starch, protein, nucleic acids, phospholipids and triacylglycerol. Bile salts from the liver emulsify dietary triacylglycerol in order to increase the effectiveness of the pancreatic lipase.

Starch is converted into maltose by the pancreatic amylase and lactose, maltose and sucrose are converted into their constituent hexoses by membrane-bound disaccharidases on the surface of the enterocytes lining the small intestine. Glucose and fructose absorption by the small intestine is followed by the metabolism of a proportion of these two hexoses into lactate and alanine which then enter the portal vein together with galactose and the remaining glucose and fructose for transfer to the liver. In this way the small intestine is able to satisfy its energy requirements and also reduce the concentration gradient against which glucose is absorbed. Alanine and lactate are the liver's preferred substrates for gluconeogenesis, and they can also be used as energy-supplying substrates by the liver.

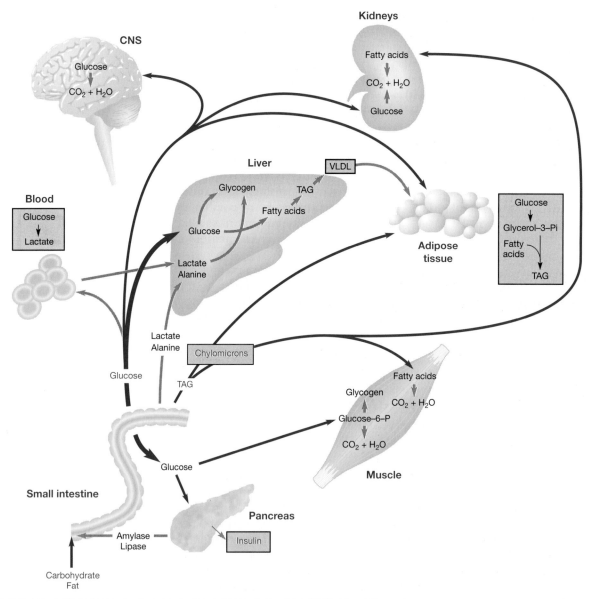

Figure 5.4 Interactions between tissues during nutrient absorption. TAG, triacylglycerol.

Proteins are rapidly converted into short peptides by the proteolytic enzymes, trypsin and chymotrypsin, secreted by the pancreas. Dipeptides and tripeptides are absorbed by the small intestine and converted into free amino acids by cytoplasmic peptidases. The fact that the amino acids are absorbed mainly as short peptides allows the intestine to maintain the relatively high cytoplasmic amino acid levels required for protein synthesis without having to absorb the amino acids against unfavourable concentration gradients. The amino acid mixture which enters the circulatory system in the small intestine tends to mirror that in normal blood, rather than the proportions in dietary protein. This is achieved by the catabolism of those amino acids present at excessive levels and the synthesis of non-essential amino acids present at low concentrations. Further adjustments to the amino acid concentrations are carried out by metabolism in the liver and muscle tissue.

Dietary nucleic acids are converted into 3'-nucleotides by pancreatic ribonuclease. These are dephosphorylated and then, with the exception of adenosine and cytidine, the nucleosides are absorbed by the small intestine. Adenosine is converted into inosine before absorption and cytidine is poorly absorbed. After uptake the nucleosides undergo phosphorolysis within the enterocytes to yield free bases plus ribose-phosphate. The purines are largely converted into the free radical scavenger urate and the pyrimidines end up as uracil which is catabolized in the liver.

Dietary triacylglycerol is emulsified by the bile salts and then hydrolysed by pancreatic lipase. Monoacylglycerol and the free fatty acids are absorbed in the small intestine where they are converted back into triacylglycerol and passed into the lymph circulation in the form of chylomicrons. The chylomicrons also contain the cholesterol and phospholipids which are absorbed by the small intestine. Since the chylomicrons do not enter the portal vein, they bypass the liver so that adipose tissue and muscle can extract some of the fatty acids before the remnant chylomicron particles which have a higher proportion of cholesterol are taken up by the liver. Short-chain fatty acids pass directly into the portal vein and are metabolized by the liver as an energy source.

5.4 Changes in tissue interrelationships during exercise

Table 5.1 shows the metabolic rates of the major energy-consuming human tissues in a resting individual. On a per organ basis the brain, liver and kidneys are comparable to skeletal muscle at rest. When the energy consumption is expressed per kilogram, it is clear that the kidneys and the heart have higher rates of energy consumption than the other tissues. However, it is apparent from the table that during exercise the energy consumption of skeletal muscle changes by two orders of magnitude to a value similar to that of the kidneys. Given the fact that muscle represents approximately half the human body weight, it is clear that massive changes in the supply of substrates for ATP production must take place in order to support exercise.

As muscles begin to contract there is an immediate release of adrenaline which mobilizes muscle glycogen by increasing the rate of glycogen phosphorolysis in muscle. Increased muscle activity also causes an initial drop in the blood glucose, triggering the secretion of glucagon which has two important effects on substrate supply for the muscles. The first is to stimulate the rate at which the liver releases glucose from its glycogen stores, and the second is the stimulation of gluconeogenesis by the liver. The release of adrenaline by the adrenal medulla

Table 5.1 Tissue weights and approximate oxygen consumption in a 70 kg man

Tissue	Total weight (kg)	Resting O_2 consumption mmol/day	mmol/min/kg tissue
Adipose tissue*	8.30		
Blood**	1.10		
Brain	1.39	3,400	1.7
Gastrointestinal tract	2.40	3,400	1.0
Heart	0.29	1,900	4.5
Kidneys	0.28	2,900	7.2
Liver	1.56	3,600	1.6
Skeletal muscle	28.5	3,300	0.08
Skeletal muscle (severe exercise)	28.5	260,000	6.3

*No estimate of O_2 consumption is available, but the rate is low.
**Red blood cells do not consume O_2.

occurs as a result of stimulation from the CNS, and it is accompanied by the release of noradrenaline, which also stimulates the hormone-sensitive lipase of adipose tissue. The combined effects of adrenaline and noradrenaline on adipose tissue ensure that the muscles have a greatly increased supply of fatty acids to prevent them from depleting the blood glucose level too much. In order to increase its metabolic rate by such a large amount, skeletal muscle requires an increased oxygen supply and this is also a consequence of the adrenaline secretion. Adrenaline improves the blood flow to muscle by increasing the heart rate and constricting the arterial blood supply to organs such as the digestive tract and the skin.

The changes in substrate supply and the interchange of metabolites between tissues during exercise are summarized in Figure 5.5. The advantage of having the mobilization of substrates for muscle contraction linked to the secretion of adrenaline and noradrenaline by the adrenal medulla is that the CNS can also send signals to the medulla to anticipate exercise. Excitement or fear is likely to require a large increase in muscle activity, but before this occurs the two hormones from the adrenal medulla can flood the muscles with glucose-phosphate and the blood with fatty acids. This ensures that the sudden increase in exercise will not cause too great a reduction the level of blood glucose. Release of fatty acids is necessary during exercise since, as Table 5.2 shows, they represent the body's main energy store.

Table 5.2 Available energy stores in a 70 kg man (kilojoules)

Tissue	Glycogen (+ glucose)	Triacylglycerol	Available protein
Adipose tissue	330	566,000	200
Blood	250	200	0
CNS	30	0	0
Liver	1,650	1,900	1,650
Muscle	5,000	1,900	100,000
Total	7,260	570,000	101,850
as %	1	84	15

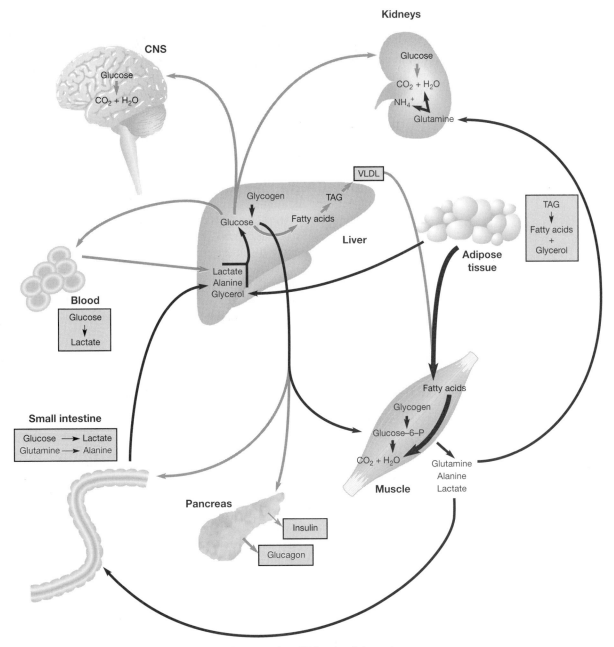

Figure 5.5 The relationships between tissues during exercise. TAG, triacylglycerol.

5.5 Protection

The body requires protection from the potentially hostile environment at all times and this is a major function of the blood. However, changes in the type and level of protection are needed as a consequence of feeding or changes in muscle activity.

The protection against infection, which is provided by the immune system, as well as by phagocytes and bacteriocidal enzymes, operates on a continuous basis, but it is clear that there is an increased risk of exposure to pathogens during feeding. The small intestine has groups of antibody-producing cells close to the epithelial surface that respond rapidly to foreign antigens entering the digestive system during feeding. As indicated in section 12.6, the speed with which the immune system can supply antibodies against a foreign antigen will depend on whether the body has been previously exposed to the particular antigen.

Increased muscular activity is usually needed to protect an individual. However, this is likely to provide a greater risk of injury, and the clotting mechanism is always available to deal with such emergencies.

The major alteration in the demand for protective mechanisms caused by feeding is a consequence of an increased requirement for urea synthesis. This is due to the fact that nitrogen intake must be balanced by nitrogen excretion, and consequently nitrogen elimination by the liver and kidneys must be adjusted to match the increased intake. More protection against free radicals and xenobiotics is also needed during feeding and this is aided by the virtually quantitative conversion of dietary purines into urate which is released into the blood.

Increased exercise is also associated with an elevated release of nitrogen from muscles in the form of glutamine and alanine, but the most important demand on the protective mechanisms is the need to eliminate large amounts of carbon dioxide produced by active muscles. Severe exercise also results in the formation of large amounts of lactate which can alter the blood pH. Consequently the liver must respond by removing the lactate from the blood and converting it back to glucose.

5.6 The selective basis of integration and control

The metabolic integration among the eight tissues is summarized in Figure 5.3, but it should be clear that the peripheral nervous system provides direct links between the CNS and the other seven tissues. These nerve pathways report information from the organs to the CNS and in most cases can also allow direct stimulation of the organ by the CNS. The integration of the information from the organs within the higher centres of the brain is determined by the physical links between neurones and the formation of particular neurotransmitters and receptors.

Metabolic integration is also strongly dependent on the secretions of the endocrine system, much of which is controlled by the CNS. If the hormones secreted by endocrine cells enter the general circulation the specificity of their actions is dependent on specific receptors on the membranes of cells in the target organs and the nature of the internal second messengers. Local hormones can exert their effects on adjacent cells without entering the general circulation.

In a resting individual the integrative actions of the nervous and endocrine systems are not particularly apparent. However, any significant change in activity or environmental conditions immediately reveals the complexity of the control mechanisms.

The operation of the integrative controls is most evident on the initiation of exercise or as a result of fear or excitement. In these conditions the release of adrenergic hormones causes an immediate increase in heart rate and a rise in blood pressure. There is also a shift in the circulatory pattern so that more blood is pumped through the muscles and the CNS whereas the blood supply to the digestive organs is reduced by vasoconstriction. As indicated in section 5.4 the hormonal changes mobilize glucose and fatty acids to provide substrates for the increased energy demand by the muscles.

Consumption of food also causes an integrated response. The blood supply to the digestive system increases and there is a general vasoconstriction of the blood vessels supplying skeletal muscles and the skin. As soon as there is an increase in the glucose concentration in the blood the pancreas will increase the secretion of insulin. This stimulates the uptake of glucose and amino acids by muscle and adipose tissue, thus increasing the storage of glycogen and triacylglycerol. Even before glucose absorption occurs the presence of food in the digestive tract causes a sophisticated response by the CNS. As a result, secretion of the hormones and enzymes associated with the digestion of food will increase. If feeding occurs at the same time as severe exercise, excitement or fear, there is an immediate conflict between the changes induced by the absorption of food and the effects of the adrenergic hormones. The release of adrenaline and noradrenaline override the effects of the food and indigestion often occurs.

5.7 *Summary of the functions and metabolic contributions of tissues*

Figure 5.2 indicates which tissues support the four main requirements of the body and it also lists the main areas of metabolism in each tissue. The principal processes of the eight tissues covered in Part 2 are summarized below.

Adipose tissue contains the most important store of energy-supplying substrates in the body. The storage of triacylglycerol in white adipose tissue is the body's main energy reserve (see Table 5.2). The release of free fatty acids by the hormone-sensitive lipase provides the body with a controlled supply of oxidizable substrate. Brown adipose tissue is concerned with maintaining body temperature, particularly in the newborn.

The **blood** is chiefly involved in transport and protection. The chief feature of blood cell metabolism is the production of lactate by red cells. The biosynthesis of antibody proteins by lymphocytes is an important feature of protection as is the formation, and subsequent removal, of blood clots.

The **central nervous system** is chiefly concerned with the integration of the body. Its metabolism is mainly characterized by the consumption of energy-suppling substrates. However, the synthesis of specialized neurotransmitters and other neurosecretory substances such as adrenaline and noradrenaline plays an important part in the integration of metabolism.

The **kidneys** have a significant metabolic role in the oxidation of glutamine and the secretion of ammonia into the lumen of the tubule to control the acidity of the blood and urine. During periods of starvation the kidneys are also major contributors to gluconeogenesis. However, the main metabolic importance of the kidneys is their high metabolic rate due to the energy cost of the reabsorption of nutrients from the kidney tubules.

The **liver's** principal metabolic functions are concerned with homeostasis and the biosynthesis of a wide range of compounds. In order to fulfil its role as a regulator of nutrient levels the liver synthesizes glucose (either by breaking down glycogen or by gluconeogenesis), as well as triacylglycerol, ketone bodies, non-essential amino acids and urea. Cholesterol biosynthesis supplies this essential membrane constituent and also provides bile salts for the emulsification of dietary fats. The biosynthesis of albumin is important for the maintenance of the osmolarity of the blood. In addition to forming urea in order to protect the body against ammonia, the liver detoxifies a range of foreign compounds by metabolism, hydroxylation or conjugation and excretion in the bile.

Muscle metabolism is mainly devoted to the production of ATP to support muscle contraction and the storage of energy-supplying substrates in the form of glycogen or triacylglycerol. In addition muscle plays an important role as the principal site of branched chain amino acid catabolism with the release of the nitrogen from these amino acids in the form of glutamine. The initiation of muscle contraction depends on a rise in cytoplasmic Ca^{2+}. Muscle cells can store Ca^{2+} in the sarcoplasmic reticulum and it is rapidly released following stimulation by a motor neurone. Muscle protein also provides the second largest energy store in the body (see Table 5.2).

Metabolism in the **pancreas** is particularly directed toward the biosynthesis and secretion of digestive enzymes and the hormones insulin and glucagon. It forms the digestive enzymes amylase, carboxypeptidase, chymotrypsin, lipase, ribonuclease and trypsin which play a crucial role in the hydrolysis of fats, nucleic acids, proteins and starch. Glucagon and insulin, the endocrine secretions of the pancreatic α- and β-cells, control the level of blood glucose as well as its formation and storage in various tissues of the body. Insulin is also important for the storage of fatty acids by adipose tissue.

The **small intestine** which is responsible for the absorption of nutrients requires a substantial input of energy. Even when food is not being absorbed the intestine has a significant metabolic role in the conversion of glutamine to alanine plus NH_4^+. In addition to acting as a physical barrier, the protective function of the small intestine includes the production of antibodies by the immune cells within the lining of the gut, the conversion of dietary purines into the free radical scavenger urate and the trapping of some foreign molecules within the enterocytes.

In the chapters that follow we shall examine the metabolism of each of the eight tissues in detail. In this chapter the links between the tissues have been introduced and at the end of each of the next eight chapters the importance of these interrelationships for each tissue will be stressed. These links are important for the overall integration of metabolism considered in Chapter 14.

E X E R C I S E S

1. List the energy-supplying tissues and indicate the major substrates each tissue provides for the body.

2. Describe the cooperation between tissues in controlling the blood glucose concentration.

3. List the forms of protection provided by the blood.

4. How does feeding alter the provision of energy-supplying substrates?

5. How does exercise alter the metabolic balance between tissues?

6. How does exercise alter the requirements for protection?

7. Fear or excitement causes the release of adrenaline; how does this change the availability of energy-supplying substrates?

8. How is the liver involved in excretion?

9. What does the pancreas contribute to metabolic integration?

10. In what way are the small intestine, kidneys and the liver important for protection?

Further reading

Dow, J., Lindsay, G. & Morrison, J. (1996) *Biochemistry, Molecules, Cells and the Body*, Addison-Wesley, Chapters 11–15.

Frayn, K.N. (1996) *Metabolic Regulation: A Human Perspective*, Portland Press, Chapters 1–3.

Lang, F., Busch, G.L., Ritter, M., Volkl, H., Waldegger, S., Gulbins, E. & Haussinger, D. (1998) Functional significance of cell volume regulatory mechanisms. *Physiological Reviews* **78**, 247–306.

Rolfe, D.F.S. & Brown, G.C. (1997) Cellular energy utilizational and molecular origin of standard metabolic rate in mammals. *Physiological Reviews* **77**, 731–758.

The liver

The liver plays a central role in human metabolism. Its principal functions are metabolic homeostasis, biosynthesis and detoxification.

The liver makes crucial contributions to carbohydrate, lipid and nitrogen metabolism. It controls blood glucose, synthesizes fatty acids and cholesterol, and degrades excess amino acids, converting the nitrogen into urea.

6.1 What are the functions of the liver?

As indicated in the previous chapter the principal functions of the liver are the metabolic interconversions responsible for homeostasis, biosynthesis and detoxification. The interconversions of metabolites by the liver are particularly important for its homeostatic function of maintaining a relatively constant supply of essential nutrients for the non-hepatic tissues, and for the storage of excess nutrients absorbed during feeding. The metabolism of the liver can be visualized as an integrated set of metabolic pathways which are balanced so that they can either supply or remove key metabolites circulating through the body in the blood. When metabolite concentrations in the blood change, the pathways react quickly to restore the normal levels. The biosynthetic processes that occur in the liver include the production of albumin to maintain the osmotic pressure of the blood, the formation of bile salts for the digestion and absorption of lipids and the synthesis of fatty acids, ketone bodies and triacylglycerols. The major detoxification process in the liver is the synthesis of urea for the excretion of nitrogen; and detoxification processes in the liver are also important for the elimination of drugs and other foreign compounds that enter the body.

Figure 6.1 summarizes the principal metabolic processes that take place in the liver. All of the central pathways shown in Figure 5.1 are active in hepatocytes, and in addition there are a number of important specialized pathways such as urea synthesis and the formation of bile salts, cholesterol, creatine and ketone bodies. The detoxification of xenobiotics is also an important feature of liver metabolism. Figure 6.1 also identifies those figures that give the details of the specialized metabolic pathways in the liver.

Homeostasis

Because of the number of specialized functions performed by the liver it is easy to overlook the importance of the coordinating role that the liver plays in most areas of metabolism. This aspect of liver function is best described by the term 'homeo-

CHAPTER 6

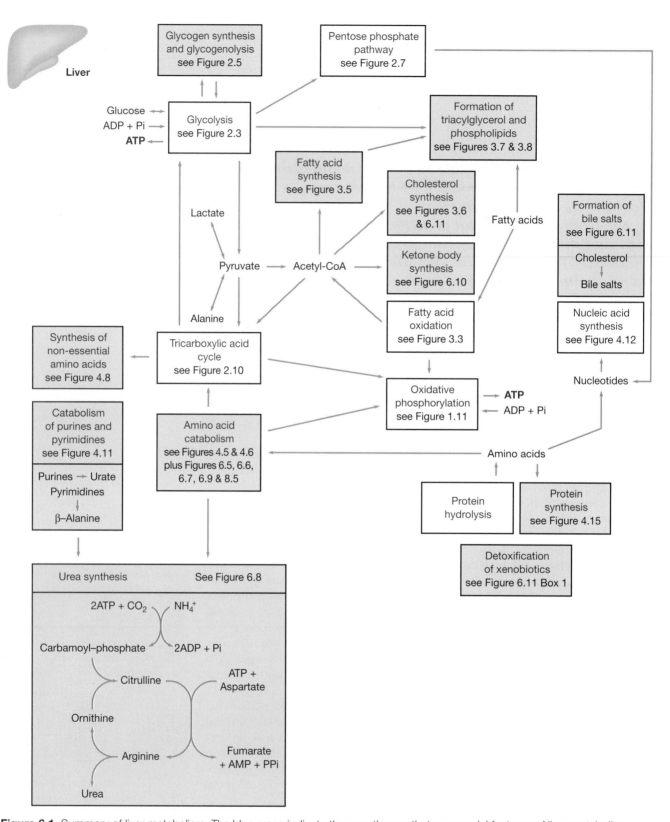

Figure 6.1 Summary of liver metabolism. The blue areas indicate those pathways that are special features of liver metabolism.

stasis', the maintenance of a stable internal environment for the body as a whole. The liver helps to achieve this stability by monitoring the concentrations of many circulating metabolites and responding to abnormal levels by adding or removing the metabolites from the blood. As described in Chapter 5 the classical example of this homeostatic action is the liver's response to changes in blood glucose: a rise in blood sugar is countered by the uptake of glucose by the liver and a fall in blood sugar by glucose production. Although the homeostatic response may be less effective for changes in the concentrations of blood constituents other than glucose, the same pattern of response is made to changes in blood concentrations of other important constituents such as amino acids and lipids. The nature of the blood supply to the liver aids this homeostatic function. Blood comes to the liver from two sources: arterial blood from the aorta via the hepatic artery, and venous blood drained from many internal organs by way of the hepatic portal vein. The fact that the blood from the small intestine passes to the liver through the hepatic portal vein makes it possible for the liver to moderate the increases in blood nutrient levels caused by the absorption of food.

Biosynthesis

Embryologically the liver is derived from the gut and the mature liver plays an important role in the digestion and absorption of lipids by its secretion of bile salts. The liver's origins are also responsible for the epithelial nature of the hepatocytes: one face of each liver cell is on a sinusoid which gives it direct contact with the blood, while the other face is on a small branch of the bile duct. The liver is the main site of cholesterol synthesis and it also controls the cholesterol content of the blood by regulating the rate of synthesis and by the excretion of excess cholesterol into the bile. Bile salts are formed from cholesterol by the liver and are stored in the gall bladder until they are released into the upper end of the small intestine. Bile salts help to break up fat particles, giving a larger surface for the action of the pancreatic lipases which convert them into fatty acids and monoacylglycerols. The bile salts are also involved in the absorption of the monoacylglycerols and other lipids by the small intestine. Ketone bodies are synthesized by the liver from excess fatty acids. A wide range of plasma proteins (e.g. albumin and fibrinogen) are also synthesized in the liver.

Detoxification

In addition to urea synthesis the liver has three main strategies for detoxification. Compounds may be degraded by a catabolic pathway, modified (e.g. by hydroxylation) or conjugated with glycine, glucuronate or sulphate. If the modified compounds are returned to the blood the structural changes may prevent them from entering other cells and stop their reabsorption by the epithelial cells lining the kidney tubules (see Chapter 13). The polarized nature of the hepatocytes is also important for the liver's protective function since some of the compounds it detoxifies can be excreted into the bile. The liver also detoxifies alcohol as described in section 6.8.

6.2 The cellular organization of the liver and its blood supply

Hepatocytes are arranged in stacks so that one side of every cell borders a blood vessel or sinusoid (see Figure 6.2a). This face of the hepatocyte is extended by irregular projections into the extracellular space which resemble the brush border of the intestine and the epithelial lining of the kidney tubules. A small area on the opposite side of each hepatocyte borders a bile canaliculus and the epithelial func-

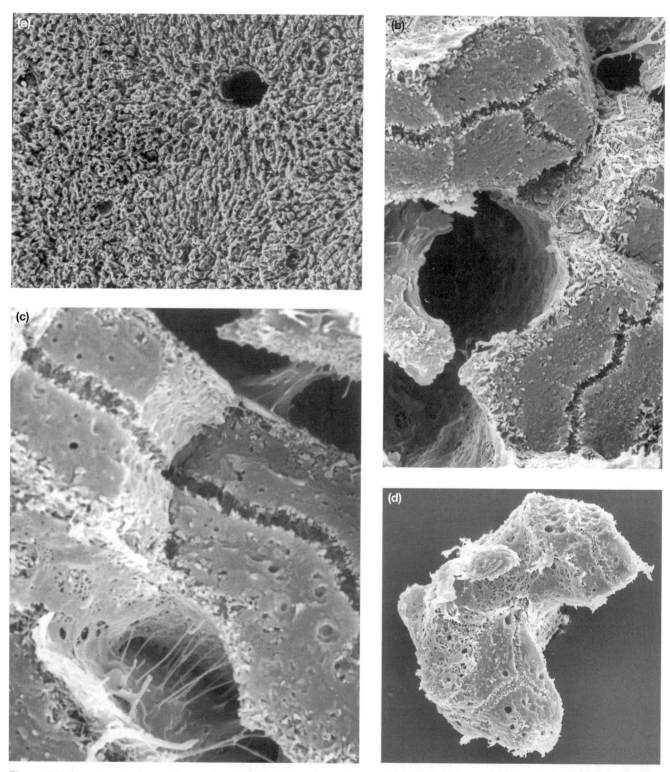

Figure 6.2 Scanning electron micrographs of liver tissue. (a) Low power micrograph showing the arrangement of cells around a branch of the hepatic artery × 110. (b) Groups of hepatocytes bordering a sinusoid × 5500. (c) The relationship between hepatocytes and the bile canaliculus × 5500. (d) An isolated hepatocyte × 2150. Micrographs supplied by P.G. Humpherson.

tion of the liver is illustrated by the fact that bile salts absorbed from the blood by the hepatocytes are recycled by excretion into the bile. Most of the remaining surface of the cuboidal hepatocyte is closely applied to its neighbouring cells. The scanning electron micrographs of rat liver in Figure 6.2 show how mammalian hepatocytes have a large proportion of their plasma membrane bordering on a sinusoid and a small area of membrane along a bile canaliculus.

The liver consists mainly of parenchymal cells which make up more than 90% of its total volume; most of the remaining cells are reticulocytes, which are responsible for degradation of red cells and their contents, or endothelial cells lining the various blood vessels. Two main blood vessels feed the liver, the hepatic artery and the portal vein, and it is drained by the the vena cava. The blood vessels entering the liver divide into a large number of branches and the arterial and portal blood mixes in the sinusoids that serve all of the hepatocytes. This arrangement ensures that the liver cells receive a proportion of oxygenated blood directly from the heart and at the same time they are able to monitor any changes in the composition of the blood coming from the intestine and other specialized organs such as the kidneys. The capacity to detect the presence of nutrients absorbed from the small intestine enables the liver to moderate the large increases in amino acids, glucose and other sugars following a meal. Although the overall organization of the liver resembles a sponge, it is important to recognize that the mixing of arterial and venous blood does not occur evenly throughout the liver, so that some hepatocytes will be well oxygenated with blood from the hepatic artery while others receive a larger proportion of venous blood which has a low oxygen content. A great deal of research on liver function is carried out with isolated hepatocytes (see Figure 6.2d) in which all sides of the cell are exposed to the same conditions. Consequently, to gain a true picture of hepatocyte function in the organ as a whole, it is also necessary to study the metabolism of the intact liver.

6.3 Regulation of blood metabolite levels by the liver

The liver is the principal organ responsible for monitoring and regulating the blood levels of nutrients and other organic constituents. The circulating concentrations of glucose, fatty acids and most of the amino acids are kept within reasonably narrow limits. In addition, the homeostatic actions of the liver extend to plasma proteins and the cholesterol-carrying LDL. Many minor organic constituents and foreign compounds such as drugs are either removed from the blood by the liver or converted into a form that can be excreted by the kidneys.

Control of blood glucose

The control of blood glucose is the most effective regulatory system operated by the liver. Neurones in the brain and other parts of the CNS rely on a continual supply of glucose so that it is important that the blood glucose concentration does not fall much below 5 mM or fluctuate too rapidly. At the other extreme, excessively high blood glucose levels can distort the metabolism of extrahepatic tissues. The absorption of a large amount of glucose by the intestine causes a rise in blood sugar. As mentioned in Chapter 5, the increased glucose concentration directly stimulates the secretion of insulin by the pancreas which immediately reduces the blood glucose by increasing entry into muscle and adipose tissue, but the metabolism of glucose by the liver also helps to bring the blood glucose back to the normal 5 mM level. The fate of excess glucose removed by the liver depends on the

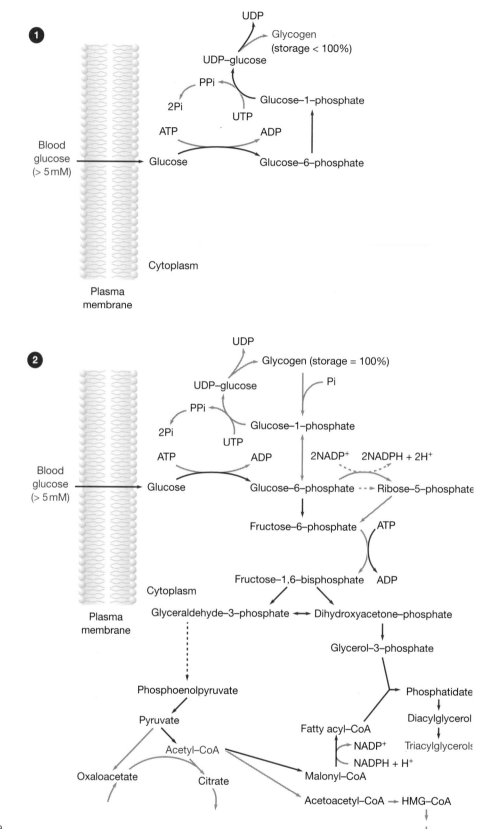

Liver

Figure 6.3(a)
Metabolic responses by the liver to a
high blood glucose.

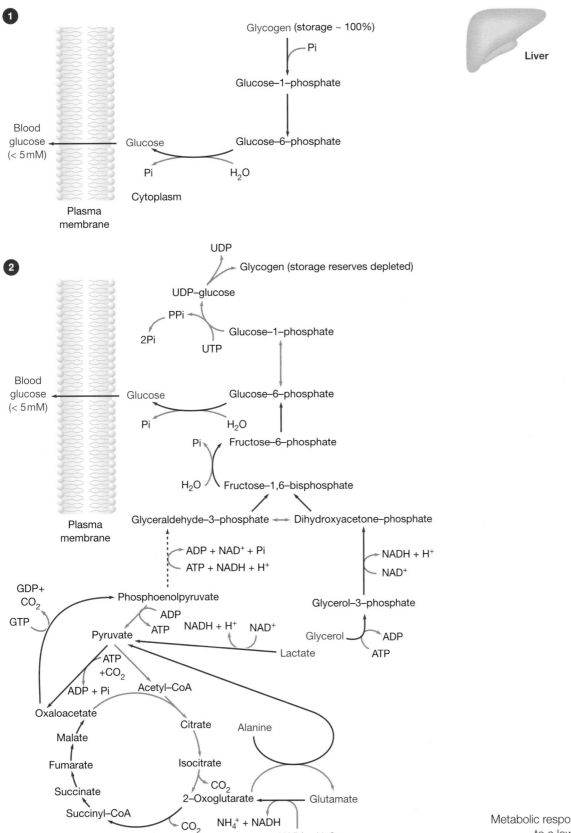

1

Glycogen (storage ~ 100%)

Pi

Glucose–1–phosphate

Glucose–6–phosphate

Blood glucose (< 5mM) ← Glucose

Pi   H₂O

Cytoplasm

Plasma membrane

Liver

2

UDP

Glycogen (storage reserves depleted)

UDP–glucose

PPi

2Pi   Glucose–1–phosphate

UTP

Blood glucose (< 5mM) ← Glucose   Glucose–6–phosphate

Pi   H₂O

Pi   Fructose–6–phosphate

H₂O   Fructose–1,6–bisphosphate

Glyceraldehyde–3–phosphate ⇌ Dihydroxyacetone–phosphate

Plasma membrane

ADP + NAD⁺ + Pi   NADH + H⁺

ATP + NADH + H⁺   NAD⁺

GDP+ CO₂   Phosphoenolpyruvate   Glycerol–3–phosphate

GTP   ADP   NADH + H⁺   NAD⁺

ATP

Pyruvate   Lactate   Glycerol   ADP

ATP   ATP

+CO₂

ADP + Pi   Acetyl–CoA

Oxaloacetate   Citrate   Alanine

Malate   Isocitrate

Fumarate   CO₂

Succinate   2–Oxoglutarate ← Glutamate

Succinyl–CoA   CO₂   NH₄⁺ + NADH

NAD⁺ + H₂O

Figure 6.3(b)
Metabolic responses by the liver to a low blood glucose.

nutritional state, as illustrated in Figure 6.3. In a fed individual the stores of liver glycogen are well stocked so that relatively little of the incoming glucose will be converted into glycogen. Nevertheless, restoration of liver glycogen stores is the first priority for the glucose taken up by the liver, regardless of the nutritional state. The stored glycogen enables the liver to react to a sudden drop in blood glucose by converting its glycogen into glucose phosphates (see Figure 6.3b). The presence of glucose-6-phosphatase in the liver makes it possible for this tissue to release glucose into the blood, in contrast to muscle where the enzyme is absent. The location of the glucose-6-phosphatase on the luminal side of the endoplasmic reticulum membranes separates it from the glucokinase and helps to prevent futile cycling at the expense of ATP since the entry of glucose-6-phosphate into the endoplasmic reticulum lumen and the exit of glucose will be influenced by the concentrations of these metabolites in the liver cytoplasm. After liver glycogen has been exhausted the liver still releases glucose in response to low levels in the blood, and under these conditions the glucose is produced by gluconeogenesis (see Figure 6.3b).

Once the demand for glycogen storage has been met, the liver converts excess glucose into other metabolites through the central pathways (see Figure 6.3a). It is important to recognize that feeding the glucose carbons into the central pathways enables *any* requirement for a particular metabolite formed from a central pathway intermediate to be satisfied. For example, demands for pentose phosphate or NADPH can be met by the oxidation of glucose-6-phosphate through the pentose phosphate pathway; if glycerol-3-phosphate is needed it can be formed by reduction of dihydroxyacetone-phosphate. Most of the excess glucose carbons are converted into pyruvate and their fate is influenced by the concentrations of other nutrients in the blood. If glucose intake by the intestine is not associated with the digestion and absorption of protein constituents, there may be a need for the synthesis of non-essential amino acids either directly from pyruvate or by way of one of the TCA cycle intermediates. Once such demands have been met (or if the dietary sources of glucose are mixed with protein), the excess glucose will be converted to acetyl-CoA for conversion into fatty acids or cholesterol. Of course it is necessary to make the proviso that sufficient oxaloacetate and acetyl-CoA must be formed from pyruvate to ensure that the TCA cycle functions rapidly enough to satisfy the demand for ATP in the liver.

What is the effect of the intake of sucrose?

It was pointed out in Part 1 that a large intake of sucrose is likely to distort carbohydrate metabolism because fructose bypasses the phosphofructokinase control point in glycolysis by direct conversion into three-carbon intermediates (see Figure 2.2). There is some conversion of fructose to lactate in the small intestine but most of the fructose metabolism takes place in the liver. Since the liver also metabolizes the glucose that is absorbed with fructose, it might be concluded that once the glycogen stocks are replenished both sugars should have the same effect. However there are several reasons why fructose can cause greater increases in the rate of acetyl-CoA production than the equivalent amount of glucose. Since fructokinase has a much lower K_m than glucokinase, fructose entering the liver by the hepatic portal vein will be converted into acetyl-CoA even when the blood glucose concentration is within the normal range. Secondly, because fructose comes mainly from sucrose, it will enter the circulation together with an equivalent amount of glucose. Therefore although the glucose will be used initially to top up glycogen stocks and to supply the energy requirements of non-hepatic cells, the fructose will enter the central pathways in the liver to be converted mainly into acetyl-CoA. A final danger associated with fructose intake is that it is only elevated levels of blood glucose that are capable of triggering the satiation reflex in the brain which helps to discourage further eating.

Regulation of vascular amino acid concentrations

The liver also plays a major role in regulating the amino acid concentrations in the blood. As indicated in Chapter 5, a meal containing protein results in absorption of peptides and amino acids by the small intestine. Although metabolism in the intestine helps to convert the amino acid intake into a physiological mixture, the digestion of protein will lead to a sharp rise in the amino acid levels in the hepatic portal vein and and consequently also in the hepatocytes. The liver will remove the amino nitrogen from the excess amino acids by a combination of transamination and deamination (see Figure 4.4a) and convert the nitrogen into urea. The only exceptions are the branched chain amino acids, leucine, isoleucine and valine, which are degraded in skeletal muscle (see Figure 8.5). The liver's response to a deficiency of amino acids in the blood is more complex. Only the non-essential amino acids can be synthesized from central metabolites, but it should be noted that the rate of protein synthesis in the liver and other metabolically active tissues is very sensitive to the cytoplasmic amino acid concentrations. Since a drop in blood amino acid concentrations is reflected in the cytoplasm, the rate of protein synthesis in tissues such as the liver will decline. When the cell is in a steady state protein synthesis is balanced by protein breakdown, but a sudden drop in the rate of synthesis will increase the supply of all 20 amino acids because it will take some time for the rate of degradation to adjust to the lower rate of synthesis.

Regulation of lipid levels in the blood

The liver is also involved in the regulation of fatty acid and cholesterol levels in the blood but for these constituents, as pointed out in the last chapter, interactions between the liver and other tissues are particularly important. Short-chain fatty acids pass directly to the liver via the hepatic portal vein and the production of acetyl-CoA from these fatty acids will tend to reduce the rate at which hexoses are metabolized by the glycolytic pathway. However, it is clear that in the liver excess acetyl-CoA from any source will be converted either into fatty acids and then tri-acylglycerol for release in the form of VLDL or into ketone bodies which are released directly into the blood. The glycerol released by the lipoprotein lipase in other tissues is taken up by the liver where it enters the central pathways as glycerol-phosphate which can be used in a variety of ways such as the formation of glucose, acetyl-CoA or even pentose phosphate.

As the triacylglycerol is removed from the chylomicrons or VLDL these lipoprotein particles are converted into chylomicron remnants and IDL, respectively. Some of the IDL is then converted into LDL which delivers cholesterol to cells all around the body for use in the formation of membranes. Any deficiency in the supply of cholesterol from the diet is made up by the liver which synthesizes it from acetyl-CoA (see Figures 3.6 and 6.11) Excess dietary cholesterol should be excreted by the liver into the bile. However, this is not a fully effective means of eliminating the excess, since the cholesterol can be reabsorbed by the small intestine. Moderate levels of cholesterol in the diet should not lead to excessive blood levels provided that the regulation of cholesterol biosynthesis in the liver operates correctly. Nevertheless, it is important to note that a proportion of lipoprotein cholesterol is always present in the form of the lipid-soluble cholesteryl esters. Therefore a high dietary intake will tend to provide a higher level of cholesteryl esters in the blood lipoproteins. These esters can be deposited in foam cells beneath the endothelial lining of blood vessels causing bulges that interfere with blood flow in arteries (see section 12.9). It is not certain what initiates formation of these cholesteryl ester deposits but they are known to cause dangerous narrowing of the vessels in the heart and the brain.

6.4 Glycogen synthesis, glycogenolysis and gluconeogenesis

The capacity of the liver to sustain an adequate level of glucose in the blood while at the same time preventing the blood glucose concentration from rising to excessive levels is a consequence of four features of liver metabolism. Two of these processes are concerned with the supply of glucose and two with its removal.

Removal of excess blood glucose by the liver

The simplest way for the liver to deal with excess glucose is to convert it into glycogen (Figure 6.3a). The highly branched nature of the glycogen molecules (see Figure 2.5) allows them to accept large numbers of glucose units as UDP-glucose at the same time. Because of the vast number of acceptor sites for glucose units, the speed of the synthesis is dependent on the number of active glycogen synthetase molecules available. An increase in glucose concentration is accompanied by the secretion of insulin and this stimulates the phosphatase enzyme which converts the inactive phosphorylated form of glycogen synthetase into the active dephosphorylated form (see Figure 1.13).

Figure 6.3(a) shows that a second way of removing excess glucose is to convert it into triacylglycerol via acetyl-CoA and fatty acyl-CoA. This is a reasonable expectation in hepatocytes when there is an excess of glucose-6-phosphate, the glycogen store is replete and the energy requirements of the cell have been satisfied. The conversion of glucose into fatty acids under these conditions is further enhanced by insulin which stimulates the activity of both pyruvate dehydrogenase and acetyl-CoA carboxylase. In the former case it stimulates the phosphatase responsible for activating pyruvate dehydrogenase, whereas the activity of the acetyl-CoA carboxylase is enhanced by polymerization of the enzyme. Because acetyl-CoA is produced from pyruvate within the mitochondria and fatty acids are synthesized in the cytoplasm, the acetyl-CoA must be exported from the mitochondrial matrix either as citrate or by the carnitine acyltransferase (see Figure 6.10). The second part of Figure 6.3(a) also shows that the acetyl-CoA formed from excess glucose could be used to form cholesterol, but this does not normally happen because cholesterol synthesis is under strict control (see section 6.10).

How does the liver prevent the blood glucose concentration from falling?

The two main ways in which the liver can supply blood glucose are the degradation of glycogen and synthesis from a variety of substrates such as alanine, lactate, glycerol and TCA cycle intermediates (see Figure 6.3b). The generation of free glucose by the liver is called glycogenolysis when it is derived from glycogen and gluconeogenesis when other carbon sources are used.

In Chapter 2 the degradation of glycogen was described in detail (section 2.3), but at this point it is important to consider what special features apply to glycogenolysis in the liver. The release of glucose phosphates from glycogen is controlled by the enzyme glycogen phosphorylase (Figure 2.5b), and the activity of this enzyme can be stimulated in three different ways. The most basic control, which operates mainly in muscle, is the stimulation of phosphorylase b by 5'-AMP which only occurs when the ATP/ADP ratio is reduced. A low blood glucose will stimulate the secretion of glucagon by the pancreas, and this hormone initiates the cyclic-AMP cascade (Figure 1.13), resulting in the phosphorylation of phosphorylase b which converts it into the active form, phosphorylase a. The third

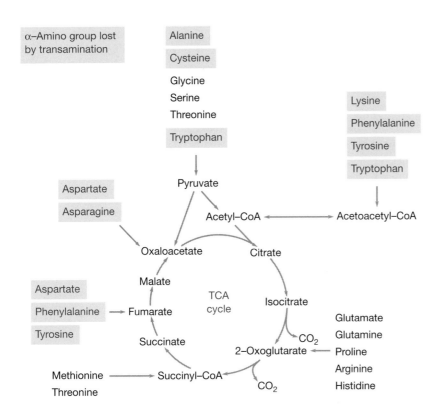

Liver

Figure 6.4(a)
Summary of amino acid
catabolism in the liver.

method of stimulating glycogen phosphorolysis is through adrenaline secretion. This hormone is produced by the adrenal medulla in response to a signal from the CNS that extra glucose is going to be required because extra exertion is anticipated or is already taking place. Adrenaline also combines with a receptor which activates the cyclic-AMP cascade (see Figure 1.13).

When liver glycogen is depleted, gluconeogenesis takes over. Figures 2.4 and 6.3(b) chart the pathway from the main substrates lactate and alanine, but it is important to remember that all but two of the amino acid carbon skeletons can generate TCA cycle intermediates (see Figure 6.4a) and therefore can provide carbons for gluconeogenesis. In addition, Figure 6.3(b) shows that the glycerol which is released from triacylglycerol in adipose tissue by triacylglycerol lipase and is removed from the blood by the liver can serve as a substrate for gluconeogenesis. Control of gluconeogenesis occurs again on three levels. Since all the major substrates except glycerol must enter the pathway using mitochondrial enzymes, the TCA cycle must be saturated with substrate so that citrate can be exported to the cytoplasm. Citrate lyase then yields the oxaloacetate for conversion to phosphoenolpyruvate. The rise in cytoplasmic citrate increases gluconeogenesis since it inhibits phosphofructokinase, thereby stimulating conversion of fructose-1,6-bisphosphate into fructose-6-phosphate. A second level of control over gluconeogenesis is provided by the supply of substrates from outside the liver. Lactate and alanine come chiefly from muscle in the sense that their availability will be strongly influenced by the level of muscle activity. Nevertheless it should be recognized that the red blood cells and the small intestine are also important sources of lactate. Recent studies have shown that a major source of alanine, which again is related to muscle activity, results from the production of glutamine in muscle and its conversion to alanine in the small intestine. The control of glycerol supplies from the adipose tissue takes us into the third level of regulation by hormones, particularly adrenaline and noradrenaline which stimulate the hormone-sensitive lipase in adipose tissue. Glucagon, which is secreted in response to a fall in blood glucose, also has a direct effect on the gluconeogenic pathway. It does this by decreasing the concentration of the regulatory molecule fructose-2,6-bisphosphate (see section

Liver

Overall reaction

A 2 Alanine + 2 2–Oxoglutarate + ATP + NH_4^+ ⟶ 3 Glutamate + ADP + Pi + CO_2 + H_2O

B 2 Alanine + 2–Oxoglutarate + ATP + NAD^+ ⟶ 2 Glutamate + ADP + Pi + NADH + CO_2

Conversion of alanine into glutamate

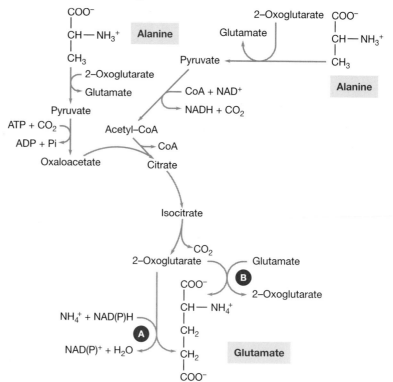

Conversion of alanine into glutamine

Overall reaction

A 2 Alanine + 2–Oxoglutarate + 2 ATP + NH_4^+ ⟶ Glutamine + Glutamate + 2 ADP + 2 Pi + CO_2 + H_2O

B 2 Alanine + 2 ATP + NAD^+ ⟶ Glutamine + 2 ADP + 2 Pi + NADH + CO_2

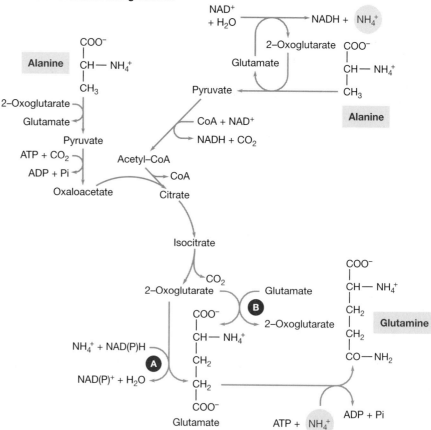

Figure 6.4(b)

Examples of amino acid interconversions in the liver.

2.3 and Figure 2.3). Glucagon reduces the concentration of fructose-2,6-bisphosphate by its effects on the multifunctional enzyme system, inhibiting the phosphofructokinase-2 activity and stimulating the fructose-2,6-bisphosphatase activity. An increase in glucose supply has the reverse effect on the multifunctional system and raises the fructose-2,6-bisphosphate concentration.

What enables the liver to respond to changes in blood glucose concentration?

The liver differs from most tissues except the pancreas by having a glucose transport system in the plasma membrane that allows the glucose concentration in the hepatocyte cytosol to equilibrate with that in the blood and a glucokinase enzyme with a high K_m to catalyse the initial phosphorylation of glucose. The presence of glucose-6-phosphatase also distinguishes the liver from most other tissues because it enables the liver to produce free glucose. By having these two enzymes the liver is able to respond to an increase in blood glucose by the conversion of glucose to glucose-6-phosphate. It reacts to a low blood glucose by the hydrolysis of glucose-6-phosphate. When the hydrolysis of glucose-6-phosphate is examined more closely it is found to occur only in the lumen of the endoplasmic reticulum of the hepatocytes. This means that the glucose-6-phosphate must be transported into the endoplasmic reticulum by a transporter so that the glucose-6-phosphatase which is bound to the inside of the endoplasmic reticulum membrane can hydrolyse it. After hydrolysis the glucose and phosphate must be transported back into the cytoplasm. Localization of the hydrolytic step in a separate compartment helps to reduce the futile cycling of glucose and glucose-6-phosphate.

6.5 Catabolism and interconversion of amino acids by the liver

The general features of amino acid catabolism were considered in Chapter 4 and they are summarized for the 17 amino acids metabolized by the liver in Figure 6.4(a). Removal of the amino group by transamination and deamination (Figure 4.4a) is normally followed by conversion of the carbon skeleton into pyruvate, acetyl-CoA or one of the intermediates in the TCA cycle. Details of the catabolism of alanine, asparagine, aspartate, glutamate, glutamine, glycine and serine to pyruvate, oxaloacetate or 2-oxoglutarate are shown in Figure 4.6. Although the catabolism of the other amino acids is somewhat more complicated the principles are the same: the nitrogen is converted into a non-toxic waste product and the carbon skeletons are channelled into the central metabolic pathways. In this way the amino acid carbons can be used to meet whatever metabolic requirements the cell needs to satisfy at the time.

Synthesis and degradation of non-essential amino acids

Amino acid metabolism in the liver serves two main purposes: to achieve a balance between nitrogen excretion and nitrogen intake, and to help maintain the concentrations of all 20 amino acids in the blood within the normal range. It should be clear from a comparison of Figure 4.8 with Figure 4.6 that there is no problem in converting an excess of most non-essential amino acids (e.g. alanine) into others (e.g. glutamate) through the TCA cycle. In this example, which is shown in outline in Figure 6.4b, two alanines need to be transaminated to yield two pyruvates One of these is carboxylated to form oxaloacetate, while the other is decarboxylated to acetyl-CoA. These two products are then converted to 2-oxoglutarate via citrate, and the final addition of the amino group to form glutamate could be by either glutamate dehydrogenase or transamination. It is important to recognize that a true conversion of alanine to glutamate cannot be achieved simply by transamination of alanine with 2-oxoglutarate, since there is no way that the resulting pyruvate can be converted to 2-oxoglutarate without the addition of acetyl-CoA or oxaloacetate. In fact, since each alanine must be transaminated it will be necessary for one of the glutamates formed in the transamination to be deaminated in order to maintain the 2-oxoglutarate levels. The NH_4^+ released can be converted into urea (see section 6.6). An alternative would be to use the NH_4^+ released in the deamination to convert the glutamate formed from the two alanines into glutamine (see Figure 6.4b) at the expense of an ATP. The glutamine can then be used to form carbamoyl-phosphate for pyrimidine synthesis (see Figure 4.9).

Similar reaction patterns apply to the conversion of excess alanine into aspartate or asparagine, although in these examples only a single alanine is required since the fourth carbon is added by the carboxylation of pyruvate to form oxaloacetate. Obviously it is also possible to form aspartate from any other amino acid which has a carbon skeleton that can be converted into oxaloacetate or one of the other TCA cycle intermediates. Formation of asparagine from aspartate merely requires the ATP-dependent addition of an NH_4^+ ion. The same pattern of reactions can be used to convert any amino acid that can form 2-oxoglutarate into glutamate or into glutamine, if sufficient NH_4^+ is available. Even an excess of histidine can be used to produce either glutamate or glutamine (see Figure 6.7). Figure 4.8 also indicates how amino acids that can yield oxaloacetate or 2-oxoglutarate can produce arginine, proline or serine. As indicated in the sections that follow, the reason why the same principles cannot normally be used to synthesize the essential amino acids is due to the inability to form the corresponding 2-oxo-acids.

Catabolism of essential amino acids

The liver is the main site of the catabolism of excess amino acids entering the body from the small intestine as a result of the intake of dietary protein. Although, as emphasized above, only the net synthesis of the non-essential amino acids can occur in mammals, it should be stressed that catabolism of all 20 amino acids must occur in order to maintain nitrogen balance. For catabolism of 17 amino acids the liver is quantitatively the most important organ although some breakdown does occur in tissues such as muscle, intestine and the kidneys. Some catabolism of the three branched chain amino acids, isoleucine, leucine and valine, has been shown to occur in adipose tissue, but muscle is the only quantitatively important catabolic site for these amino acids (see Figure 8.5). Some of the consequences of the catabolism of branched chain amino acids in muscle will be considered in the Chapter 8.

Metabolism of sulphur-containing amino acids; the S-adenosylmethionine cycle

Catabolism and interconversion of the two sulphur-containing amino acids, cysteine and methionine, is shown in Figure 6.5. Although an excess of methionine can be used to make up for deficiencies of cysteine, the reverse cannot occur. Methionine can be formed from homocysteine, as shown in Figure 6.5, by the transfer of a methyl group from N^5-methyl-tetrahydrofolate via vitamin B_{12} (see Figure 6.5, Boxes 1 and 3), but no quantitatively significant pathway is available to form homocysteine from cysteine. The catabolism of methionine involves the transfer of the sulphur to serine, producing cysteine. The final steps in the pathway require the carboxylation of propionyl-CoA to form methylmalonyl-CoA which undergoes rearrangement to form succinyl-CoA. Vitamin B_{12} (see Figure 6.5, Box 2) is the coenzyme for the methylmalonyl-CoA mutase reaction.

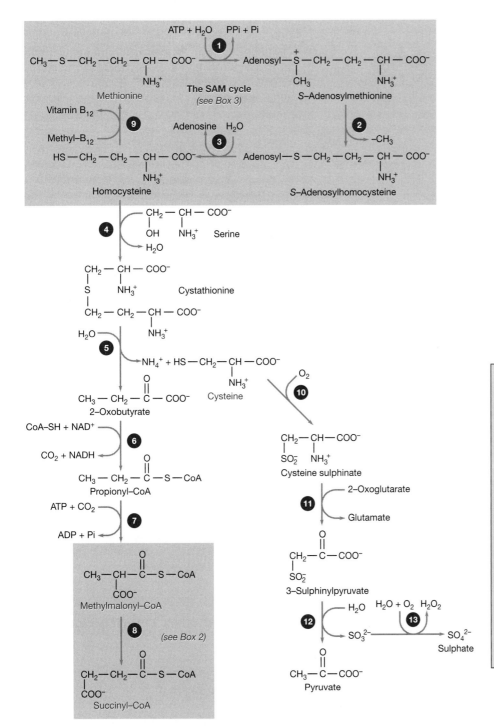

Liver

Enzymes

1 Methionine adenosyltransferase
2 Methyltransferase
3 Adenosylhomocysteinase
4 Cystathionine β–synthase
5 Cystathionine γ–lyase
6 2–Oxobutyrate dehydrogenase
7 Propionyl–CoA carboxylase
8 Methylmalonyl–CoA mutase
9 Homocysteine methyltransferase
10 Cysteine dioxygenase
11 Transaminase
12 Hydrolysis (non-enzymatic)
13 Sulphite oxidase

Figure 6.5
Metabolism of methionine and cysteine in the liver.

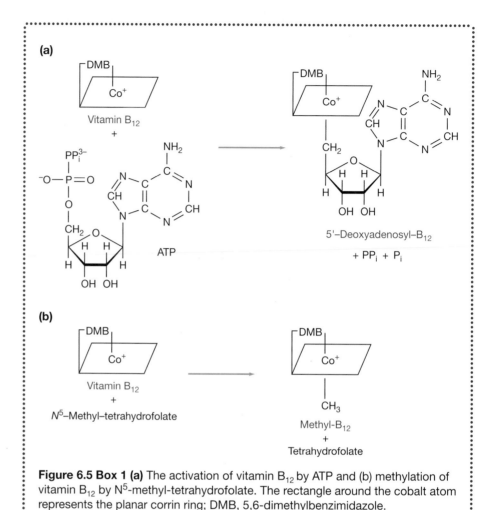

Figure 6.5 Box 1 (a) The activation of vitamin B_{12} by ATP and (b) methylation of vitamin B_{12} by N^5-methyl-tetrahydrofolate. The rectangle around the cobalt atom represents the planar corrin ring; DMB, 5,6-dimethylbenzimidazole.

Figure 6.5, Box 3, also highlights the metabolic significance of methionine for methyl group transfer via S-adenosylmethionine. This pathway is important for the methylation of amino acid side chains, such as lysine or histidine, during the post-translational modification of proteins. It is also responsible for the formation of carnitine, which is important for the transfer of fatty acids into the mitochondrial matrix (see Figure 3.2), and in the conversion of phosphatidyl ethanolamine into phosphatidyl choline (see Figure 3.8). The synthesis of creatine in the liver (see Figure 6.5, Box 4) involves the addition of a methyl group by S-adenosylmethionine. The S-adenosylmethionine cycle (SAM cycle) also plays an important role in the synthesis of adrenaline and noradrenaline by the adrenal medulla (see Figure 11.7). Recent evidence suggests that a rise in plasma homocysteine is associated with folate deficiency and vascular disease.

Catabolism of threonine, lysine and tryptophan; dioxygenase reactions

Not all the amino acid nitrogens are removed by the combination of transamination and the deamination of glutamate shown in Figure 4.4(a). The catabolic pathways for lysine, tryptophan and threonine, which are described in Figure 6.6, involve quite different nitrogen removal techniques. For lysine the ε-amino group

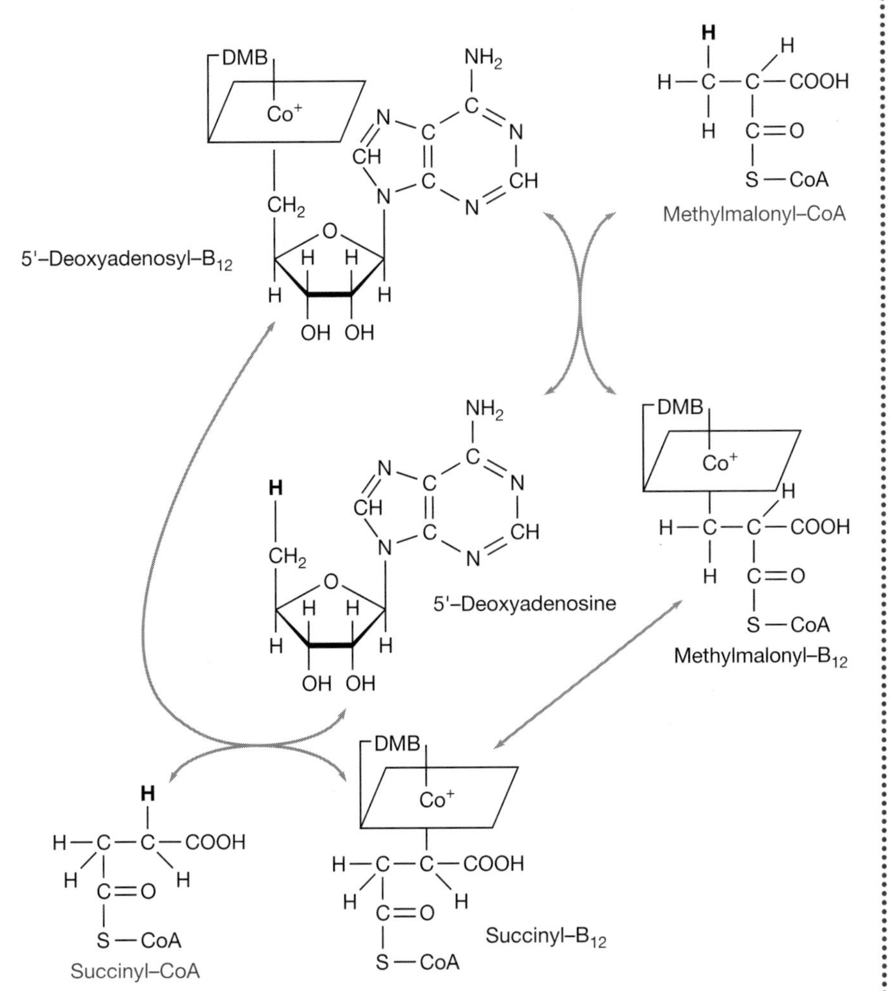

Figure 6.5 Box 2 The steps of the methylmalonyl-CoA mutase reaction.

is lost through the addition of 2-oxoglutarate, followed by the oxidative removal of glutamate; a further oxidative step yields 2-aminoadipate which then undergoes transamination forming 2-oxoadipate. In the case of tryptophan the nitrogen-containing five-membered ring is opened by a dioxygenase reaction which involves the addition of both atoms of an oxygen molecule (see Figure 6.6a), and the α-amino nitrogen is removed by the formation of alanine. A further dioxygenase step is required to open the six-membered ring and after a decarboxylation the pathway joins that for lysine at 2-oxoadipate. In the case of threonine (Figure 6.6b) there are alternative pathways: direct deamination by threonine dehydratase or oxidation to aminoacetone followed by deamination by monoamine oxidase.

Breakdown of phenylalanine and tyrosine

Direct oxidation by molecular oxygen is also responsible for the catabolism of phenylalanine and tyrosine. Addition of the tyrosine hydroxyl group is the consequence of a monooxygenase reaction (see Figure 6.9, Box 1A, and section 6.7) in which one of the atoms in molecular oxygen is used to form the hydroxyl group in the presence of a reducing agent, tetrahydrobiopterin, while the other

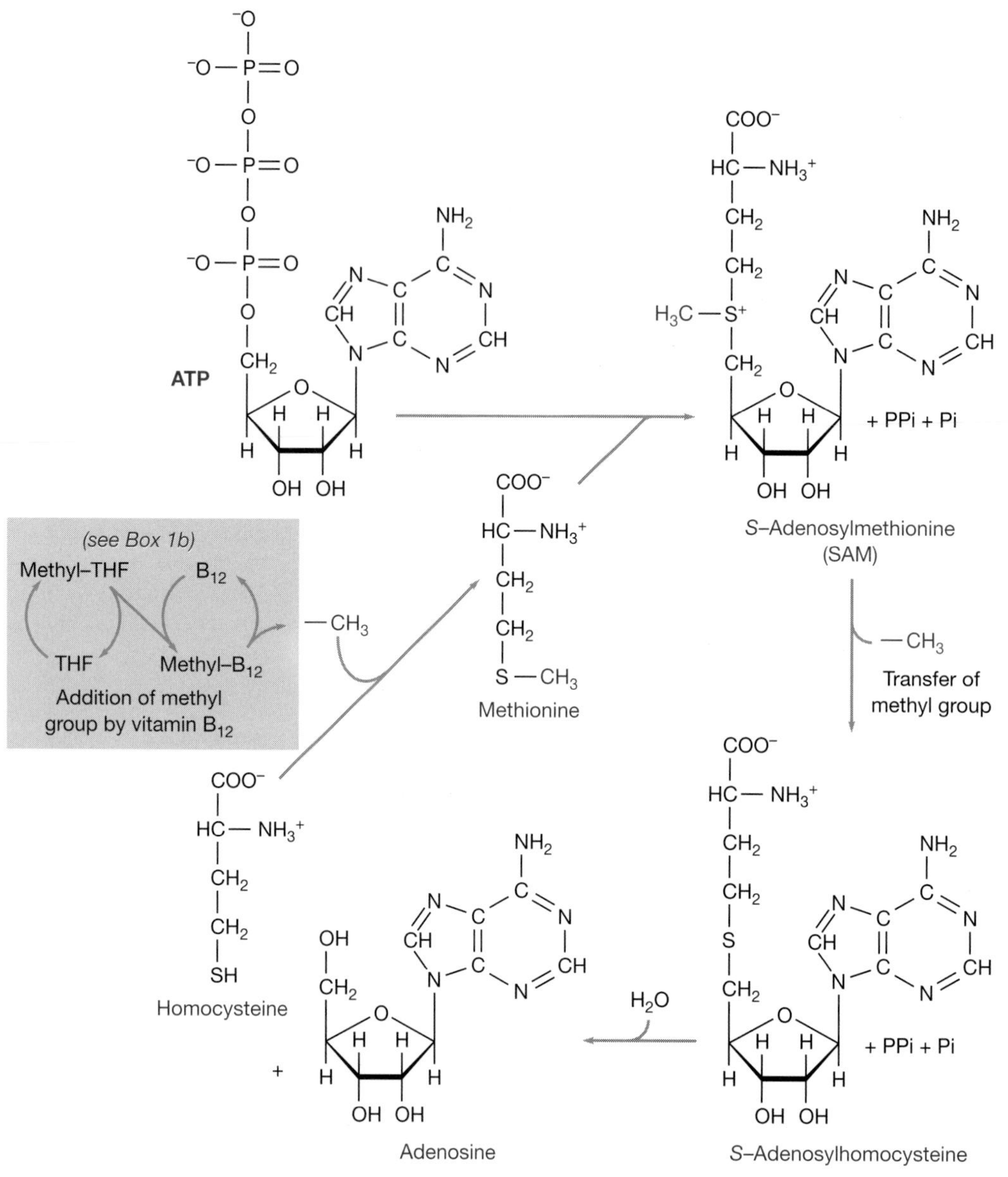

Figure 6.5 Box 3 The S–adenosylmethionine (SAM) cycle.

oxygen forms water. Tyrosine loses its amino group to 2-oxoglutarate by transamination producing 4-hydroxyphenylpyruvate which then requires two successive dioxygenase steps to break up the benzene ring. The final products are acetoacetate and fumarate, providing both acetyl-CoA and (effectively) oxaloacetate for the TCA cycle.

Catabolism of histidine, proline and arginine

The formation of arginine and proline from glutamate has already been shown in Figure 4.8, and a similar pathway is responsible for catabolism of these amino

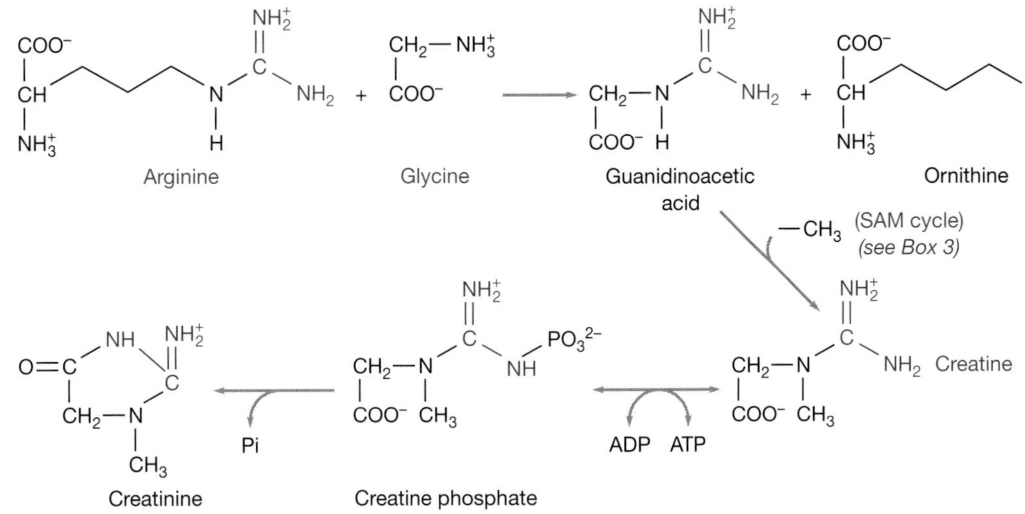

Figure 6.5 Box 4 The role of the SAM cycle in the formation of creatine by the liver.

acids as shown in Figure 6.7. Histidine is also degraded to glutamate by a pathway that involves transfer of a formimino group to tetrahydrofolate (Figure 6.7).

6.6 Urea synthesis

Quantitatively the most important detoxification process in the liver is the conversion of NH_4^+ and excess amino nitrogen into urea. In view of the need to balance nitrogen excretion with nitrogen intake, as discussed in previous chapters, the liver's capacity for urea synthesis must be adequate to allow for the maximum nitrogen intake. The general pattern of the urea synthesis cycle is shown in Figure 4.4(a), which illustrates one of its important characteristics, namely the fact that only one of the two urea nitrogens comes from NH_4^+ with the other coming directly from aspartate. This allows excessive levels of many individual amino acids to be reduced through transamination to form aspartate without relying on deamination, which in most cases must be channelled through glutamate. It is also important to recognize that the two urea nitrogens are added in separate parts of the cell.

The formation of citrulline from ornithine

Figure 6.8 shows that conversion of ornithine to citrulline, which requires the addition of NH_4^+ as carbamoyl-phosphate, takes place in the mitochondrial matrix where most of the glutamate deamination occurs. Furthermore, any NH_4^+ released in the cytoplasm will enter the matrix at the expense of the membrane potential (negative inside) across the inner mitochondrial membrane. Localization of the ornithine to citrulline step and the associated deamination of glutamate within the mitochondrial matrix makes it possible to use NADPH-dependent amination of 2-oxoglutarate in the cytoplasm to generate additional cytoplasmic glutamate at the same time that the NAD^+-dependent deamination of glutamate in the mitochondrial matrix is supplying NH_4^+ for urea synthesis.

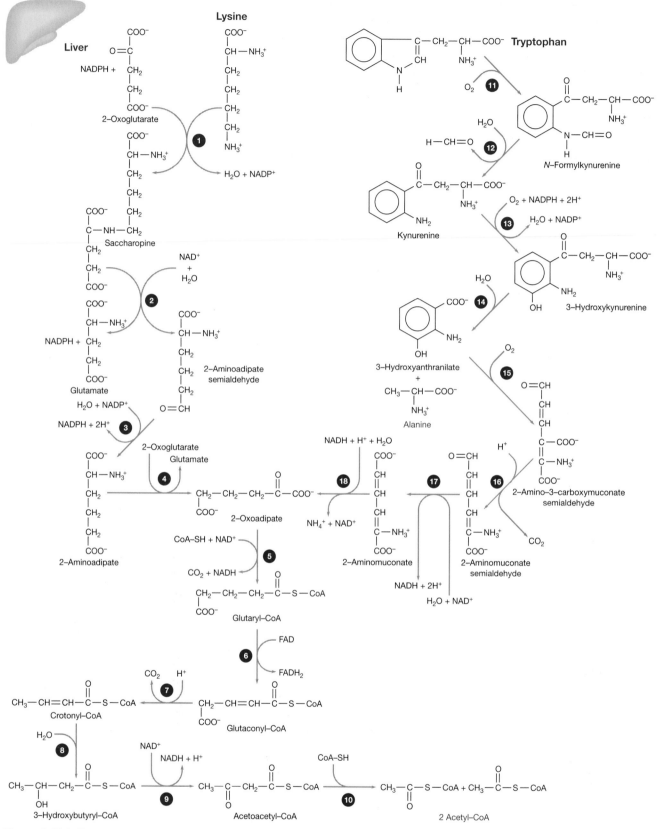

Figure 6.6(a) The catabolism of lysine and tryptophan by the liver.

Enzymes responsible for the catabolism of lysine and tryptophan

1. Saccharopine dehydrogenase
2. Saccharopine dehydrogenase
3. Aminoadipate semialdehyde dehydrogenase
4. 2–Aminoadipate aminotransferase
5. 2–Oxoadipate dehydrogenase
6. Glutaryl–CoA dehydrogenase
7. Decarboxylation
8. Enoyl–CoA hydratase
9. 3–Hydroxybutyryl–CoA dehydrogenase
10. Acetyl–CoA acetyltransferase

11. Tryptophan 2,3–dioxygenase
12. Formamidase
13. Kynurenine 3–monooxygenase
14. Kynureninase
15. 3–Hydroxyanthranilate 3,4–dioxygenase
16. Aminocarboxymuconate semialdehyde decarboxylase
17. Aminomuconate semialdehyde dehydrogenase
18. Aminomuconate reductase

Figure 6.6(a)
Continued

Liver

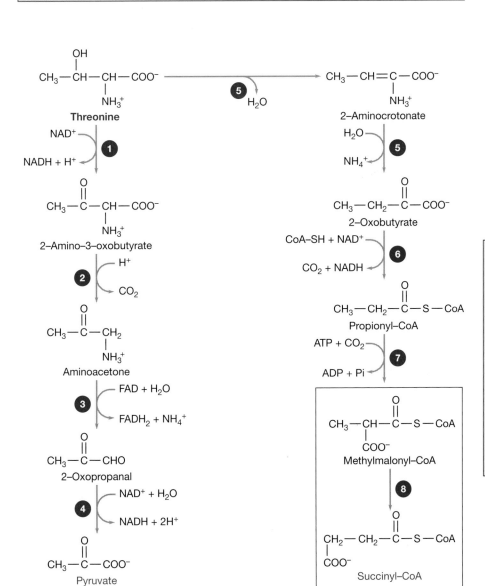

Enzymes

Major pathway:

1. Threonine dehydrogenase
2. Decarboxylation
3. Monoamine oxidase
4. Aldehyde dehydrogenase

Alternative pathway:

5. Threonine dehydratase
6. 2–Oxobutyrate dehydrogenase
7. Propionyl–CoA carboxylase
8. Methylmalonyl–CoA mutase

(see Figure 6.5 Box 2)

Figure 6.6(b)
Alternative pathways for threonine catabolism in the liver.

Liver

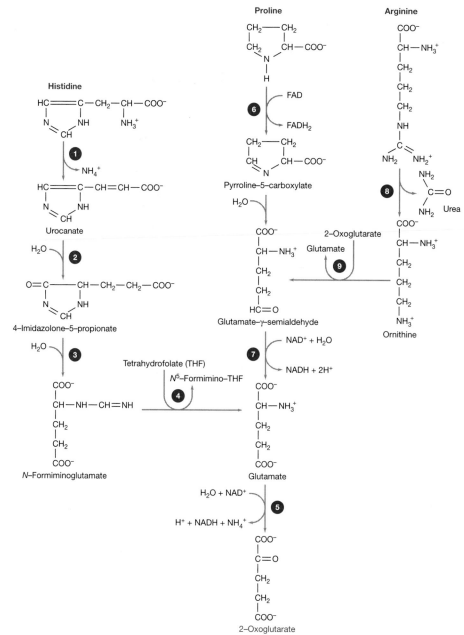

Enzymes

1. Histidine–ammonia lyase
2. Urocanate hydratase
3. Imidazolonepropionase
4. Glutamate formiminotransferase
5. Glutamate dehydrogenase
6. Proline dehydrogenase
7. Glutamate–γ–semialdehyde dehydrogenase
8. Arginase
9. Ornithine–oxoacid aminotransferase

Figure 6.7

Catabolism of histidine, proline and arginine by the liver.

Arginine is synthesized and broken down in the cytoplasm

The conversion of citrulline to arginine which occurs in the cytoplasm is aided by the cytoplasmic location of most of the transaminases. As indicated in Figure 6.8, the addition of aspartate to citrulline produces argininosuccinate which splits to yield arginine and fumarate. The latter is usually hydrated to form malate which may enter the mitochondrial matrix by the electroneutral dicarboxylic acid transporter in exchange for 2-oxoglutarate (see Figure 2.12). Within the matrix the malate will be oxidized to oxaloacetate for reconversion to aspartate by transamination. At this point it is important to consider the potential role of the malate–aspartate shuttle in the operation of the urea synthesis process. Aspartate generated within the mitochondrial matrix by transamination of

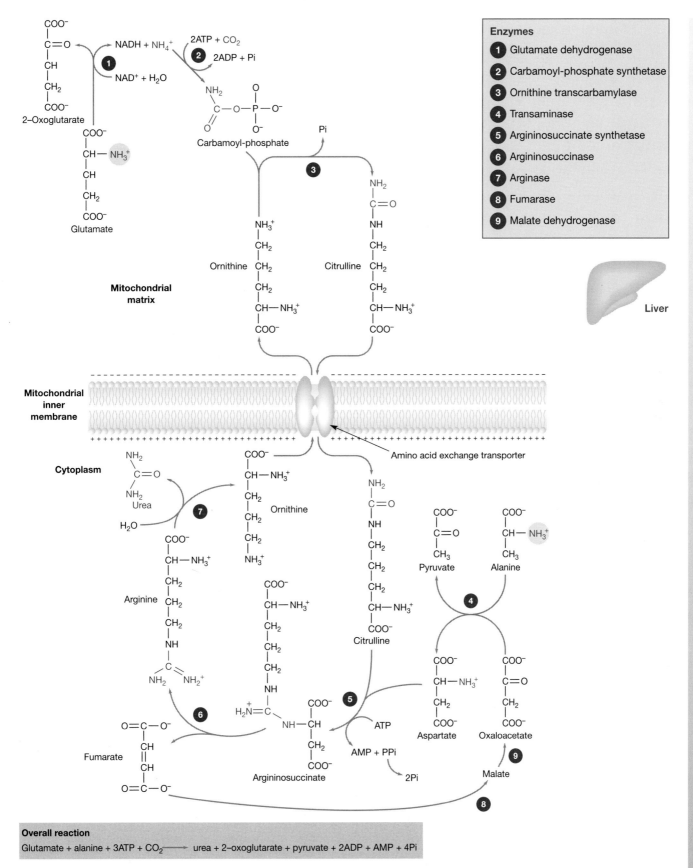

Enzymes

1. Glutamate dehydrogenase
2. Carbamoyl-phosphate synthetase
3. Ornithine transcarbamylase
4. Transaminase
5. Argininosuccinate synthetase
6. Argininosuccinase
7. Arginase
8. Fumarase
9. Malate dehydrogenase

Liver

Overall reaction

Glutamate + alanine + 3ATP + CO_2 ⟶ urea + 2–oxoglutarate + pyruvate + 2ADP + AMP + 4Pi

Figure 6.8 Details of the reactions responsible for urea synthesis in the mitochondrial matrix and the cytoplasm.

oxaloacetate will exit in exchange for glutamate (Figure 2.12). This exchange will effectively provide glutamate for deamination in the matrix forming NH_4^+ for carbamoyl-phosphate synthesis and aspartate for the formation of argininosuccinate in the cytoplasm. The former will yield 2-oxoglutarate in the matrix while the latter yields fumarate and then malate in the cytoplasm. The exchange of the cytoplasmic malate for matrix 2-oxoglutarate completes the cycle. The effect of the malate–aspartate shuttle is to ensure that an adequate supply of nitrogen is available in the mitochondrial matrix and the liver cytoplasm for the separate phases of the urea cycle.

The final step of the urea cycle is the arginase step which also occurs in the cytoplasm. This releases urea in the cytoplasm so that it can diffuse out across the plasma membrane into the blood. The other product of the cycle is ornithine which re-enters the mitochondrial matrix in exchange for citrulline via an exchange transporter in the mitochondrial inner membrane.

How can tissues other than the liver avoid the toxic effects of ammonia?

It is important to emphasize that the synthesis of urea is restricted to the liver. As a consequence, most of the other tissues in the body must be protected from the accumulation of ammonia released during the catabolism of amino acids and the nucleobases. This is achieved through the action of cytoplasmic glutamine synthetase:

$$\text{Glutamate}^- + NH_4^+ + ATP \rightarrow \text{glutamine} + ADP + Pi \tag{6.1}$$

If there is a shortage of glutamate for this reaction, it can be formed from 2-oxoglutarate by cytoplasmic glutamate dehydrogenase (Eq. 6.2) driven by the high NADPH/NADP+ ratio in the cytoplasm. This reaction also depletes the cytoplasmic NH_4^+:

$$\text{2-Oxoglutarate}^{2-} + NH_4^+ + NADPH + H^+ \rightarrow \text{glutamate}^- + NADP^+ + H_2O \tag{6.2}$$

As we shall see in later chapters there are two tissues which release the amide nitrogen from circulating glutamine, the small intestine and the kidneys. In the latter case the NH_3 is used to adjust the pH of the urine. However, the small intestine converts vascular glutamine into alanine which the liver uses as a substrate for gluconeogenesis. Some of the glutamine nitrogen is released into the hepatic portal blood as NH_4^+ by the intestine (see Figure 10.7), but this is not a hazard since it is removed by the liver before it enters the general circulation.

6.7 Dioxygenase and monooxygenase reactions

In section 6.5 we considered several pathways in which the direct participation of molecular oxygen was involved in the catabolism of amino acids. However, it is

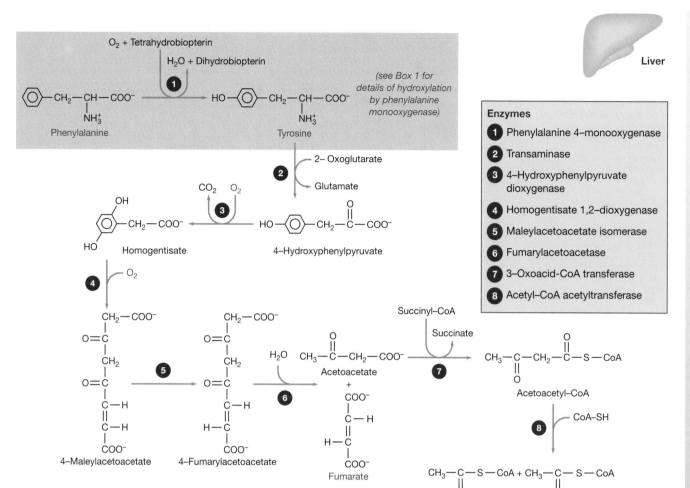

Figure 6.9 Metabolism of phenylalanine and tyrosine in the liver.

important to recognize that both dioxygenase and monooxygenase reactions play a crucial role in many other areas of metabolism, both anabolic and catabolic. Many of these reactions occur in other tissues as well as the liver. For example, Figure 6.9, Box 1b, shows how molecular oxygen is involved in the hydroxylation of proline and lysine. Hydroxyproline (and hydroxylysine) are important constituents of collagen, a common protein that is important in connective tissue and joints. A crucial feature of the hydroxylation reaction is the fact that ascorbate is required to keep the iron atom in its reduced state. The absence of ascorbate causes collagen synthesis to stop within a short time.

Monooxygenases are responsible for the hydroxylation of fatty acids in a variety of tissues and for the hydroxylation of steroid hormones in the adrenal cortex. These reactions require the participation of the cytochrome P-450 system (Figure 6.11, Box 1) which is associated with the endoplasmic reticulum. This is also true for the hydroxylation of cholecalciferol to form 1,25-dihydroxycholecalciferol, the active form of vitamin D (see Figure 3.12a). In this case the first of the two hydroxylations occurs in the liver and the second in the kidney cortex.

175

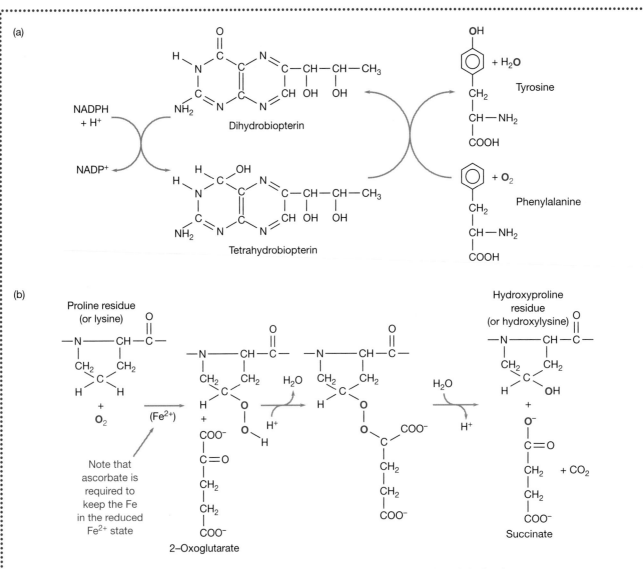

Figure 6.9 Box 1 (a) The reaction responsible for the formation of tyrosine from phenylalanine by phenylalanine 4-monooxygenase. (b) The hydroxylation of a proline residue in a protein by prolyl 4-hydroxylase. A similar reaction is carried out by lysine hydroxylase to form hydroxylysine residues.

6.8 *Detoxification reactions*

As indicated in section 6.6, the most important detoxification process that occurs in the liver is the conversion of ammonia and the amino groups of amino acids into urea. However, the liver is also responsible for the detoxification of steroid hormones, drugs and other foreign compounds known as xenobiotics using the P-450 monooxygenase reactions (see Figure 6.11, Box 1). The effect of the hydroxylation process is to make the compounds more hydrophilic so that they may be eliminated in the urine.

Detoxification of alcohol

Another important detoxification process that occurs in the liver is the oxidation of alcohol. There are three separate enzyme systems for dealing with alcohol. The most active enzyme is alcohol dehydrogenase, which oxidizes ethanol to acetaldehyde:

$$CH_3-CH_2-OH + NAD^+ \rightarrow CH_3-CHO + NADH + H^+ \tag{6.3}$$
$$\text{ethanol} \qquad\qquad\qquad \text{acetaldehyde}$$

There is also a monooxygenase system which involves the cytochrome P-450 hydroxylation system (see Figure 6.11, Box 1) which also produces acetaldehyde, but forms hydrogen peroxide as well:

$$CH_3-CH_2-OH + NADPH + H^+ + 2O_2 \rightarrow CH_3-CHO + 2H_2O_2 + NADP^+ \tag{6.4}$$

Since the ethanol monooxygenase system uses the cytochrome P-450 system, it is likely that the presence of alcohol will reduce the capacity of the liver to detoxify drugs. The hydrogen peroxide formed in Eq. 6.4 will be converted to water plus oxygen (Eq. 6.5) by catalase present in the liver peroxisomes. The catalase enzyme can also convert ethanol to acetaldehyde at the expense of hydrogen peroxide (Eq. 6.6):

$$2H_2O_2 \rightarrow O_2 + 2H_2O \tag{6.5}$$

$$CH_3-CH_2-OH + H_2O_2 \rightarrow CH_3-CHO + 2H_2O \tag{6.6}$$

The final stage in the detoxification of ethanol in the liver is the oxidation of acetaldehyde to acetate (Eq. 6.7); the acetate is then converted to acetyl-CoA at the expense of ATP (Eq. 6.8):

$$CH_3-CHO + NAD^+ + H_2O \rightarrow CH_3-COO^- + NADH + 2H^+ \tag{6.7}$$

$$CH_3-COO^- + ATP + CoA-SH \rightarrow CH_3-CO-S-CoA + AMP + PPi \tag{6.8}$$

The acetyl-CoA will then be available for oxidation by the TCA cycle or for conversion into fatty acids.

Conjugation of toxic compounds

Another detoxification mechanism which takes place in the liver involves conjugating the toxic compound with glycine, glucuronate or sulphate. In some cases, e.g. the steroid hormones, conjugation occurs after hydroxylation. The conjugation process makes the unwanted compounds more water soluble so that they can be eliminated in the urine. The conjugation of salicylic acid (a catabolite of aspirin) with glycine occurs prior to its excretion by the kidneys. However, the conjugation of bile acids with glycine results in their excretion in the bile rather than the urine. The conjugation of steroids with glucuronate or sulphate is followed by their excretion in the kidneys.

The liver can also modify foreign compounds by acetylation or methylation. Unfortunately when sulphonamide drugs were first introduced acetylation made the drugs less water soluble, so that there were cases of kidney damage following sulphonamide treatment when the water intake was insufficient. This example underlines one of the problems associated with the introduction of a new drug, namely the importance of discovering whether the body has an acceptable method of detoxifying and excreting the drug.

6.9 Synthesis of triacylglycerols and ketone bodies: the role of cell compartmentation

Because of its homeostatic functions the liver will generate acetyl-CoA from a variety of metabolites when excessive concentrations are present in the blood. Acetyl-CoA is formed within the mitochondrial matrix, mainly from pyruvate or as a consequence of the β-oxidation of fatty acids. The fate of the acetyl-CoA in the liver will depend on the balance of substrates available. If adequate supples of carbohydrates or amino acid carbon skeletons are available, excessive acetyl-CoA levels stimulate the carboxylation of pyruvate to form oxaloacetate which makes it possible for citrate synthetase to convert the acetyl-CoA into citrate. Some of this citrate will be used in the TCA cycle to satisfy the demand for ATP in the hepatocytes, but excess citrate will be exported from the mitochondrial matrix in exchange for malate (Figure 6.10). The electrogenic exchange of citrate (with three negative charges) for malate (with two negative charges) is driven by the membrane potential across the mitochondrial inner membrane. As a consequence, citrate export to the cytoplasm will decrease whenever the mitochondrial membrane potential is reduced by an increased demand for ATP. Out in the cytoplasm citrate lyase converts the citrate back into acetyl-CoA plus oxaloacetate. The rise in matrix citrate also slows its formation from acetyl-CoA which may allow some of the excess acetyl groups to be transferred directly to the cytoplasm by the carnitine transferase system (see Figure 6.10).

When is excess acetyl-CoA used for triacylglycerol synthesis?

Cytoplasmic acetyl-CoA carboxylase converts much of the acetyl-CoA into malonyl-CoA which is required for the synthesis of fatty acyl-CoA as shown in Figure 3.5. Because the amount of coenzyme A in the cytoplasm is limited, fatty acid synthesis can only continue if the fatty acyl-CoA is esterified to form triacylglycerol (see Figure 3.7). Since the glycerol-3-phosphate backbone of triacylglycerol is formed from dihydroxyacetone-phosphate, an adequate supply of carbohydrate is necessary to support the biosynthesis of triacylglycerols. An alternative fate for cytoplasmic acetyl-CoA in the liver is the synthesis of cholesterol (see Figures 3.6 and 6.11) which does not require intermediates from the carbohydrate pathway. However, as indicated in the next section, cholesterol biosynthesis is normally strictly regulated to avoid excessive cholesterol levels in the blood.

Ketone body synthesis

When there is a shortage of pyruvate and oxaloacetate the mitochondrial β-oxidation of fatty acids provides most of the electrons for oxidative phosphorylation and this will cause the matrix acetyl-CoA to rise sharply. As pointed out above, the higher levels of acetyl-CoA could increase the rate at which acetyl groups are trans-

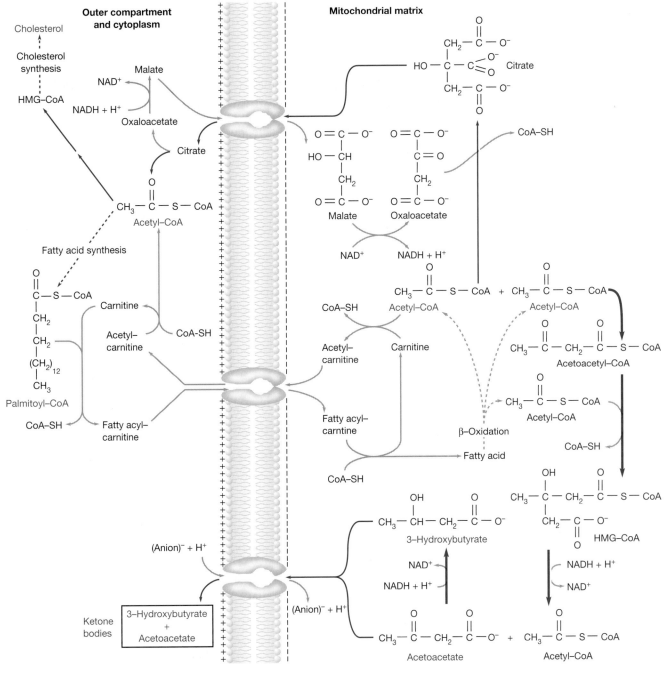

Figure 6.10 Ketone body synthesis in the liver and the relationship between these reactions and the synthesis of triacylglycerol and cholesterol.

Liver

ferred to the cytoplasm by carnitine, but only if cytoplasmic carbohydrate levels are adequate to maintain triacylglycerol synthesis. Thus, when there is a shortage of carbohydrate an alternative fate for acetyl-CoA is required in order to keep free coenzyme A available for the oxidation of fatty acids in the mitochondrial matrix. The solution to this problem is provided by formation of the ketone bodies acetoacetate and 3-hydroxybutyrate from the excess acetyl-CoA as shown in Figure 6.10. This process provides the main fate of the surplus acetyl-CoA formed by β-oxidation of fatty acids in the liver when no dietary carbohydrate is available during either short or long periods of starvation. However, the sharp rise in vascular ketone body concentrations during starvation can cause severe acidosis.

Once they are formed in the mitochondrial matrix the ketone bodies are transported out into the cytoplasm. Since both ketone bodies have a negative charge, their exit is likely to be an electrogenic export of negatively charged molecules in exchange for anions entering with a proton (as shown for the exchange of glutamate for aspartate in Figure 2.12). As in the case of citrate export from the mitochondrial matrix, such a process would be influenced by the membrane potential.

Finally, it should be recognized that in the liver there is also a link between the formation of ketone bodies and gluconeogenesis. Whenever there is a reduction in blood glucose the liver responds by releasing additional glucose. During periods of starvation liver glycogen will be exhausted and it is essential for glucose to be synthesized from three- or four-carbon precursors. As indicated in Figure 2.4, the pyruvate formed from either lactate or alanine is a major substrate for gluconeogenesis, but in order to participate in this process the pyruvate must be transferred into the mitochondrial matrix for conversion into oxaloacetate. Under these conditions there will be an excess of acetyl-CoA from fatty acid oxidation, and the high rate of β-oxidation ensures that most of the citrate formed from oxaloacetate plus acetyl-CoA will be exported into the cytoplasm. Once the citrate is released from the mitochondrial matrix, citrate lyase will release the oxaloacetate for conversion into phosphoenolpyruvate and subsequent conversion to free glucose. The entry of the pyruvate together with a proton can balance the exit of the ketone bodies.

6.10 Synthesis of cholesterol and bile salts: biliary secretion and enterohepatic circulation

Although virtually all cells have the capacity to synthesize cholesterol, the major sites of cholesterol formation are the liver and the small intestine. Figure 3.6 shows the initial steps of cholesterol synthesis, and the final steps are shown in Figure 6.11. The amount of cholesterol formed by the liver is regulated by the level of cholesterol entering the liver. This important role of the liver in cholesterol homeostasis is essential in order to prevent excessive plasma cholesterol levels, which is seen as a major cause of coronary heart disease and cerebrovascular accidents or strokes. These problems appear to be the result of the storage of excess cholesterol in the form of cholesteryl esters which can be deposited in foam cells beneath the endothelial lining of arteries. Nevertheless, it is important to recognize that cholesterol is an essential component of the membranes in all cells as well as serving as the precursor for bile salts and steroid hormones.

Control of blood cholesterol concentration

Our modern diet is relatively high in cholesterol, and the liver can respond to increased levels of cholesterol in the blood in two ways: by reducing the rate of synthesis and by increasing the rate of cholesterol excretion in the bile. When the system is working in a well-regulated manner the excretion of neutral sterols in the faeces roughly balances the average intake of dietary cholesterol (500 mg/day). A higher level of cholesterol in the diet is balanced by a reduction in the rate of cholesterol synthesis in the liver. One of the problems of using sterol excretion in the bile to reduce cholesterol levels is that the small intestine can reabsorb the sterols which are then released into the lymph in chylomicrons. This effect is partially countered by the continual loss of the enterocytes lining the small intestine which helps to increase the cholesterol content of the faeces. Also sterols excreted in the bile bind to dietary fibre which helps to prevent reabsorption.

Formation of bile salts

Bile salts are formed by the liver from cholesterol as shown in Figure 6.11(b). The bile salts are secreted into the bile canaliculi and stored in the gall bladder which opens off the main bile duct. Large quantities of bile salts are released into the intestine when the gall bladder contracts in response to the secretion of the hormone cholecystokinin by the duodenum (the top end of the small intestine). Bile salts are formed from cholic acid, a derivative of cholesterol, by conjugation with glycine and taurine. This structure gives them detergent properties which enables the bile salts to play a key role in the absorption of dietary lipids. Bile salts are reabsorbed by the small intestine and returned to the liver for re-excretion in the

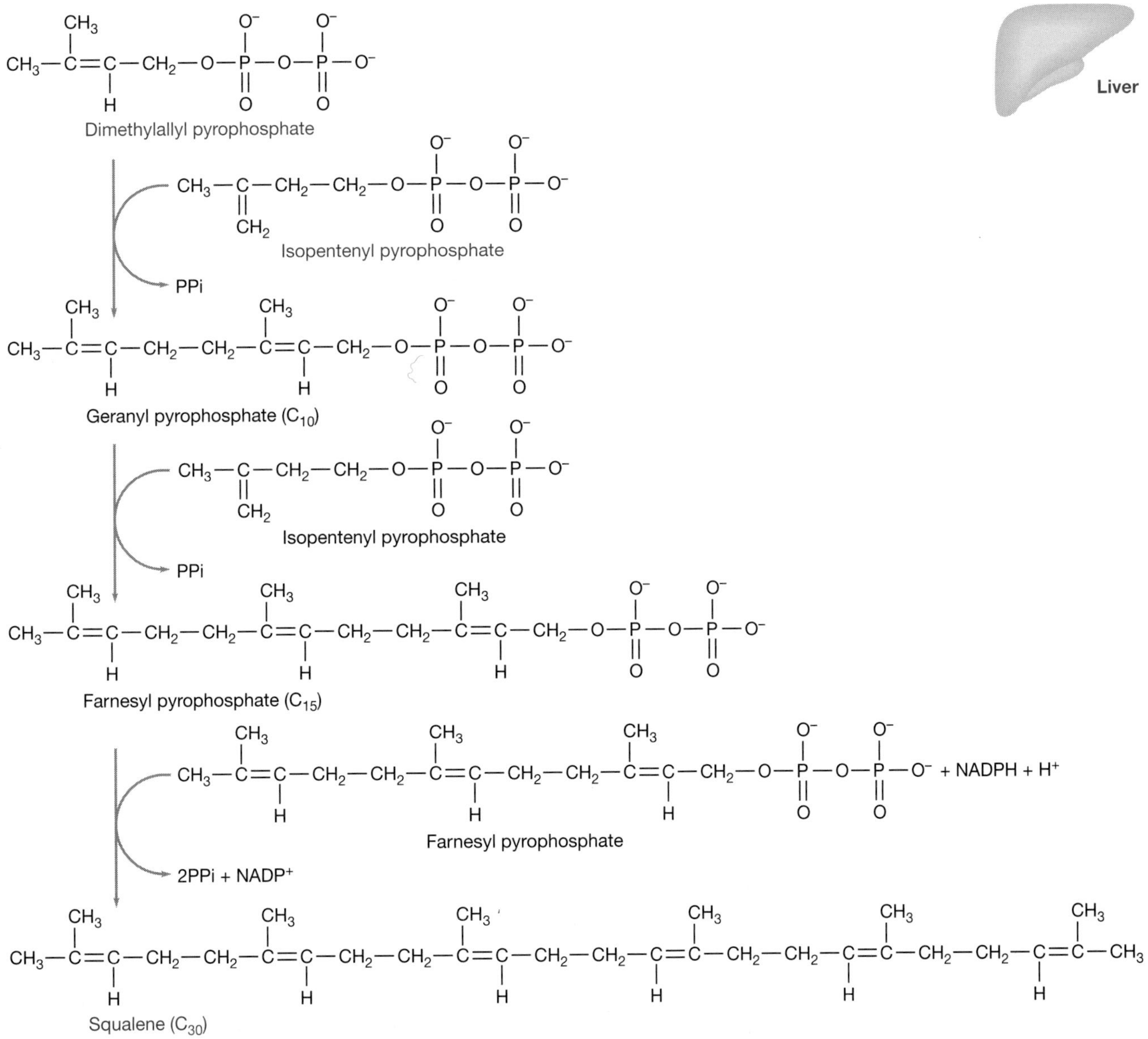

Liver

Figure 6.11(a) The synthesis of squalene from five-carbon precursors.

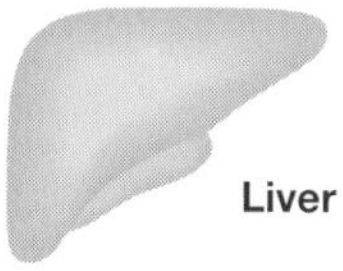

Liver

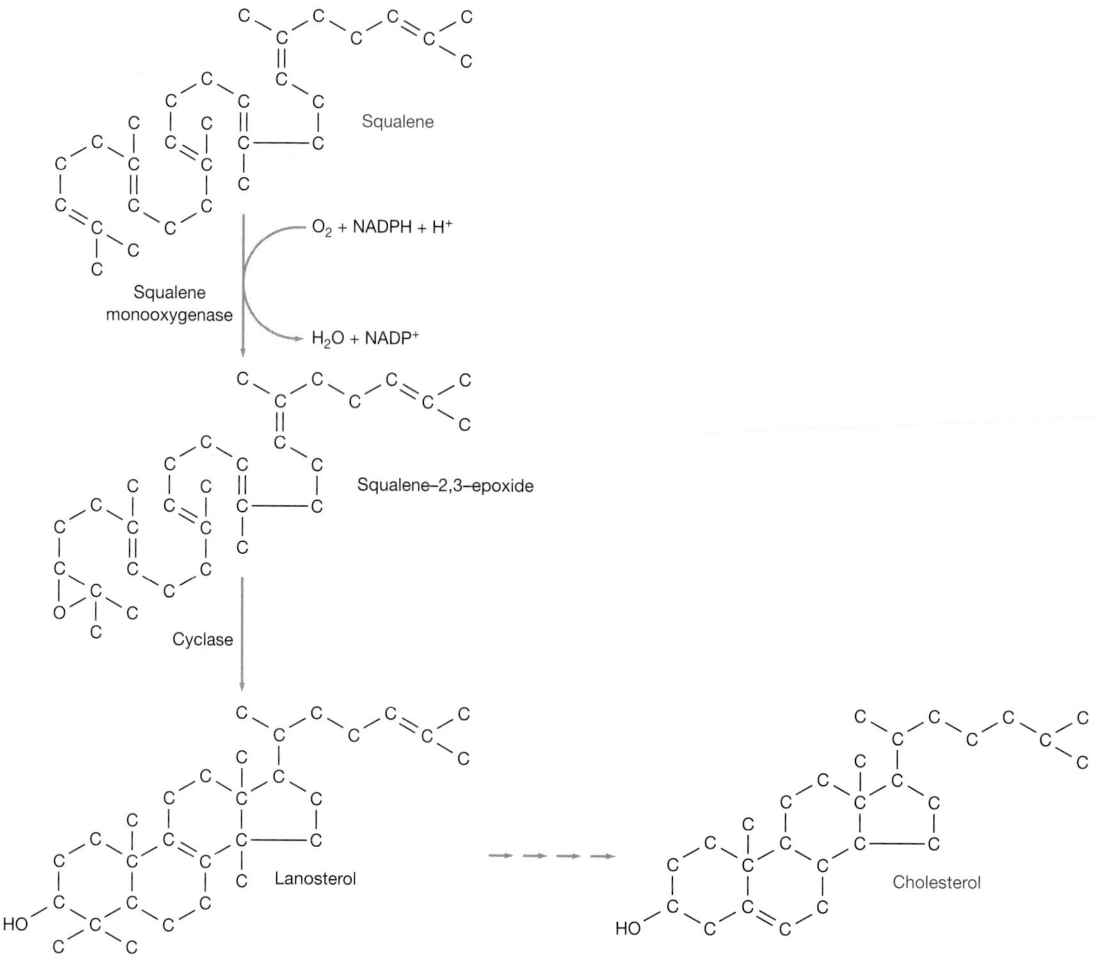

Squalene

O_2 + NADPH + H$^+$

Squalene monooxygenase

H_2O + NADP$^+$

Squalene–2,3–epoxide

Cyclase

Lanosterol

Cholesterol

Conversion of cholesterol into bile acids. The first step involves hydroxylation of carbon 7 by cholesterol 7α–monooxygenase. See Box 1 for the role of cytochrome P–450 in this process.

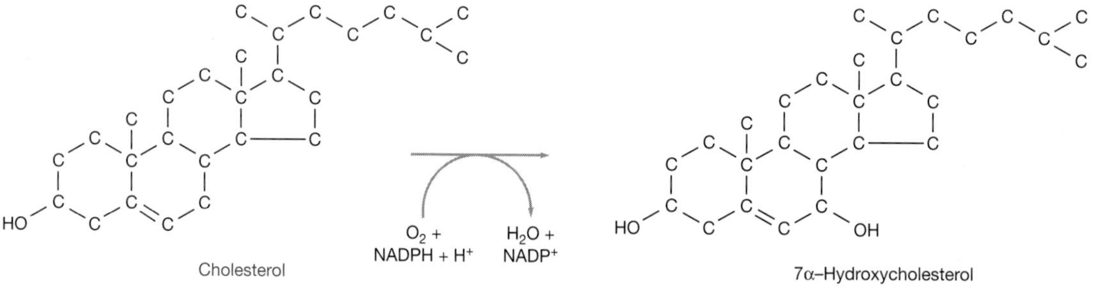

Cholesterol

O_2 + NADPH + H$^+$

H_2O + NADP$^+$

7α–Hydroxycholesterol

The formation of the bile acids requires further modification of the cholesterol nucleus and the side chain.

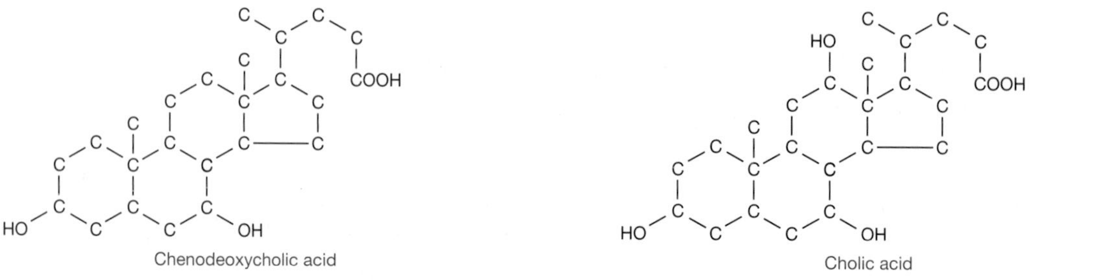

COOH

Chenodeoxycholic acid

COOH

Cholic acid

Figure 6.11(b) The conversion of squalene into cholesterol and the formation of bile salts.

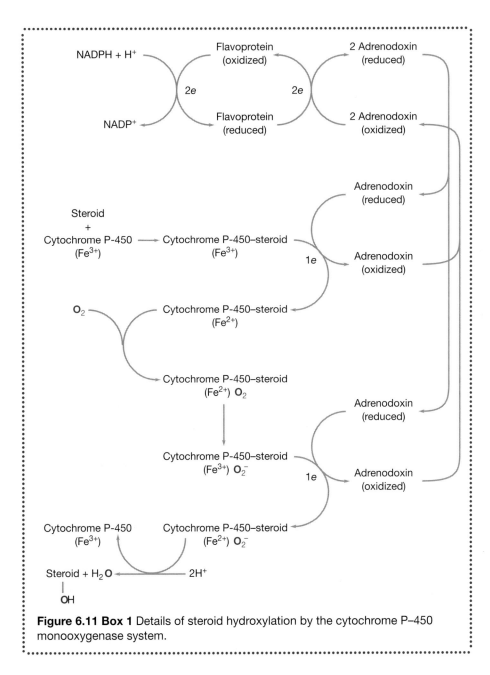

Figure 6.11 Box 1 Details of steroid hydroxylation by the cytochrome P–450 monooxygenase system.

bile. This process is known as the enterohepatic circulation of the bile salts, although approximately 10% are lost each day in the faeces.

6.11 Structure, synthesis and secretion of lipoproteins

The general characteristics of lipoproteins were described briefly in Chapter 3, and we now need to look in more detail at the interaction of four types (VLDL, IDL, LDL and HDL) with the liver. The formation and release of VLDL into the blood is the mechanism by which the liver transfers fatty acids to peripheral tissues. These lipoproteins consist of more than 50% triacylglycerol which is synthesized by the liver. VLDL contains a higher proportion of free cholesterol and cholesteryl esters than the chylomicrons and more protein. VLDLs are released into the hepatic vein and have a relatively short half-life. As the triacylglycerol is removed from VLDL by lipoprotein lipase in peripheral tissues, the density of the particle increases and the apoprotein content changes so that they become IDLs. At this stage the IDL particles are either taken up by the liver or converted into the cholesterol-rich LDL by triacylglycerol lipase on the surface of the hepatocytes. The LDLs donate cholesterol to peripheral tissues, as well as returning it to the liver where more than 50% of the LDL is taken up. Conversion of IDL into LDL requires the removal of two of its apoproteins and their transfer to HDL. Whereas IDL and LDL interact with the liver, HDL is chiefly concerned with the removal of cholesterol from peripheral cells. The transfer of cholesterol back to the liver by HDL appears to involve the transfer of cholesteryl esters to IDL, LDL or to chylomicron remnants so that it can be taken into the liver by endocytosis. The plasma cholesterol associated with HDL poses less risk to the vascular system.

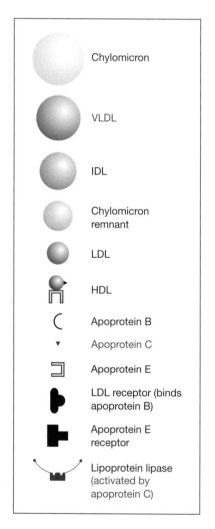

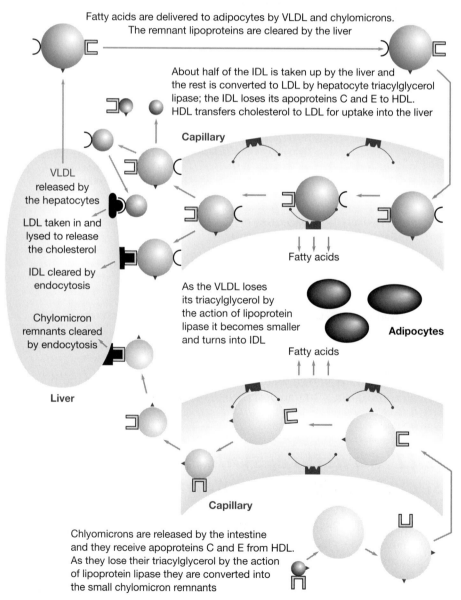

Figure 6.12(a)
Lipoprotein interactions with the liver.

The importance of lipoprotein receptors on hepatocytes

An important feature of the relationship between the liver and the lipoprotein particles is provided by the LDL receptor protein on the hepatocyte membrane. This receptor can either bind the LDL apoprotein B-100 or apoprotein E which has sufficient amino acid sequence homology with apoprotein B-100 to bind to the LDL receptor. Thus it is possible for the liver to take up IDL because of the presence of apoprotein E which becomes more prominent on the particle surface with the reduction in triacylglycerol content and can bind to either the LDL or apoprotein E receptor. The liver is also able to take up chylomicron remnants because HDL transfers apoprotein E to these particles. HDL participates in the release of fatty acids from the chylomicrons and VLDL by providing them with apoprotein C which helps to bind these particles to the endothelial lipoprotein lipase. Figure 6.12(a) provides a summary of lipoprotein interactions with the liver.

HDL carries excess cholesterol back to the liver

Figure 6.12(b) illustrates the role of HDL in transferring excess cholesterol from the extrahepatic tissues back to the liver. This is important for the control of cholesterol synthesis and excretion by the liver. Uptake of cholesteryl esters by the liver as a result of endocytosis of the IDL or LDL particles is followed by disruption of the lipoproteins and lysis of the cholesteryl esters with the release of free cholesterol. If the free cholesterol level in the liver is high, it inhibits the HMG-CoA reductase, thereby reducing the rate of cholesterol synthesis, and stimulating the rate of cholesteryl ester synthesis for biliary excretion. Higher free cholesterol levels also inhibit the synthesis of the LDL receptors, but the net effect of higher cholesterol concentrations in the liver is to reduce synthesis and encourage excretion of bile salts and cholesteryl esters. In cases where the control breaks down and the individual suffers from high plasma cholesterol, two

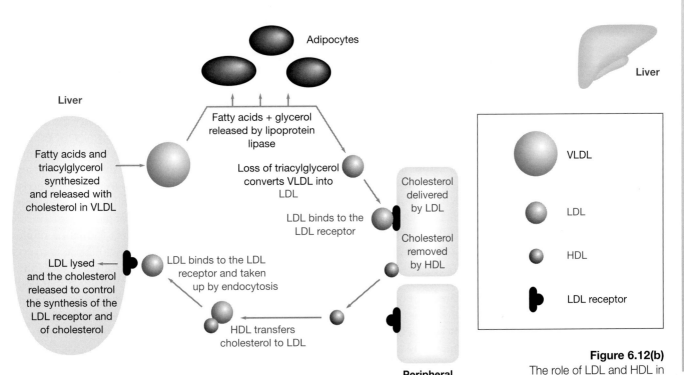

Figure 6.12(b)
The role of LDL and HDL in cholesterol transport.

techniques can be used to reduce the blood cholesterol. Cholesterol synthesis can be inhibited by drugs that reduce the activity of HMG-CoA reductase. Alternatively, increasing the fibre content of the diet can increase the excretion of bile salts and cholesteryl esters in the faeces because they bind to the fibre.

6.12 Biosynthesis of plasma proteins

The plasma proteins synthesized by the liver serve a variety of functions. In order to maintain the osmolarity of the blood it is essential to have an adequate protein content. The most common plasma protein is albumin, which is also important for the transport of fatty acids, a number of ions and other minor plasma constituents.

Other prominent plasma proteins are fibrinogen, the soluble precursor of the clot-forming fibrin, and the iron-binding protein transferrin. Blood plasma also contains a vast range of globular proteins including the antibodies. Virtually all of the plasma proteins except the immunoglobulins are synthesized by the liver, and this represents one of the major biosynthetic processes occurring in hepatocytes. Starvation results in a reduction in the availability of amino acids for protein synthesis, and the rate of protein synthesis in the liver is particularly sensitive to reduction in amino acid levels. As a consequence, individuals who are unable to eat need to be fed with amino acids parenterally to maintain their plasma protein levels.

6.13 Overview of the regulation of nutrient levels by the liver

The preceding sections have dealt in detail with the various metabolic functions of the liver and at this point it is useful to summarize the regulatory effects that these processes exert on nutrient levels in the blood.

How does the liver respond to the various dietary hexoses?

The liver has a very different response to the arrival of the three dietary hexoses as a consequence of the difference in the K_m values of the initial enzymes for each of the hexoses. Galactokinase, which has a low K_m, rapidly converts all the incoming galactose into glucose-1-phosphate (see Figure 2.2) providing substrate for glycogen synthesis, glycolysis and the pentose phosphate pathway. In the liver glucose is phosphorylated by glucokinase with a K_m of about 10 mM with the consequence that at blood concentrations below 5 mM there is net release of glucose as a result of the action of glucose-6-phosphatase. Above 5 mM there is net formation of glucose-6-phosphate, thus removing glucose from the blood. Fructokinase converts fructose into fructose-1-phosphate which is then split into dihydroxyacetone-phosphate and glyceraldehyde. The latter is phosphorylated by ATP so that both three-carbon products are fed directly into the lower part of the glycolytic pathway after the phosphofructokinase control point. As a consequence low levels of incoming fructose will provide the acetyl-CoA necessary to keep the TCA cycle operating and thus allow the glucose arriving at the liver to be converted into glycogen. Higher concentrations of fructose will still enter the three-carbon end of the glycolytic pathway and excess acetyl-CoA will be converted into fatty acids. Thus, as the concentrations of hexoses reaching the liver rise, they will be dealt with quite differently. Fructose will produce fatty acids whereas glucose and galactose will replenish liver glycogen. When the maximum levels of liver glycogen have been achieved, further differences in the fate of the hexoses become apparent. Fructose will continue to be converted into fatty acids and this will also be the fate of the excess hexose phosphates formed from incoming galactose. However, much of the excess glucose will be passed on to other tissues and the consequent rise in blood glucose will cause insulin secretion to increase. As pointed out in Chapter 5, the combination of elevated blood glucose and higher insulin levels will help to increase the glycogen stores in muscles, but much of the excess glucose will contribute to the storage of triacylglycerol in adipose tissue.

What is the fate of amino acids taken up by the liver?

Amino acids reaching the liver are also used in a variety of ways depending on the general metabolic state of the liver. When dietary protein is not being absorbed, the liver together with muscle and the small intestine maintains relatively stable concentrations of all 20 amino acids in the blood in order to sustain protein synthesis throughout the entire body. As shown in Figure 4.8, deficiencies in the non-essential amino acids can be remedied by formation of their carbon skeletons from central metabolites and the transfer of an amino group from another amino acid. These reactions are dependent on an adequate supply of amino nitrogen and the availability of key coenzymes such as tetrahydrofolate, derived from folic acid. Exceptions to this pattern of supply occur for cysteine and tyrosine which require adequate sources of methionine and phenylalanine, respectively, and histidine which has its own biosynthetic pathway. A drop in the blood level of any of the essential amino acids can only be overcome by a net breakdown of protein. However, it is important to recognize that this is really a consequence of a shift in the balance between the rates of protein synthesis and protein hydrolysis, as a result of suboptimal blood concentrations of one or more of the essential amino acids.

During the digestion and absorption of protein the hepatic portal blood contains higher than normal concentrations of almost all of the 20 amino acids. When these excessive levels of amino acids reach the liver the concentrations of 17 of them will be reduced by the liver. The three branched chain amino acids, isoleucine, leucine and valine, are metabolized mainly by the muscles. The first stage of metabolism of most of the amino acids in the liver is the removal of the amino group by transamination, and this is followed by the conversion of the carbon skeletons into acetyl-CoA or one of the constituents of the TCA cycle (Figure 6.4a). If the liver is short of glycogen, the TCA cycle intermediates can be converted into oxaloacetate and then phosphoenolpyruvate which serves as a substrate for glucose-6-phosphate formation by the gluconeogenesis pathway (see Figure 2.4). The glucose-6-phosphate is converted directly into blood glucose if the concentration is low, but if this is not the case it forms glycogen. However, if there is no shortage of blood glucose or liver glycogen the carbon skeletons of the amino acids are converted into acetyl-CoA and then into fatty acids. In this way excess protein intake contributes to the storage of carbon in the form of triacylglycerol.

Response of the liver to changes in vascular lipid concentrations

The influence of the liver on circulating lipid levels is complicated because adipose tissue, intestine and muscle are also involved in a major way. Most of the dietary lipids absorbed by the small intestine are packaged into chylomicrons and released into the lymph. This enables dietary triacylglycerol to bypass the liver so that the endothelial lipoprotein lipase can release the constituent fatty acids directly for use by adipose tissue and muscle. This leaves the chylomicron remnant, which is relatively rich in cholesterol and is taken up by the liver which degrades it completely releasing the remaining fatty acids together with the cholesterol and the apoproteins. When the blood contains excessive levels of fatty acids, usually as a result of their release from adipose tissue during starvation, these are taken up by the liver and converted into acetyl-CoA. Under these conditions most of the acetyl-CoA will be converted into ketone bodies. It is important to note that medium- and short-chain fatty acids absorbed by the small intestine and the colon are not released in chylomicrons but pass directly into the portal circulation. These fatty acids are taken up by the liver and degraded to acetyl-CoA by β-oxidation. As indicated earlier in this chapter, the fate of acetyl-CoA in the liver depends on the availability of carbohydrate; if the latter is plentiful the acetyl-CoA will be converted into triacylglycerol and released in VLDL particles. However, if carbohydrate is in short supply, ketone bodies will be produced with the consequential risk of acidosis.

6.14 Hormonal modulation of basic control mechanisms in the liver

The principal hormones which influence the regulatory actions of the liver are adrenaline, glucagon and insulin. From an overall viewpoint insulin acts to promote the storage of glucose and fatty acids and to increase the rate of protein synthesis. These effects are countered by the increased levels of cyclic AMP due to stimulation of adenyl cyclase by either glucagon or adrenaline binding to a specific receptor on the cell membrane (see Figure 1.13). Higher cyclic AMP levels effectively cause the liver to release glucose, decrease the formation of triacylglycerol and increase the degradation of amino acids.

Hormonal controls of glucose metabolism in the liver

Insulin stimulates glycogen synthesis by increasing the activity of the protein phosphatase (PP1) which converts glycogen synthetase into its active dephosphorylated form and glycogen phosphorylase into the inactive dephosphorylated phosphorylase b. Cyclic AMP, on the other hand, increases glycogen breakdown by stimulating protein kinase A (PKA) to phosphorylate glycogen synthetase and phosphorylase converting them to the inactive and active forms, respectively. Similar opposing effects of insulin and cyclic AMP operate on glycolysis and gluconeogenesis. Insulin increases the level of the regulatory molecule fructose-2,6-bisphosphate (see section 2.3) which increases the rate of glycolysis whereas cyclic AMP decreases fructose-2,6-bisphosphate thus promoting gluconeogenesis. Cyclic AMP and insulin also have opposing regulatory effects on pyruvate kinase. The cyclic AMP-dependent phosphorylation by PKA inhibits pyruvate kinase leading to a stimulation of gluconeogenesis, and this is reversed by insulin.

Hormonal control of triacylglycerol synthesis in the liver

Formation of triacylglycerol by the liver is also subject to the opposing effects of insulin and cyclic AMP. It is possible that both the stimulation of lipogenesis by insulin and the inhibition by elevated cyclic AMP levels operate at several levels, but the initial effects appear to be on the activity of acetyl-CoA carboxylase. The stimulation of acetyl-CoA carboxylase activity by insulin increases the rate of malonyl-CoA formation which stimulates the rate of fatty acid synthesis and inhibits the transfer of acyl-carnitine into the mitochondrial matrix for β-oxidation. The inhibition of acetyl-CoA carboxylase by cyclic AMP can explain both the inhibition of lipogenesis and the stimulation of ketone body synthesis by glucagon.

Do hormones influence amino acid metabolism in the liver?

The hormonal effects on amino acid metabolism by the liver are less clearly understood. However, it is known that insulin stimulates amino acid transport into the liver which would explain an increase in protein synthesis. The stimulation of gluconeogenesis by glucagon through its increase in cyclic AMP levels would tend to increase amino acid catabolism and reduce the amount of amino acids available for protein synthesis.

6.15 Interactions between the liver and other tissues

Because of its pivotal role in regulating the levels of nutrients in the blood it is obvious that the liver has interactions with all the tissues in the body. Nevertheless, it may be helpful in understanding the metabolism of the other tissues discussed in this book to summarize each of their interactions with the liver. The main features of these interrelationships are shown schematically in Figure 6.13.

During feeding sugars, amino acids and short-chain fatty acids are transferred from the intestine to the liver together with bile salts and a substantial amount of lactate. Between meals the intestine still contributes alanine and lactate to the liver as a result of metabolizing the glucose supplied by the liver and the glutamine from muscles. Adipose tissue receives fatty acids from the liver in the form of triacylglycerol travelling in VLDL particles, both during feeding and in the postabsorptive period. Glycerol released from adipose tissue returns to the liver and when a reduction in blood glucose prompts the net release of fatty acids by adipocytes some of these are also taken up by the liver. Details of the liver's relationship to the intestine and adipose tissue has already been covered in section 6.13.

Glucagon and insulin, which are secreted by the pancreatic α- and β-cells respectively, help the liver to regulate nutrient storage and release. The liver also has a special relationship with the kidneys, as described in Chapter 13, because together they are responsible for the excretion of all the waste products except CO_2.

The principal links between the liver and the muscles, blood and CNS are mainly concerned with the supply of substrates. Nevertheless these relationships are all reciprocal. Muscle receives glucose and fatty acids from the liver and sends lactate plus amino acids in the reverse direction. Blood cells depend on

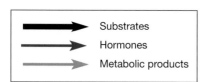

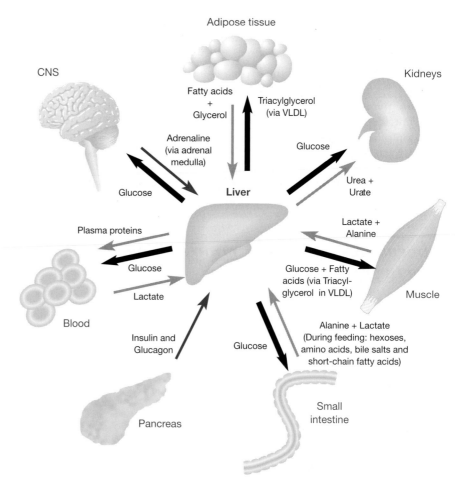

Figure 6.13
Summary of the metabolic interactions between the liver and other tissues.

the liver for their glucose supply which the red blood cells convert to lactate that is returned to the liver, and the liver also contributes most of the plasma proteins. The CNS relies on the liver for its glucose supply. It also depends on the maintenance of vascular amino acid levels as substrates for protein synthesis and the synthesis of neurotransmitters. Nitrogen is released from the CNS in the form of glutamine which reaches the liver as alanine after being processed by the intestine.

E X E R C I S E S

1. Why is glucokinase important for the liver's role in regulating blood glucose?

2. How does the liver respond to a decline in blood glucose when liver glycogen has been exhausted?

3. List the major sources of acetyl-CoA for fatty acid synthesis in liver.

4. What part do the folic acid and vitamin B_{12} coenzymes play in the *S*-adenosylmethionine cycle?

5. Distinguish between a monooxygenase and a dioxygenase reaction.

6.   Distinguish between the way in which amino nitrogen is used to convert ornithine to citrulline, and to convert citrulline to arginine.

7.   How can the cytochrome P-450 system help to detoxify xenobiotics?

8.   What makes the liver switch from fatty acid synthesis to the formation of ketone bodies?

9.   What does the liver do to prevent excessive blood cholesterol?

10.   How do HDLs transfer cholesterol back to the liver?

11.   Summarize the effects of insulin and adrenaline on glycogen formation and breakdown in the liver.

12.   How does feeding alter the sources of carbon used by the liver for glycogen synthesis?

Further reading

Bender, D.A. (1985) *Amino Acid Metabolism*, 2nd edition, Wiley.

Dow, J., Lindsay, G. & Morrison, J. (1996) *Biochemistry, Molecules, Cells and the Body*, Addison-Wesley, Chapters 10 & 13.

Felig, P. (1975) Amino acid metabolism in man, *Annual Review of Biochemistry* **44**, 933–955.

Frayn, K.N. (1996) *Metabolic Regulation: A Human Perspective*, Portland Press, Chapters 3 & 8.

Hers, H.-G. & Hue, L. (1983) Gluconeogenesis and related aspects of glycolysis, *Annual Review of Biochemistry* **52**, 617–653.

Hillgartner, F.B., Salati, L.M. & Goodridge, A.G. (1995) Physiological and molecular mechanisms involved in nutritional regulation of fatty acid synthesis. *Physiological Reviews* **75**, 47–76.

McGarry, J.D. & Foster, D.W. (1980) Regulation of hepatic fatty acid oxidation and ketone body production, *Annual Review of Biochemistry* **49**, 395–420.

Nordlie, R.C. (1984) Fine tuning of blood glucose concentrations, *Trends in Biochemical Sciences* **10**, 70–75.

Tall, A. (1995) Plasma lipid transfer proteins, *Annual Review of Biochemistry* **64**, 235–257.

White, D.A. and Baxter, M. eds (1994) *Hormones and Metabolic Control*, 2nd edition, Arnold, Chapters 2 & 8.

Adipose tissue

The body's main energy reserve is triacylglycerol and in humans most of it is found in white adipose tissue.

The adipose tissue energy store is mobilized by the release of fatty acids through the action of triacylglycerol lipase, which is activated by hormones secreted in response to an increased demand for energy.

7.1 Summary of the metabolism and functions of adipose tissue

There are two types of adipose tissue, white and brown. The function of white adipose tissue is to provide the body with its energy store, whereas brown adipose tissue provides a source of heat. The triacylglycerol present in adipose tissue provides the principal energy store in mammals. It represents at least 10% of the body weight in males and in females it may constitute as much as 25% of the total weight. Because of the hydrophobic nature of triacylglycerol, water makes up only 10% of the weight of adipose tissue cells, which are called adipocytes. This makes triacylglycerol the most efficient way to store energy-supplying substrates. In adipocytes triacylglycerol forms a roughly spherical droplet which occupies most of the cytoplasm. The total amount of triacylglycerol stored in adipose tissue is chiefly determined by the number of adipocytes and the extent to which the energy content of the diet exceeds the overall energy requirements of the body. The three main types of food, carbohydrate, fat and protein, can form triacylglycerol because they can all be converted into acetyl-CoA. The major synthetic pathway in adipose tissue is responsible for the formation of triacylglycerol from fatty acids and the glycerol-3-phosphate formed from blood glucose. Adipocytes also have the normal central metabolic pathways to provide the cells with ATP, as well as the reaction sequences required for the synthesis of fatty acids (see Figure 7.1).

Adipocytes synthesize a number of different lipases. In addition to the hormone-sensitive triacylglycerol lipase responsible for the controlled release of the first fatty acid from triacylglycerol, separate lipases which are not influenced by hormones remove the remaining two fatty acids. Adipocytes also secrete lipoprotein lipase which is attached by carbohydrate chains to the interior of the blood vessels carrying glucose, lipoproteins and oxygen to these cells. The lipoprotein lipase completely hydrolyses triacylglycerol to fatty acids plus glycerol in the capillaries. Glycerol released by both the intracellular and extracellular lipases is returned to the liver where it commonly serves as a substrate for gluconeogenesis. Lipoprotein lipase is also found in the capillaries which serve the heart and skeletal muscle.

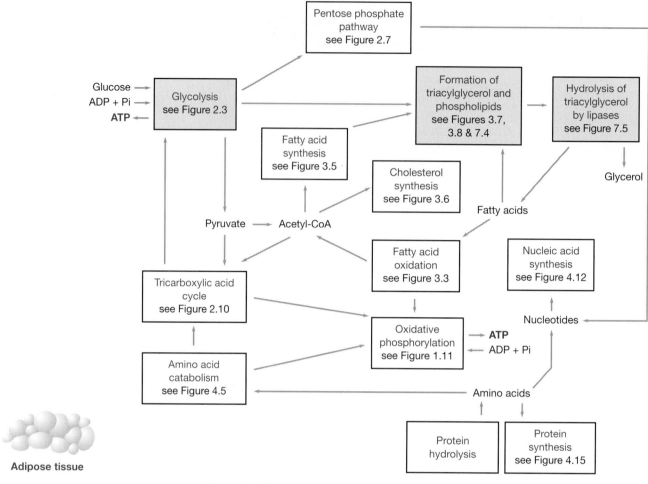

Adipose tissue

Figure 7.1 Summary of the metabolic pathways in white adipose tissue. The blue areas emphasize the pathways that are particularly important in adipocytes.

The function of the hormone-sensitive triacylglycerol lipase in white adipose tissue is to provide a controlled release of fatty acids to supply the energy requirements of most body tissues other than the CNS and the red blood cells. The release of fatty acids by the hormone-sensitive lipase is stimulated by adrenaline and noradrenaline. These hormones are secreted during muscle contraction, so that exercise has the effect of reducing the amount of stored triacylglycerol. Insulin, which is secreted by the pancreas in response to increased levels of blood glucose, stimulates the storage of triacylglycerol by adipose tissue. For this reason adipose tissue will be more likely to store excessive levels of triacylglycerol if small amounts of food (especially sugar) are consumed throughout the day, than if the same amount of energy is consumed in one or two substantial meals. This is because the presence of insulin will give a continual stimulus for triacylglycerol synthesis and there will be no need for triacylglycerol hydrolysis. Also, stressful situations which are not associated with exercise will tend to increase triacylglycerol storage, since the accompanying hormonal secretions tend to cause the liver to release glucose which is followed by a rise in insulin levels.

In addition to their role in energy storage the adipose tissue cells help to insulate the body against heat loss. Layers of adipose tissue also help to cushion internal organs. In the newborn human brown adipose tissue cells are particularly important to maintain body temperature by the oxidation of triacylglycerol by mitochondria in an 'uncoupled' manner without the synthesis of ATP.

7.2 Structure and distribution of white and brown adipose tissue

White and brown adipose tissue cells have very different functions. Both store triacylglycerol, but the brown adipose tissue uses its triacylglycerol to generate heat and not to supply other tissues with substrate. The major function of white adipose tissue, on the other hand, is to store triacylglycerol for supply to the rest of the body when it is needed.

White adipose tissue

White adipose tissue cells are mainly found in two locations: under the skin and around internal organs. The groups of adipocytes are also innervated by sympathetic nerve endings which are responsible for production of much of the noradrenaline which is responsible for stimulating the hormone-sensitive triacylglycerol lipase. Adipocytes are surrounded by loose connective tissue between thick bundles of collagen and elastin fibres (see Figure 7.2a). It is the combination of adipocytes and connective tissue proteins that supports the internal organs and protects them from mechanical damage. The layer of adipocytes and connective tissue under the skin protects the body from the cold and the extent of this protection depends on the thickness of the layer. The triacylglycerol droplet in white adipose tissue cells is surrounded by a thin layer of cytoplasm containing the nucleus (see Figure 7.2b).

Brown adipose tissue

The colour of brown adipose tissue cells is due to the large number of mitochondria that they contain. The triacylglycerol in these cells is stored in small droplets scattered among the mitochondria in the cytoplasm (see Figure 7.2b). There is considerable evidence to suggest that brown adipose tissue may be crucial for temperature control in the newborn infant where shivering does not occur. In the adult human, brown adipose tissue is probably less important, because of the prevalence of clothes and sources of heat outside the body. Brown adipose tissue is essential for temperature control in hibernating animals.

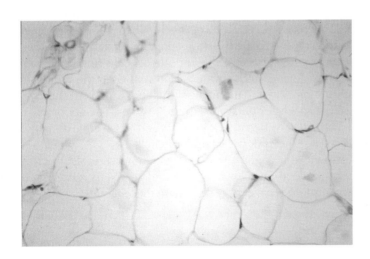

Figure 7.2(a)
Micrograph of white adipose tissue. The faintly shaded areas are thick collagen and the dark patches are capillaries. Photograph kindly supplied by Professor T.J. Ryan, University of Oxford.

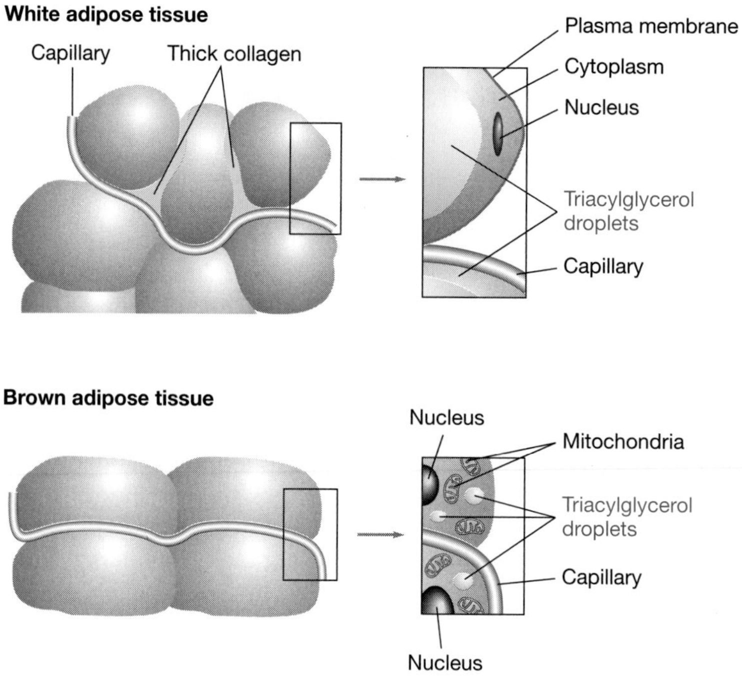

White adipose tissue

Brown adipose tissue

Figure 7.2(b)
Schematic diagrams showing the distinction between white and brown adipose tissue. The cytoplasm of the white adipocytes is largely filled with a droplet of triacylglycerol. In brown adipocytes the cytoplasm is packed with mitochondria and small droplets of triacylglycerol.

7.3 *Endothelial triacylglycerol lipase*

There are two main sources of fatty acids for the triacylglycerol stored in adipose tissue: dietary fat and triacylglycerol synthesized in the liver. Some triacylglycerol is also formed from glucose in adipocytes. In addition there is some recycling of fatty acids released from the stored triacylglycerol. However, measurements of the ratio of free fatty acids to glycerol released from adipocytes into the blood indicate that this recycling is fairly limited.

Delivery of fatty acids to adipose tissue by chylomicrons and VLDL

Dietary fatty acids and those formed in the liver are delivered to the adipose tissue by chylomicrons and VLDL, respectively. When these lipoproteins reach the capillaries in the adipose tissue they come in contact with lipoprotein lipase molecules attached to the surface of the endothelial cells lining the capillaries (see Figure 7.3). This enzyme binds to the apoprotein C on the lipoproteins as they pass through the capillaries. This anchors the lipoproteins to the enzyme so that it can release fatty acids for entry into the adipocytes. The apoprotein C, which is transferred from HDL to both chylomicrons and VLDL circulating around in the blood, also activates the endothelial lipoprotein lipase.

It is important to recognize that lipoprotein lipase is also secreted by other tissues such as skeletal muscle and heart, and serves to release free fatty acids from lipoproteins for use as energy sources in these tissues.

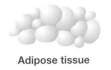

Adipose tissue

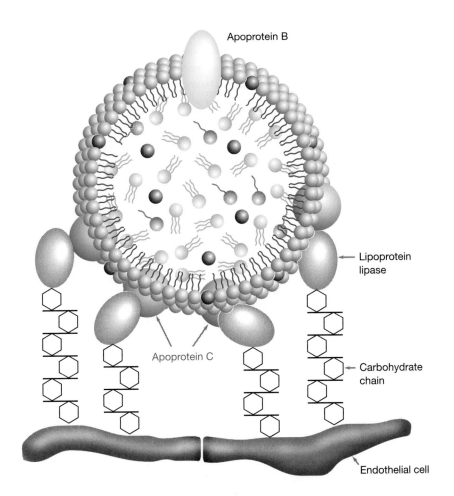

Apoprotein B

Lipoprotein
lipase

Apoprotein C

Carbohydrate
chain

Endothelial cell

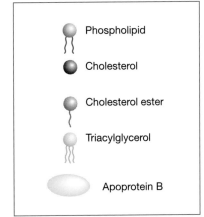

Phospholipid

Cholesterol

Cholesterol ester

Triacylglycerol

Apoprotein B

Figure 7.3
Lipoprotein lipase enzymes binding
to a chylomicron. The lipase
enzymes are attached to the
endothelial cells lining capillaries.

What controls the availability of fatty acids for triacylglycerol synthesis?

As indicated above the major source of fatty acids for triacylglycerol storage by adipose tissue is the triacylglycerol reaching the adipose tissue in the form of chylomicrons and VLDL. The rate at which chylomicrons are formed in the small intestine is directly related to the lipid content of the diet. The production of fatty acids by the liver and their conversion into triacylglycerol for release as VLDL is much more dependent on the carbohydrate and protein content of the diet and the level of fatty acids in the blood. A major controlling factor in the production of triacylglycerol by the liver would appear to be the activity of phosphatidate phosphohydrolase, a key enzyme in the production of triacylglycerol (see below). This enzyme is responsible for the production of diacylglycerol, and if its activity is depressed the phosphatidate will be used for the synthesis of phospholipids rather than for the formation of triacylglycerol. The activity of phosphatidate phosphohydrolase is increased by high levels of sugar and fat in the diet and also by alcohol or excessive levels of amino acids which result in an additional synthesis of acetyl-CoA.

It was pointed out at the beginning of this chapter that the storage of triacylglycerol in adipose tissue will be greatly modified by two related changes in conditions: increased exercise and changes in hormone levels (see section 7.6). Muscular activity depresses the storage of triacylglycerol because more fatty acid is consumed by the muscles to supply them with energy and this minimizes the fall in the glucose level in the blood which would be caused by exercise. The reduction in blood glucose also decreases the availability of glycerol-phosphate for triacylglycerol formation in the adipose tissue.

7.4 Glucose supply and the storage of triacylglycerol

As the fatty acids are released from circulating lipoproteins by the lipoprotein lipase they are transported into the adipocyte by a fatty acid transporter in the plasma membrane. In the cytoplasm they are converted into fatty acyl-CoA at the expense of ATP (Eqs 3.1 and 3.2). The initial step in synthesis of triacylglycerol is controlled by the availability of glycerol-3-phosphate for the synthesis of lysophosphatidic acid by the addition of acyl-CoA (see Figures 3.7 and 7.4). The crucial factor in making glycerol-3-phosphate available is the uptake of glucose by the adipocyte. Since these cells lack glycerol kinase, they cannot reuse glycerol released by lipase action. The plasma membrane has two glucose transporters, GLUT 1 and GLUT 4. GLUT 1 is present at low levels but provides the adipocytes

Adipose tissue

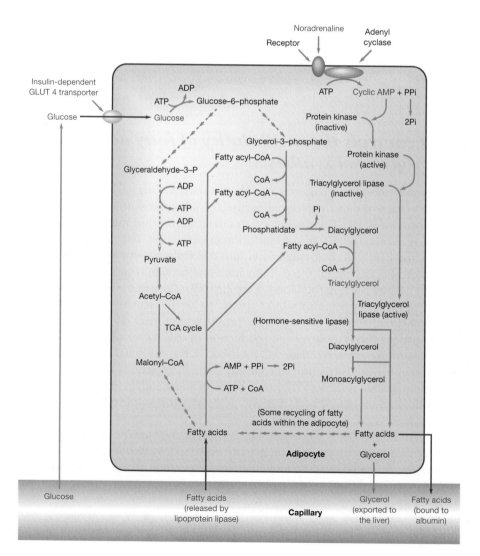

Figure 7.4
Special features of metabolism in the adipocyte.

with a minimal supply of glucose to support basal metabolism. On the other hand, adipose tissue has large amounts of GLUT 4 present in membrane vesicles, as does muscle, and the mobilization of GLUT 4 to the plasma membrane depends on the presence of insulin. The fructose transporter GLUT 5 is also found in adipose tissue so that if the uptake of fructose by the intestine exceeds the capacity of the liver to metabolize it, fructose will also be able to contribute additional glycerol-3-phosphate for triacylglycerol storage.

The fatty acid cycle

Once the first fatty acyl-CoA has been added to glycerol-phosphate the successive steps of triacylglycerol synthesis in adipocytes proceed rapidly because fatty acids are available through the action of the lipoprotein lipase in the capillaries, from lipolysis within the adipocyte or as a result of synthesis from glucose. It appears that the activity of phosphatidate phosphohydrolase, which provides an important control of triacylglycerol synthesis in liver, is not limiting in adipose tissue probably because of the high levels of fatty acid present. Figure 7.4 makes it clear that there is a cycle of triacylglycerol synthesis and hydrolysis within the adipocyte, known as the fatty acid cycle. The extent to which the fatty acids released by the hormone-sensitive lipase are actually re-esterified will largely depend on the availability of glycerol-3-phosphate. As we shall see in the next section, conditions which stimulate the hormone-sensitive triacylglycerol lipase are not normally associated with the insulin levels necessary to increase the supply of glycerol-phosphate. Nevertheless, the absorption of dietary fat and glucose presents the adipocytes with large amounts of chylomicrons or VLDL and will normally provide a good supply of glucose to form glycerol-3-phosphate. Consequently fatty acids released by lipase action within the adipocytes under these conditions will be recycled.

In addition to forming glycerol-3-phosphate, the adipocytes can use glucose via the pentose phosphate pathway to produce NADPH, and by the main glycolytic pathway to form acetyl-CoA from pyruvate. Some of the acetyl-CoA will enter the TCA cycle to supply the adipocytes with ATP, but most will be converted to malonyl-CoA and used to synthesize fatty acyl-CoA which will also be available for triacylglycerol synthesis as well as the formation of adipocyte membrane phospholipids.

7.5 Release of fatty acids from adipocytes: action of hormone-sensitive triacylglycerol lipase

Although the rate of synthesis of triacylglycerol within the adipocytes appears to depend chiefly on the availability of its constituents, the release of fatty acids is well controlled. Figure 7.5 indicates that the hormone-sensitive lipase is activated by cyclic AMP which stimulates PKA (see Figure 1.13) to phosphorylate the lipase; deactivation of the lipase is caused by protein phosphatase 1. Consequently the lipase activity will be stimulated by any hormones that increase adenyl cyclase activity, such as adrenaline or noradrenaline, and inhibited by agents that decrease it, such as adenosine and the prostaglandins (see Figure 3.11). Cyclic AMP is converted to 5'-AMP by phosphodiesterase so that any effector which alters the activity of this enzyme will also influence the level

Adipose tissue

The hydrolysis of triacylglycerol is regulated by cyclic AMP formed by adenyl cyclase. The formation of cyclic AMP is stimulated by adrenaline and noradrenaline, whereas insulin may remove cyclic AMP by stimulating phosphodiesterase

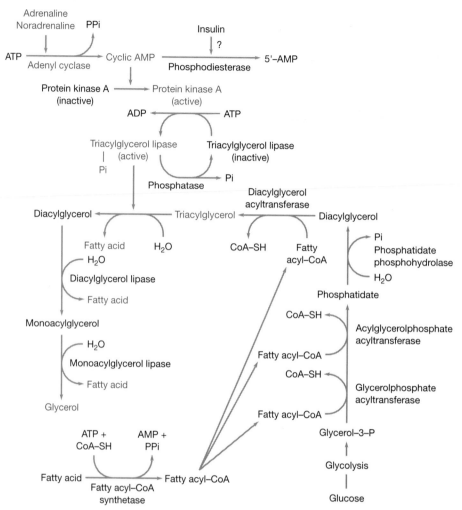

Figure 7.5

Hormonal control of the formation and hydrolysis of triacylglycerol in adipose tissue.

The formation of triacylglycerol depends on the availability of both glycerol-phosphate and fatty acids. Insulin stimulates the formation of glycerol-3-phosphate by increasing the intracellular glucose through its mobilization of GLUT 4 glucose transporters. It also increases the synthesis of the lipoprotein lipase that supplies fatty acids

of cyclic AMP. Insulin reduces the level of cyclic AMP, but it is not yet clear whether this is a result of an inhibition of adenyl cyclase or a stimulation of phosphodiesterase. Caffeine is thought to increase cyclic AMP by inhibiting phosphodiesterase, and if this is true it could stimulate the release of fatty acids from adipose tissue. Since the hormone-sensitive lipase is inactivated by protein phosphatase 1 any effectors which increase the activity of the phosphatase would also inhibit the activity of the lipase.

The lipases responsible for removing the second and third fatty acids from triacylglycerol are not hormone-sensitive, nor are they rate-limiting for the hydrolysis of triacylglycerol. Once the fatty acids are released they leave the cell by the fatty acid transporter unless they are recycled into triacylglycerol. The fatty acids circulate in the blood bound to albumin which prevents free fatty acids from endangering the integrity of membranes. Glycerol released by triacylglycerol hydrolysis also leaves the adipocyte and is normally removed from the blood by the liver.

7.6 Hormone interactions in the storage and release of fatty acids

The effects of insulin in adipocytes

The uptake of glucose by adipocytes is strongly enhanced by a rise in the concentration of insulin in the blood which increases the transfer of vesicles containing GLUT 4 transporters to the plasma membrane. The resulting rise in intracellular glucose increases the availability of glycerol-phosphate which is the rate-limiting step for the formation of triacylglycerol. Insulin also increases the synthesis of lipoprotein lipase, which is attached to the endothelial cells after secretion by the adipocytes, and in this way insulin also increases the rate of entry of fatty acids into adipocytes. As mentioned in the preceding section the decrease in cyclic AMP caused by insulin will reduce the activity of the hormone-sensitive triacylglycerol lipase and inhibit the release of fatty acids within the adipocytes. This additional insulin effect is valuable because it reduces the recycling activity of the fatty acid cycle when the storage of triacylglycerol is being stimulated.

In addition to promoting glucose entry insulin promotes the conversion of pyruvate into fatty acids and triacylglycerol by stimulating the phosphatase that converts pyruvate dehydrogenase into the active dephosphorylated form. Insulin also increases conversion of acetyl-CoA to malonyl-CoA by stimulating the acetyl-CoA carboxylase and fatty acyl-CoA transferase. In this way insulin enables the adipocytes to act as a safety net for fatty acid synthesis in case the liver and muscles are unable to deal with high levels of blood glucose. However this safety net does not operate in cases of late-onset, or non-insulin-dependent, diabetes where the insulin receptor is defective and where there are excessive lipid levels in the blood.

The actions of adrenaline and noradrenaline

Figure 7.5 shows how the breakdown of stored triacylglycerol in adipose tissue is promoted by the phosphorylation of the hormone-sensitive lipase as a result of the effect of cyclic AMP on the cyclic AMP-dependent protein kinase. The increases in cyclic AMP are the result of the action of adrenaline and noradrenaline on specific receptors which, in turn, activate the adenyl cyclase. As mentioned in section 7.5, reduction in cyclic AMP levels is caused by adenosine and prostaglandin in addition to insulin.

Exercise or excitement causes secretion of catecholamines which reduce triacylglycerol storage. The secretion of adrenaline increases cyclic AMP levels which depress phosphatidate phosphohydrolase activity in the liver and thus reduce the formation of triacylglycerol for transfer to the adipose tissue by VLDL. The release of noradrenaline from sympathetic nerve endings or its secretion from the adrenal medulla stimulates formation of cyclic AMP in adipose tissue. This increases the activity of the hormone-sensitive triacylglycerol lipase resulting in a net loss of stored triacylglycerol. Glucose utilization in exercise often causes a drop in the insulin level which stops the inhibitory effect it has on cyclic AMP levels in adipose tissue, and this also results in an increase in the activity of the hormone-sensitive triacylglycerol lipase.

7.7 *Heat production in brown adipose tissue*

The colour of brown adipose tissue is due to the high concentration of cytochromes in the mitochondria present in these cells (see Figure 7.2b). Brown adipose tissue is also rich in nerves and blood capillaries. The nerves innervating this tissue release noradrenaline in response to a drop in temperature. As in white adipocytes the noradrenaline stimulates the hormone-sensitive lipase to release fatty acids and these are then oxidized to CO_2 and water by the β-oxidation pathway and the TCA cycle within the adipocytes. However, instead of forming large amounts of ATP this fatty acid oxidation in brown adipocytes produces heat, providing what is known as non-shivering thermogenesis. It does this because the mitochondrial inner membranes in the brown adipose tissue mitochondria contain a protein called thermogenin which forms a proton channel in the inner membrane. These channels dissipate much of the proton gradient ensuring that most of the energy released during fatty acid oxidation is available as heat rather than being used to phosphorylate ADP. In order to prevent heat production when it is not needed the thermogenin proton channel is closed by ADP and GDP, and it appears that this inhibition is removed by the fatty acids released in response to noradrenaline secretion.

7.8 *The relationships between adipocytes and other tissues*

The interrelationships that adipose tissue has with the other tissues are summarized in Figure 7.6. It is important to note, as described below, that changes in conditions can lead to either a net increase or a net decrease in the amount of triacylglycerol stored in adipose tissue.

The substrates required for the storage of triacylglycerol in adipose tissue are supplied by the liver and the intestine. The fatty acids are transported as triacylglycerol in the VLDL and chylomicron lipoproteins respectively, and are released by lipoprotein lipase attached to the lining of the capillaries supplying the adipose tissue. The glycerol-3-phosphate is formed from blood glucose emanating either from the liver or from the small intestine during carbohydrate absorption. Any fructose reaching the adipose tissue can also serve as a substrate for the formation of glycerol-3-phosphate. Glycerol released by the action of the lipoprotein lipase does not enter the adipocytes but returns to the liver.

As long as fatty acids are available to the adipocyte, stimulation of triacylglycerol storage is largely a consequence of the rise in insulin secretion from the pancreas that always accompanies an increase in blood glucose. This hormone acts directly to mobilize the GLUT 4 glucose transporter from the cytoplasmic vesicles to the plasma membrane of the adipocytes. As a result the cytoplasmic glucose concentration rises, stimulating the formation of glycerol-3-phosphate which is normally rate-limiting for triacylglycerol synthesis. Insulin also stimulates fatty acid synthesis in the liver by increasing the rate of acetyl-CoA formation from glucose through its stimulation of pyruvate dehydrogenase activity and the conversion of the acetyl-CoA into malonyl-CoA by increasing the activity of acetyl-CoA carboxylase.

Hydrolysis of stored triacylglycerol is controlled by the activity of the hormone-sensitive triacylglycerol lipase of the adipocytes. The activity is stimu-

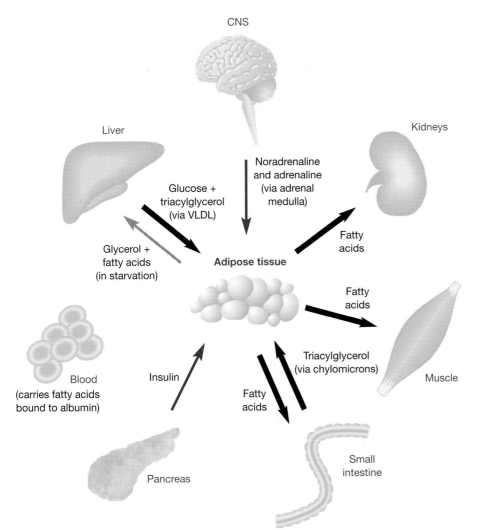

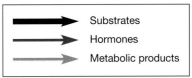

CNS

Liver

Kidneys

Glucose +
triacylglycerol
(via VLDL)

Noradrenaline
and adrenaline
(via adrenal
medulla)

Fatty
acids

Glycerol +
fatty acids
(in starvation)

Adipose tissue

Fatty
acids

Fatty
acids

Blood
(carries fatty acids
bound to albumin)

Insulin

Fatty
acids

Triacylglycerol
(via chylomicrons)

Muscle

Pancreas

Small
intestine

Substrates
Hormones
Metabolic products

Figure 7.6
Summary of the metabolic
interactions between adipocytes
and other tissues.

lated via cyclic AMP by adrenaline and noradrenaline secreted in response to stimulation from the CNS. The secretion of these hormones can either be a consequence of muscle activity or in anticipation of it. The onset of muscle activity will cause release of fatty acids from the adipocytes as a consequence of the drop in insulin levels due to a decline in blood glucose. The fall in insulin concentration stimulates fatty acid release in two ways: by reducing the availability of glycerol-3-phosphate and by removing the inhibitory effect that insulin has on cyclic AMP levels. As a result the rate of triacylglycerol hydrolysis is increased and the recycling of fatty acids within the adipocyte is reduced.

Skeletal muscle and the heart are the major consumers of fatty acid released from adipose tissue but most other metabolically active tissues such as kidneys, liver and intestine can also use fatty acids as energy-supplying substrates. The main exceptions are the CNS and the red blood cells. The blood–brain barrier prevents the access of fatty acid to the CNS, and erythrocytes cannot oxidize fatty acids because they lack mitochondria. When the release of fatty acids from adipose tissue reaches a high level due to the fall in blood sugar resulting from even mild periods of starvation, the liver converts the excess fatty acid into ketone bodies. This reduces the potential danger to membrane integrity of high fatty acid levels and also provides a substrate for the CNS when glucose levels are low. The main control of the utilization of ketone bodies is their concentration in the blood. Normally this is very low ($20\,\mu\text{M}$), but as the length of starvation increases ketone body concentration rises rapidly into the millimolar range. As the utilization of ketone bodies rises, glucose metabolism becomes progressively more inhibited even in the brain. Ketone bodies also appear to inhibit the lipolysis of triacylglycerol in adipocytes. The negative side of ketone body production during starvation is the increase in the acidity of the blood.

EXERCISES

1. How does brown adipose tissue differ from white adipose tissue?

2. Describe the actions of lipoprotein lipase.

3. What controls the formation of triacylglycerol in adipose tissue?

4. How does a high level of fructose intake influence the deposition of triacylglycerol?

5. What is the fatty acid cycle in adipose tissue?

6. How is the activity of hormone-sensitive triacylglycerol lipase regulated?

7. Why does a decline in insulin concentration increase the release of fatty acids from adipocytes?

8. How does the relationship between adipose tissue and liver change during feeding?

9. How does noradrenaline get to the adipocytes?

10. Why is it not possible for the brain and the red blood cells to use fatty acids as an energy-supplying substrate?

Further reading

Clement, K, Vaisse, C., Lahlou, N., Cabrol, S., Pelloux, V., Cassuto, D., Gourmelen, M., Dina, C., Chambaz, J., Lacorte, J-M., Basdevant, A., Bourgneres, P., Lebouc, Y., Frogue, P. & Guy-Grand, B. (1998) A mutation in the human leptin receptor gene causes obesity and pituitary dysfunction. *Nature* **392**, 398–401.

Dow, J., Lindsay, G. & Morrison, J. (1996) *Biochemistry, Molecules, Cells and the Body*, Addison-Wesley, Chapter 9.

Frayn, K.N. (1996) *Metabolic Regulation: A Human Perspective*, Portland Press, Chapter 8.

Gurr, M.I. & Harwood, J.L. (1991) *Lipid Biochemistry*, 4th edition, Chapman & Hall.

Kiberstis, P.A. & Marx, J. (1998) Regulation of body weight. *Science* **280**, 1363–1370.

White, D.A. & Baxter, M., eds (1994) *Hormones and Metabolic Control*, 2nd edition, Arnold, Chapter 2.

Muscles

Muscles are responsible for movement and they also have a metabolic role. When they are working, muscle cells require about 100 times the amount of energy that they use at rest.

Skeletal muscle cells contain an instantly available store of energy-supplying substrates in the form of glycogen; they also contain the main body proteins that can be mobilized to supply energy.

8.1 Summary of the functions of muscle cells

The function of muscle cells is straightforward: to contract. To fulfil this function for the whole organism it is essential that the contraction of individual muscles be carried out in a controlled and coordinated manner. Contraction occurs in response to nerve stimulation and is initiated by a rise in calcium ion concentration in muscle cell cytoplasm. There are several different types of muscle cells. These are classified both in terms of their anatomical location and the ways in which they are controlled, e.g. striated muscle, smooth muscle or cardiac muscle. Individual muscle cells, or fibres, can be classified on the basis of their speed of contraction and the characteristics of their metabolism, e.g. slow twitch, fast twitch (oxidative) or fast twitch (glycolytic). Whole muscles will normally contain a mixture of these three fibre types.

Given the simplicity of muscle function it is reasonable to expect that the metabolism of muscle cells will be simple too, namely to supply the ATP needed for muscle contraction and for the transport of Ca^{2+} out of the cytoplasm. Muscle cells must also have the biosynthetic and catabolic processes required for the continual recycling of cell constituents. Figure 8.1 shows that the ATP-supplying pathways are the most important metabolic features in muscle cells, although the enzymes for most of the central metabolic pathways are present.

Muscle fibre types

The three types of fibres differ in their speed of contraction, the major energy source they use and the extent to which they rely on oxidative metabolism. In order to contract, all muscle cells need to have some stored fuel. This is mainly triacylglycerol in the slow (type I) fibres, a mixture of glycogen and triacylglycerol in the fast (type IIA oxidative) fibres and glycogen in the fast (type IIB glycolytic)

CHAPTER 8

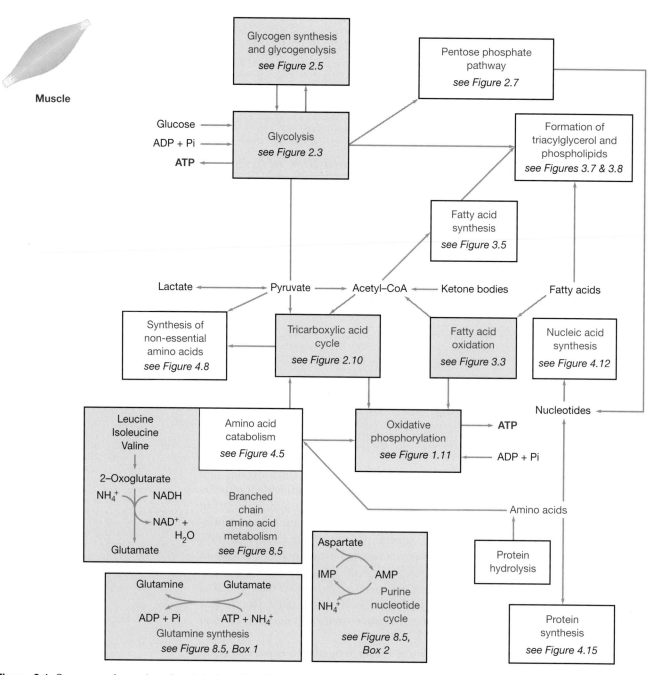

Figure 8.1 Summary of muscle cell metabolism. The blue areas indicate those metabolic processes of particular importance in muscle.

fibres. All muscle cells are also rich in protein because they are filled with actin and myosin filaments. The oxidative and glycolytic type II fibres differ mainly in terms of the availability of oxygen through the capillary bed and the prevalence of mitochondria within the muscle cell, which limits the space for contractile proteins in the oxidative fibres. The type II oxidative fibres are not completely dependent on the supply of oxygen from the capillaries since, in addition to glycogen, they contain stored oxygen bound to myoglobin and phosphocreatine (also present in the type II glycolytic fibres) which can replenish the ATP levels. All of the fibres, except for the type II glycolytic, need to retain the flexibility to use different energy sources, depending on availability.

Muscle cells also contribute to the metabolism of the whole body

In addition to supporting contraction and maintaining the cell constituents, muscle metabolism also plays an important role in the metabolism of the whole body. In part, the importance of muscle metabolism is due to the fact that skeletal muscle alone accounts for more than 40% of the body weight (see Table 5.1). However, much more significant is the fact, also evident from Table 5.1, that the rate at which oxygen is consumed by skeletal muscle, and hence its demand for substrates, can increase from about 17% of that in the whole body at rest to more than 90% during severe exercise. For these reasons muscle has an important influence on the disposal of nutrients absorbed by the intestine during feeding. The total amount of oxidizable substrate stored in muscle and adipose tissue is also influenced by the level of exercise. Furthermore, the large volume of skeletal muscle provides the most significant store of essential amino acids in the body. Although amino acids are only released by the net loss of muscle protein, this can occur for short periods without any significant reduction in muscle strength.

Figure 8.1 illustrates the fact that muscle plays a special role in amino acid metabolism because it is the principal site for the catabolism of the three branched chain amino acids. The ammonia that is released during the breakdown of these amino acids is largely released as glutamine. This is also the fate of the ammonia produced by the purine nucleotide cycle.

Other special features of muscle cell metabolism include the control mechanisms that enable the cells to form and mobilize their energy stores, and to speed up the contraction cycle. Control of the energy stores is mainly accomplished by hormonal mechanisms which regulate glucose uptake and the formation and breakdown of muscle glycogen. The speed of the contraction cycle depends on the availability of ATP for the cycle itself and for the removal of cytoplasmic Ca^{2+}. Muscle cells have three special ways to supply ATP rapidly. One is by storing creatine-phosphate for the rephosphorylation of ADP, the second is by the anaerobic production of lactate and the third is by using oxygen stored on myoglobin in the cytoplasm.

8.2 General features of muscle cell structure

In order to cause movement or generate tension, a muscle cell becomes, or attempts to become, shorter. The individual cells, or fibres, within the muscle are packed with bundles of filaments composed largely of actin and myosin proteins (see Figure 8.2). Shortening of the muscle fibres is accomplished by the thick myosin filaments and the thin actin filaments moving relative to each other as a consequence of the action of the cross-bridges. This movement is accomplished at the expense of ATP hydrolysis, so it is clear that each muscle fibre must be well organized metabolically to supply ATP at a high rate. Contraction is initiated by an increase in the Ca^{2+} content of the cytoplasm and relaxation depends on the rapid ATP-dependent removal of the Ca^{2+} ions into the sarcoplasmic reticulum or across the plasma membrane.

Most muscles contain all three fibre types, although there are variations between different muscles. Furthermore, the proportions of the three fibre types in a particular muscle differ from individual to individual. Such variations are responsible for differences in physical prowess. For example, it has been shown that successful sprinters need to have a high proportion of the muscle mass in

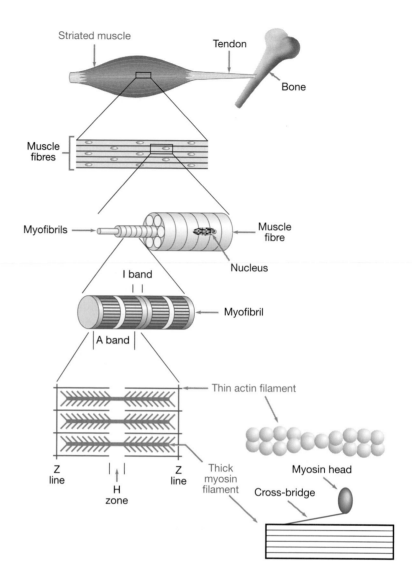

Figure 8.2
Structural organization of striated muscle showing the arrangement of filaments within a myofibril in a single muscle cell or fibre.

their legs composed of the type IIB glycolytic fibres, whereas long distance runners need a high proportion of type I and type IIA oxidative fibres. In most untrained individuals the proportions of type I and type II fibres are approximately equal, suggesting that the relative proportions of the different fibre types can be altered by training. However, it is also probable that there is a genetic basis for those individuals who are good sprinters or good marathon runners.

Type I muscle fibres

These fibres are known as slow twitch fibres since the speed of their contraction cycle is somewhat slower than that of the fast twitch fibres. Metabolically the type I fibres have a high capacity for oxidative phosphorylation, fatty acid oxidation and TCA cycle activity. As a consequence they need a good blood supply and relatively high levels of myoglobin. These fibres can also be distinguished by their stores of triacylglycerol in addition to a basic store of glycogen. Although they differ structurally, cardiac muscle fibres are metabolically similar to type I fibres.

Type IIA (oxidative) fibres

These fibres are distinguished from type I fibres by having a faster contraction cycle and relatively high glycolytic capacity. Although they are less well supplied with capillaries than the type I fibres, the type IIA fibres have a high oxidative capacity and are rich in myoglobin. They also store triacylglycerol as well as glycogen.

Type IIB (glycolytic) fibres

These fast twitch fibres have a low oxidative capacity and rely for their energy on a high rate of glycolysis. They have few mitochondria and a relatively poor blood supply, and as a consequence they do not store triacylglycerol. These fibres are only capable of sustaining contraction for a relatively short time, but the compensation for their low oxidative activity may be that they have a higher proportion of actin and myosin filaments so that they can generate more tension for a given fibre cross-sectional area. These fibres store large amounts of glycogen.

8.3 The molecular basis of contraction in striated muscle

Overall it is clear that muscle contraction involves the shortening of individual muscle cells at the expense of the energy released by the hydrolysis of ATP. When skeletal or cardiac muscle is viewed more closely it is clear that the shortening is due to the movement of the thin actin filaments over the thick myosin filaments, and that this movement is a consequence of changes in the cross-bridges that can be seen between the two classes of filaments. The general features of these changes are shown in Figure 8.3 and it should be noted that the force for the movement, the so-called 'power stroke', is a consequence of the dissociation of ADP and phosphate from the myosin headpieces rather than a result of the hydrolysis of ATP. The cause of the 'power stroke' is actually a conformational change in the myosin headpiece and such a change in a protein can often result from the dissociation of one or more ligands. Smooth muscle and cardiac muscle differ from striated muscle in their structural organization and protein composition but, although they contract more slowly, ATP still provides the energy for shortening. These muscles also require Ca^{2+} ions to initiate contraction and ATP to remove the Ca^{2+} from the cytoplasm.

The cross-bridge cycle

The binding of ATP initiates the cross-bridge cycle by dissociating the myosin headpieces from the actin filaments. At this stage the headpieces are in a low-energy configuration. The angle between the headpiece and the long helical section of the myosin molecule changes with the hydrolysis of ATP and this conformation is maintained by the binding of ADP and phosphate. The next stage is entered with the binding of Ca^{2+} ions to the troponin C component of the thin filaments. The resulting rearrangement in the thin filament structure permits the myosin headpieces in their high-energy configuration to bind to actin molecules which triggers the release of the ADP and phosphate and the 'power stroke' change in the conformational shape of the headpiece. The shape change causes the thick and thin filaments to slide relative to each other. The events of the cross-bridge cycle outlined above clearly illustrate the principal metabolic

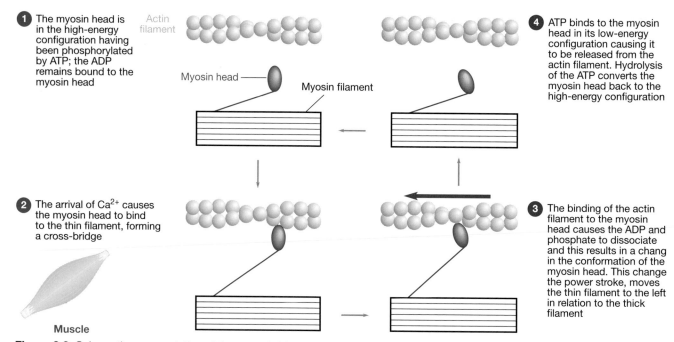

1 The myosin head is in the high-energy configuration having been phosphorylated by ATP; the ADP remains bound to the myosin head

Actin filament

Myosin head

Myosin filament

4 ATP binds to the myosin head in its low-energy configuration causing it to be released from the actin filament. Hydrolysis of the ATP converts the myosin head back to the high-energy configuration

2 The arrival of Ca^{2+} causes the myosin head to bind to the thin filament, forming a cross-bridge

Muscle

3 The binding of the actin filament to the myosin head causes the ADP and phosphate to dissociate and this results in a chang in the conformation of the myosin head. This change the power stroke, moves the thin filament to the left in relation to the thick filament

Figure 8.3 Schematic representation of the cross-bridge cycle in skeletal muscle.

requirements of muscle contraction: the phosphorylation of ADP to maintain a high ATP/ADP ratio and the removal of Ca^{2+} from the cytoplasm to keep the cytoplasmic Ca^{2+} at the resting concentration of about 1×10^{-7} M.

8.4 Excitation–contraction coupling in muscle

A muscle fibre is stimulated to contract by impulses coming from the CNS along the axons of the motor neurones. These axons terminate in an expanded region known as a motor end plate in which vesicles containing the neurotransmitter acetylcholine are stored. When the impulse reaches the motor end plate some of the vesicles empty their contents into the space between the axon terminus and the plasma membrane of the muscle fibre. The acetylcholine combines with receptors on the plasma membrane, and this opens Na^+ channels, which depolarizes the membrane of the muscle cell. The wave of depolarization extends in all directions from the motor end plate and is transmitted into the interior of the muscle fibre by narrow transverse tubules. The effect of the wave of depolarization is to cause a transient opening of Ca^{2+} channels in the sarcoplasmic reticulum membrane as well as in the plasma membrane itself (see Figure 8.4, Box 1).

Calcium ion transport and storage in the sarcoplasmic reticulum

The release of Ca^{2+} into the cytoplasm as a result of nervous stimulation of the muscle initiates contraction. Since the extracellular Ca^{2+} concentration is more than 1000 times that in the sarcoplasm, the opening of Ca^{2+} channels in the plasma membrane will cause a rapid rate of Ca^{2+} entry. In striated muscle the

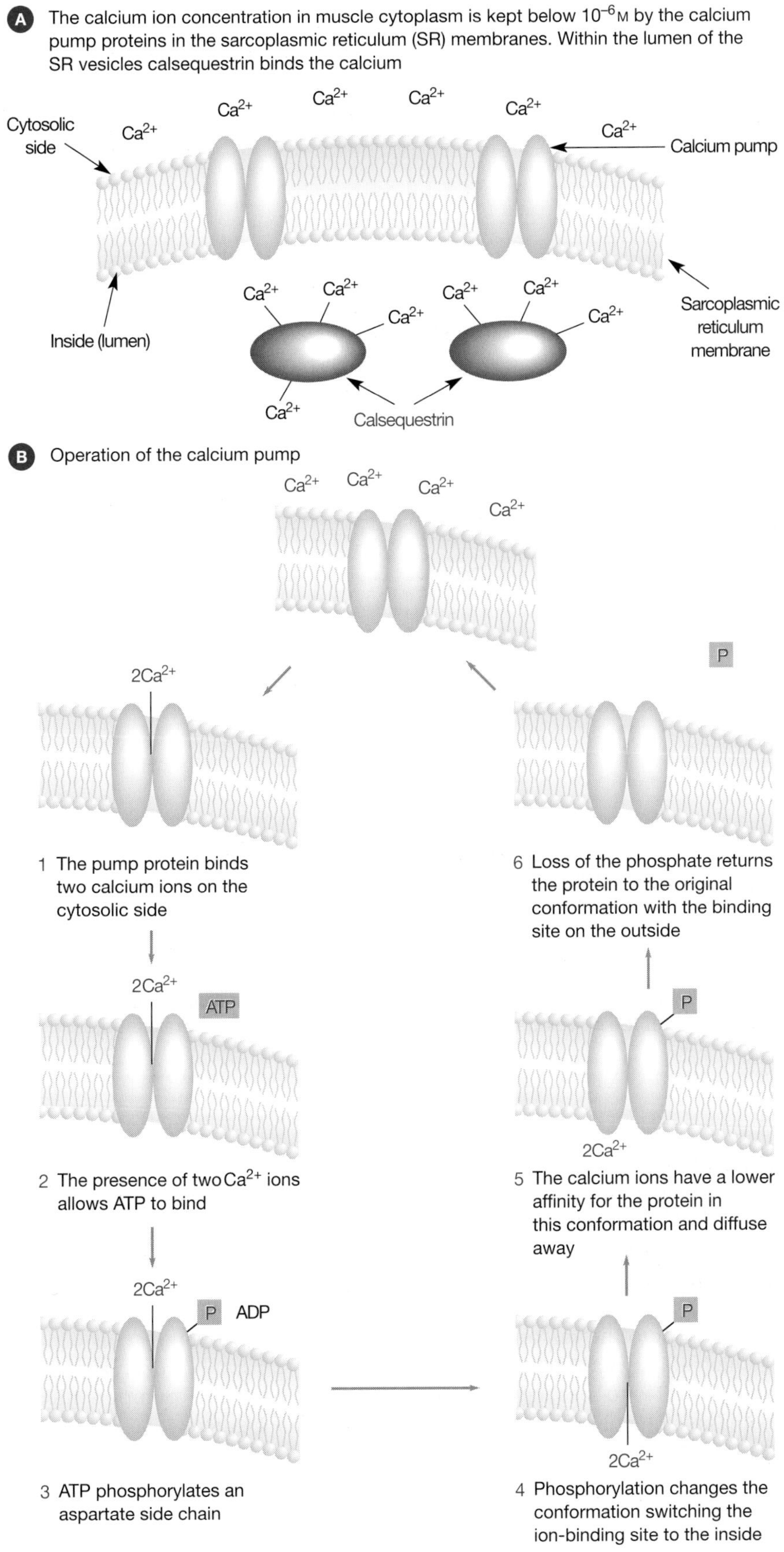
A The calcium ion concentration in muscle cytoplasm is kept below 10^{-6} M by the calcium pump proteins in the sarcoplasmic reticulum (SR) membranes. Within the lumen of the SR vesicles calsequestrin binds the calcium
Cytosolic side
Ca^{2+}
Calcium pump
Inside (lumen)
Sarcoplasmic reticulum membrane
Calsequestrin
B Operation of the calcium pump
$2Ca^{2+}$
ATP
P
ADP
1 The pump protein binds two calcium ions on the cytosolic side
2 The presence of two Ca^{2+} ions allows ATP to bind
3 ATP phosphorylates an aspartate side chain
4 Phosphorylation changes the conformation switching the ion-binding site to the inside
5 The calcium ions have a lower affinity for the protein in this conformation and diffuse away
6 Loss of the phosphate returns the protein to the original conformation with the binding site on the outside

Muscle

Figure 8.4
ATP-dependent calcium ion transport and storage in the sarcoplasmic reticulum.

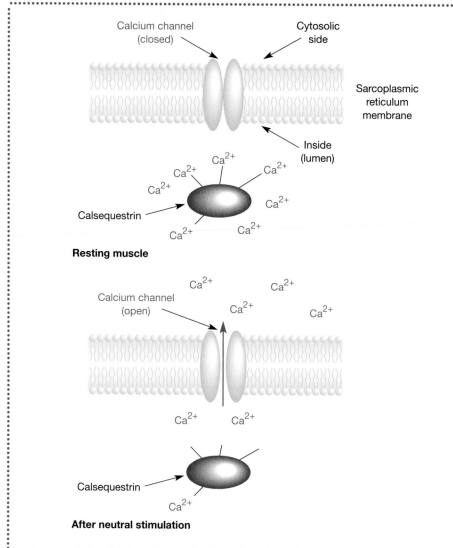

Calcium channel
(closed)

Cytosolic
side

Sarcoplasmic
reticulum
membrane

Inside
(lumen)

Ca^{2+}
Ca^{2+}
Ca^{2+}
Ca^{2+}
Ca^{2+}
Ca^{2+}
Ca^{2+}

Calsequestrin

Resting muscle

Ca^{2+}
Ca^{2+}
Calcium channel
(open)
Ca^{2+}
Ca^{2+}

Ca^{2+}
Ca^{2+}

Calsequestrin

Ca^{2+}

After neutral stimulation

Figure 8.4 Box 1 The release of calcium ions from the sarcoplasmic reticulum as a result of the opening of calcium channels caused by neutral stimulation.

opening of Ca^{2+} channels in the sarcoplasmic reticulum, where large amounts of Ca^{2+} are held bound to calsequestrin, causes a rise in Ca^{2+} concentration throughout the muscle. Following the nervous stimulation the plasma and sarcoplasmic reticulum membranes are repolarized and the Ca^{2+} channels close. In order for the muscle fibre to relax it is essential that the Ca^{2+} ion concentration be reduced to the resting level of 1×10^{-7} M. This is accomplished by the transport of Ca^{2+} into the sarcoplasmic reticulum where it is bound to calsequestrin and a high-affinity Ca^{2+}-binding protein. The Ca^{2+} transporter must be phosphorylated by ATP to be activated and two Ca^{2+} ions are pumped into the sarcoplasmic reticulum for each ATP hydrolysed (see Figure 8.4).

8.5 Energy-supplying pathways in muscle

The glycolytic pathway

The phosphorylation of ADP to form ATP occurs directly from the glycolytic pathway, and indirectly from the TCA cycle or β-oxidation of fatty acids via the oxidative phosphorylation system. Striated muscle also has a more immediate way of rephosphorylating ADP by the transfer of phosphate from creatine-phosphate as shown in Eq. 8.1:

$$\text{Creatine-phosphate} + \text{ADP} \longleftrightarrow \text{creatine} + \text{ATP} \tag{8.1}$$

The concentration of creatine-phosphate in striated muscle is approximately twice that of ATP and makes it possible to maintain a high ATP/ADP ratio during the initial stages of contraction. The rephosphorylation of ADP by creatine-phosphate provides time for the stimulation of glycogenolysis to provide the glucose-phosphate substrates for glycolysis, which is the fastest metabolic pathway in muscle for ATP production. Rapid rates of muscle contraction are normally associated with increased Ca^{2+} levels in muscle cytoplasm and the stimulation of adrenaline release from the adrenal medulla. Adrenaline increases the cyclic AMP concentration, causing PKA-mediated stimulation of glycogen phosphorylase, phosphofructokinase and pyruvate kinase in muscle. The highest rate of ATP production by glycolysis can only be sustained by NADH oxidation through the conversion of pyruvate to lactate, since the glycerol-phosphate and malate–aspartate shuttles (Figure 2.12) cannot regenerate NAD^+ as rapidly as lactate dehydrogenase. Complete oxidation of the glucose-phosphate units released from muscle glycogen can produce ATP less than half as fast as anaerobic glycolysis. However, it is important to recognize that the maximum rate of anaerobic glycolysis cannot be sustained for more than a few seconds because the accumulation of lactate inhibits the conversion of pyruvate to lactate and as it leaves the muscle cells it reduces the pH of the blood. The increased Ca^{2+} levels in active muscle cells are also important for stimulating the breakdown of muscle glycogen by phosphorylase, and increasing the rate of glycolysis by stimulating phosphofructokinase.

Oxidative phosphorylation in muscle

When muscle cells have to rely on substrates from outside the cell the maximum rate of ATP production is only about 40% of that from muscle glycogen. This is true for the complete oxidation of blood glucose as well as for the β-oxidation of fatty acids. Nevertheless, as will be considered in the next section, the rate at which both glucose and fatty acids are supplied to muscle can be increased substantially by the actions of insulin, glucagon, adrenaline and noradrenaline. These hormones have the effect of increasing the rate of entry of energy-supplying substrates from the blood. Insulin does this by mobilizing additional GLUT 4 transporters to the plasma membrane, thereby increasing the rate of glucose entry. Glucagon and adrenaline stimulate the release of glucose from the liver and noradrenaline stimulates the hormone-sensitive lipase, causing the release of fatty acids from adipose tissue. Thus, glucagon and adrenaline effectively raise the circulating levels of glucose, which increases its entry into the muscle cells. Noradrenaline has a similar effect on the level of fatty acids in the blood. As soon as fatty acids enter the muscle cell they are converted into fatty acyl-CoA at the expense of ATP, so that increasing the concentration of fatty acids in the blood increases the concentration gradient into the cell and therefore the rate of entry.

In addition to the problems of substrate supply, the rate of substrate oxidation by muscle cells is limited by the rate at which oxygen can be supplied to the mitochondria from the blood. However, the blood supply to muscles can be substantially increased by the release of adrenaline and the stimulation of the sympathetic nervous system. In addition, the supply of oxygen to striated muscle mitochondria is aided by the presence of myoglobin. Because it is a monomer the oxygen dissociates from myoglobin at a much lower concentration than it does from haemoglobin. As a consequence myoglobin stores oxygen when the rate of utilization is low and releases it when the demand for oxygen by muscle mitochondria has reduced the cytoplasmic oxygen concentration to a very low level.

8.6 The relative importance of glucose, fatty acids and ketone bodies as energy-supplying substrates for muscle

Since muscle can make such a heavy demand on the available energy-supplying substrates, as indicated in Table 5.1, it must be able to use different substrates depending on their availability. The capacity of individual muscle fibres to use a range of substrates is somewhat limited by the type of fibre, as indicated at the beginning of this chapter. The type I and type IIA (oxidative) fibres are the most versatile since they have a good oxidative capacity and stores of both glycogen and triacylglycerol. Type IIB (glycolytic) fibres are more restricted in the substrates they can use because they have a low oxidative capacity and do not store triacylglycerol. Cardiac muscle can oxidize a wide range of substrates but because it lacks adequate glycogen stores it is not adapted to carry out anaerobic glycolysis.

Since striated muscles are composed of a mixture of the three main fibre types it is possible for the muscles to alter their substrate utilization to reflect what is available. For long periods of sustained exercise it is necessary for the muscles to rely on the major energy stores in the body. As indicated in Table 5.2 the main store of energy-supplying substrates is the triacylglycerol in adipose tissue. The only other quantitatively significant form of stored energy is muscle protein, but the body does not rely on this source of substrate except under conditions of starvation.

Which energy-supplying substrates will muscle use?

For a slow rate of muscle contraction in a well-fed individual the main choice of energy substrates is between glycogen, glucose and fatty acids. In the resting state it is likely that both glucose and fatty acids from the blood will contribute most of the substrate. In this way the stores of glycogen and triacylglycerol in the muscle will be preserved. Immediately after a meal the choice between the two substrates will depend largely on the blood glucose concentration, since high levels of glucose are accompanied by a rise in insulin levels which increases the rate of glucose entry and inhibits fatty acid utilization. With a normal blood glucose level fatty acids may become the favoured substrate, particularly if circulating levels of chylomicrons or VLDL are high. Under these conditions the increased rate of fatty acid entry will inhibit glucose utilization in muscle. Low blood glucose levels are associated with an elevation of glucagon and noradrenaline secretion which will stimulate glucose release by the liver and the release of free fatty acids from adipose tissue. Under these conditions, the increased entry of fatty acids will strongly inhibit glucose oxidation. During periods of mild starvation the release of fatty acids from adipose tissue will also lead to formation of ketone bodies by the liver, and these will also replace glucose as an oxidizable substrate. It has also been discovered that a rise in the circulating levels of ketone bodies reduces the rate of lipolysis in adipose tissue.

How does strenuous exercise change substrate utilization?

The pattern of substrate utilization changes dramatically with the initiation of severe exercise. In order to achieve a high rate of contraction the muscle will make use of its glycogen stores especially in the type IIB glycolytic fibres. However, long periods of hard exercise will mean that the major substrate must become fatty acid released from adipose tissue. Nevertheless, it is interesting to note that even in a prolonged period of severe exercise the muscles must continue to use a certain proportion of muscle glycogen as fuel in addition to the fatty acids.

The control processes responsible for the balance between the utilization of glycogen, glucose and fatty acids operate at several levels. An increase in the glucose concentration in the blood, particularly in the hepatic portal vein, causes a rise in insulin levels which stimulates glucose utilization in muscle and decreases the rate of triacylglycerol lipolysis in adipose tissue. Both of these effects are largely the result of an increased mobilization of the GLUT 4 transporters in both tissues by insulin. The effect of an increased availability of fatty acids is to reduce the rate of glycolysis by inhibiting hexokinase, phosphofructokinase and pyruvate dehydrogenase. This appears to be due to the increased production of acetyl-CoA as a consequence of the β-oxidation of the fatty acids in the mitochondrial matrix. This leads directly to the production of citrate which is transported out of the mitochondria in exchange for malate. In the cytoplasm the citrate inhibits phosphofructokinase, causing a rise in glucose-6-phosphate which inhibits hexokinase. The rise in matrix acetyl-CoA stimulates pyruvate dehydrogenase kinase to phosphorylate pyruvate dehydrogenase converting it into an inactive form. This change reduces the rate at which pyruvate is used as a substrate for the TCA cycle, and channels it into oxaloacetate to act as a catalyst for the oxidation by the cycle of the acetyl-CoA from fatty acids.

8.7 Amino acid metabolism in muscle

Branched chain amino acid metabolism

Muscle is the major site for the catabolism of the branched chain amino acids and the pathways are shown in Figure 8.5. These amino acids provide a considerable energy input for muscle cells. Both isoleucine and valine yield succinyl-CoA which, after conversion to phosphoenolpyruvate, can either serve as a source of

Muscle

Enzymes

Leucine

1. Leucine aminotransferase
2. 2–Oxoisovalerate dehydrogenase
3. Isovaleryl–CoA dehydrogenase
4. Methylglutaconyl–CoA carboxylase
5. Methylglutaconyl–CoA hydratase
6. Hydroxymethylglutaryl–CoA lyase

Valine

7. Valine aminotransferase
8. 2–Oxoisovalerate dehydrogenase
9. Acyl–CoA dehydrogenase
10. Enoyl–CoA hydratase
11. 3–Hydroxyisobutyryl–CoA hydrolase
12. 3–Hydroxyisobutyrate dehydrogenase
13. Methylmalonate semialdehyde dehydrogenase
14. Propionyl–CoA carboxylase
15. Methylmalonyl–CoA mutase

Isoleucine

16. Isoleucine aminotransferase
17. 2–Oxoisovalerate dehydrogenase
18. Acyl–CoA dehydrogenase
19. Enoyl–CoA hydratase
20. 3–Hydroxybutyrl–CoA dehydrogenase
21. Acyl–CoA acyltransferase

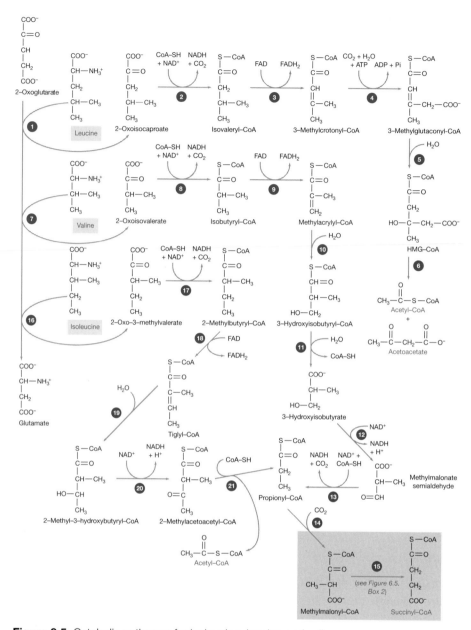

Figure 8.5 Catabolic pathways for isoleucine, leucine and valine.

acetyl-CoA for the TCA cycle or be converted into glycogen. Furthermore, isoleucine yields an additional acetyl-CoA. Leucine effectively forms three molecules of acetyl-CoA and all three pathways feed electrons into the respiratory chain so that they produce additional ATPs.

Muscle cells also have the potential to use a number of the common non-essential amino acids such as alanine, aspartate and glutamate as energy-supplying substrates. The use of amino acid carbon skeletons as an energy source could be particularly important during starvation in view of the fact that muscle provides the main source of mobilizable protein (see Table 5.2). However, there is a major difficulty for muscle and other tissues in using amino acids as an energy source because catabolism of all the amino acids releases ammonia which is potentially highly toxic. As a consequence it appears that, with the exception of the three branched chain amino acids, mobilization of muscle protein results in the release of the amino acids into the blood and their subsequent conversion into glucose or ketone bodies by the liver.

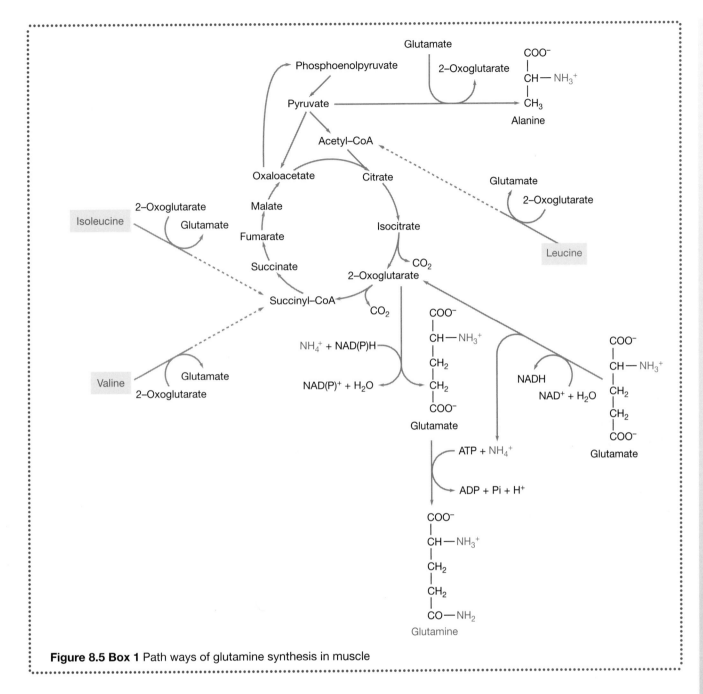

Figure 8.5 Box 1 Path ways of glutamine synthesis in muscle

Production of glutamine by muscle

Even when muscle is not suffering a net loss of protein it is still metabolizing the three branched chain amino acids in order to help maintain nitrogen balance. Consequently, muscle cells must have a mechanism for dealing with the nitrogen released during amino acid catabolism. Figure 8.5, Box 1, shows how the formation of glutamine is linked to the removal of amino groups during the catabolism of the three branched chain amino acids. The concentration of glutamine in the blood is higher than that of any of the other amino acids and represents about 20% of the total circulating amino acid. Muscle metabolism is the source of most of the vascular glutamine since a considerable proportion of the glutamine absorbed from the lumen of the small intestine is used as a substrate by the enterocytes. When nutrient absorption is not occurring the intestine metabolizes

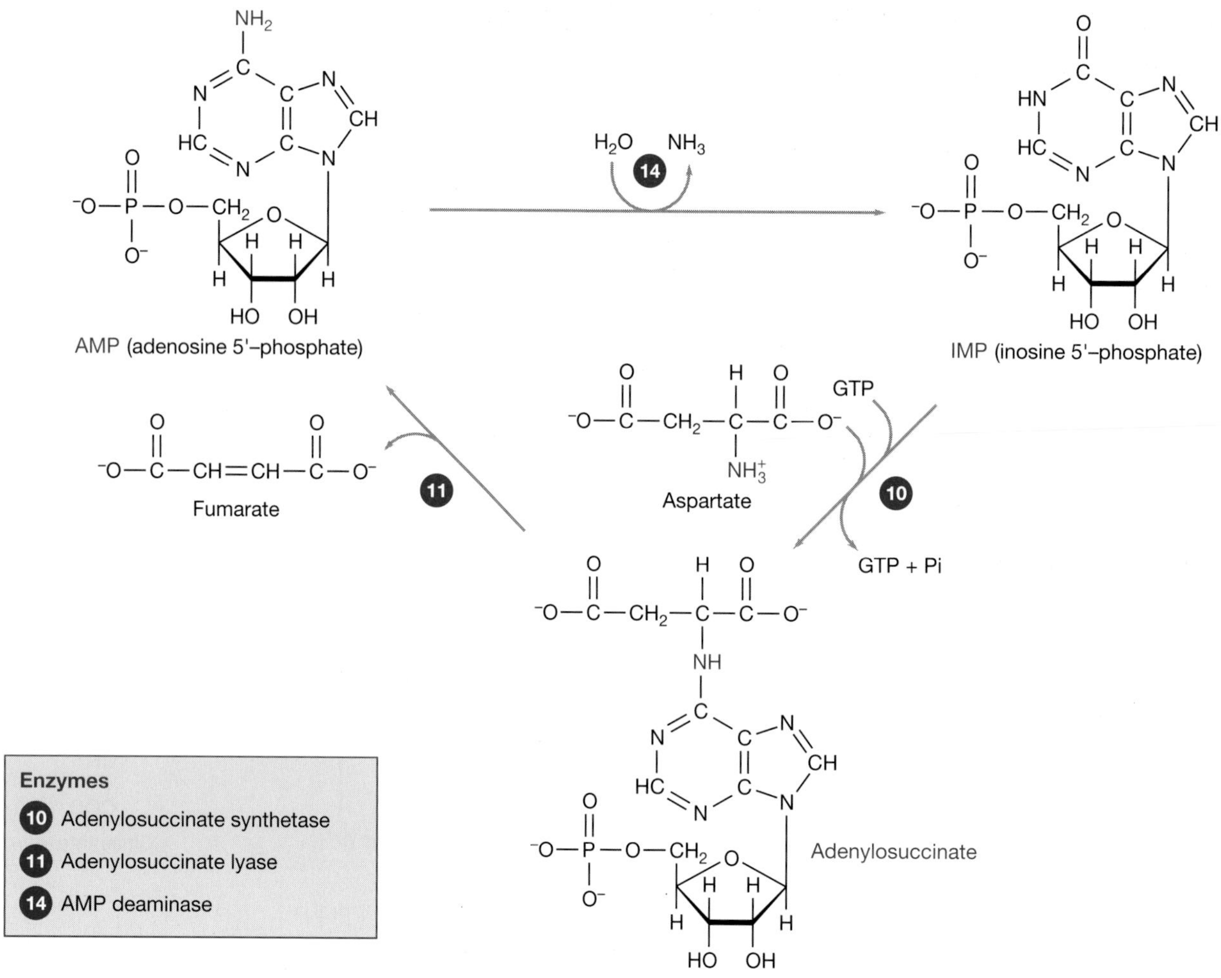

Figure 8.5 Box 2 The purine nucleotide cycle.

vascular glutamine and releases the nitrogen into the hepatic portal blood largely as alanine plus a small amount of ammonia.

The purine nucleotide cycle

Muscle cells are also a particularly active location for the purine nucleotide cycle in which AMP is deaminated to IMP and subsequently converted back into AMP at the expense of aspartate (see Figure 8.5, Box 2). Although some ammonia is released by muscle it appears that glutamine production is the main route used by muscle to export nitrogen. As indicated in the next section, alanine is also released by muscle, but this appears to be more closely related to the rate of glycolysis than to the rate of degradation of amino acids or purines.

8.8 Metabolic relationships between muscle and other tissues

Muscle depends on liver and adipose tissue for its substrate supply under normal conditions when nutrients are not being absorbed by the small intestine. The demand for substrate will be determined by the rate of muscle contraction. For the interactions shown in Figure 8.6 and described below a moderate level of exercise has been assumed.

The fast type IIB glycolytic fibres depend on their glycogen stores for substrate during contraction, but in order to replenish their glycogen they rely on glucose from the liver. This will be derived either from liver glycogen or by gluconeogenesis. The release of glucose by the liver is stimulated by the formation of cyclic AMP in response to adrenaline secreted by the adrenal medulla on stimulation by the nervous system. Glucagon secreted by the pancreas as a consequence of a drop in blood glucose also stimulates cyclic AMP formation and the release of glucose by the liver. It should be noted that the secretion of adrenaline will also stimulate the phosphorolysis of muscle glycogen to yield additional substrate for glycolysis even at high blood glucose levels.

The consequence of a high rate of glycolysis in muscle is the formation of a large amount of lactate which will be returned to the liver to serve as a substrate for gluconeogenesis. The newly formed glucose then comes back to the muscles forming a cycle known as the Cori cycle. In well-oxygenated muscle it is likely that a proportion of the pyruvate produced in glycolysis will be transaminated with glutamate or aspartate to form alanine. This also returns to the liver as a substrate for gluconeogenesis and has the added advantage that it also transports ammonia back to the liver for conversion into urea. The extent to which the glucose/

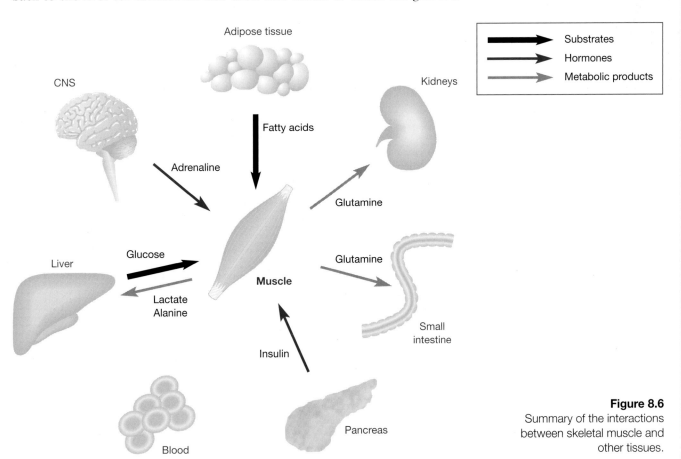

Figure 8.6
Summary of the interactions between skeletal muscle and other tissues.

alanine cycle operates between muscle and liver is uncertain. However it is important to note that for this cycle to operate, the NADH formed during glycolysis must be oxidized by the mitochondria through the glycerol-phosphate or malate–aspartate shuttles (see Figure 2.12).

For the type I fibres, type IIA oxidative fibres and cardiac muscle the supply of fatty acids from adipose tissue provides the major substrate input. The release of fatty acids by the hormone-sensitive triacylglycerol lipase in adipose tissue is promoted by glucagon, adrenaline and noradrenaline. As the level of fatty acids rises, the acetyl-CoA produced inhibits glycolysis in the oxidative fibres and promotes the utilization of fatty acids.

The relationships described above are altered during feeding and in the period immediately afterwards. Absorption of nutrients affects the utilization of both glucose and fatty acids. In the former case the increase in the glucose content of the hepatic portal blood stimulates the release of insulin by the pancreas. Although the insulin will inhibit glucose production by the liver, it also increases the uptake of glucose into muscle and adipose tissue. As a consequence fatty acid release from adipose tissue will be inhibited and muscle will obtain more of its ATP from glucose catabolism. However, the release of chylomicrons rich in triacylglycerol from the intestine will provide the muscles with an alternative source of fatty acids and counteracts the effects of insulin to some extent.

Nitrogen metabolism in muscle is largely governed by two factors: the levels of essential amino acids in the circulation, and the need to prevent the ammonia content of muscles from rising to toxic levels. If excessive levels of the three branched chain amino acids are present they will be degraded and the nitrogen exported in the form of glutamine. On the other hand, if there is a deficiency of essential amino acids, protein synthesis in muscle slows and there is a net release of virtually all amino acids. Some glutamine formation will occur during any period of exercise in order to ensure that ammonia is exported from the muscle in a non-toxic form. Once the glutamine is released it will either be used in the kidneys to prevent the urine from becoming too acid, or as a substrate for the formation of alanine in the small intestine.

EXERCISES

1. What is the distinction between type I and type IIA muscle fibres?

2. What is the relationship between ATP and phosphocreatine in supplying energy for muscle contraction?

3. What is responsible for the power stroke in the cross-bridge cycle?

4. How does a nerve impulse initiate contraction of a muscle fibre?

5. Why are transverse tubules important in large muscle fibres?

6. What is the role of calsequestrin?

7. How does insulin influence glucose metabolism in muscle cells?

8. What does muscle contribute to whole body amino acid metabolism?

9. Why do muscle cells produce glutamine?

10. Distinguish between the Cori cycle and the glucose/alanine cycle.

Further reading

Cooke, R. (1997) Actinomycin interactions in striated muscle. *Physiological Reviews* **77**, 671–697.

Frayn, K.N. (1996) *Metabolic Regulation: A Human Perspective*, Portland Press, Chapter 7.

Fritta, R.H. (1994) Cellular mechanisms of muscle fatigue. *Physiological Reviews* **74**, 49–94.

Juel, C. (1997) Lactate-proton cotransport in skeletal muscle *Physiological Reviews* **77**, 321–358.

Rayment, I. *et al*. (1993) Structure of the actin–myosin complex and its implications for muscle contraction, *Science* **261**, 58–65.

Snell, K. (1979) Alanine as a gluconeogenic carrier, *Trends in Biochemical Sciences* **4**, 124–128.

Stryer, L. (1995) *Biochemistry*, 4th edition, W.H. Freeman, Chapter 15.

Sugi, H., ed. (1992) *Muscle Contraction and Cell Motility*, Springer-Verlag.

The pancreas

Pancreatic secretions play a key role in digestion and metabolic control. The pancreas secretes enzymes responsible for the digestion of starch, lipids, proteins and nucleic acids.

Maintenance of a stable blood glucose concentration is dependent on the pancreatic hormones insulin and glucagon.

9.1 Pancreatic secretions are important for nutrient absorption and the control of blood glucose concentration

The pancreas has two main functions, exocrine production of enzymes and endocrine formation of hormones. The digestive enzymes are synthesized and secreted by pancreatic acinar cells, and the hormones glucagon and insulin are formed and released by the α-cells and β-cells, respectively, of the islets of Langerhans. As indicated in Figure 9.1, these processes make protein synthesis one of the key features of pancreatic metabolism.

Pancreatic digestive enzymes play a crucial role in the digestion of all the major types of food: starch, lipids, protein and nucleic acids. The release of the digestive enzymes into the top end of the small intestine allows the products of digestion to be absorbed by the intestine as soon as they are released. Absorption of the products of pancreatic enzyme digestion by the intestinal epithelium is preceded by further hydrolysis by membrane-bound enzymes in some cases (see Chapter 10).

Another feature of the pancreatic digestive enzymes is that they are most active at neutral pH. Consequently, it is essential that the pH of the acidic stomach contents is adjusted to neutral as they enter the intestine. This is accomplished by the secretion of bicarbonate by the pancreas. Since the digestive enzymes secreted by the pancreas are active at the pH of the pancreatic juice, it is essential that the proteases are released in an inactive form in order to avoid damage to pancreatic tissue. The enzymes are not activated until they reach the small intestine.

Scattered among the groups of polarized acinar cells the pancreas has specialized islet cells which are responsible for the secretion of insulin and glucagon. Insulin is a small protein consisting of two polypeptide chains, but it is synthesized as proinsulin, a single polypeptide chain, which is processed within the β-cells prior to release as insulin. Glucagon is a polypeptide rather than a protein, but is nevertheless formed as a normal gene product. The islets of Langerhans

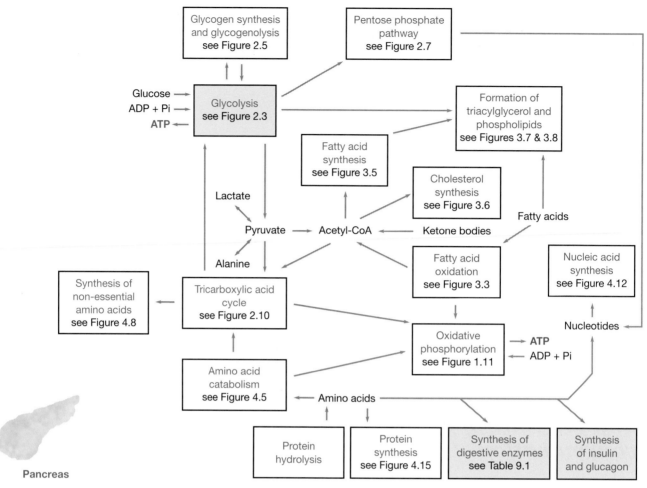

Figure 9.1 Summary of metabolism in the pancreas. Blue areas show the important role of the pancreas in synthesizing digestive enzymes and the hormones responsible for regulating blood glucose concentration.

cells have the high K_m GLUT 2 glucose transporter so that, like the liver, the cytoplasmic glucose concentration in these cells will reflect that in the blood. This enables the β-cells to respond to a high glucose level by secreting insulin, whereas the α-cells release glucagon when the glucose concentration is low.

9.2 Structure and organization of the pancreas

The pancreas is located below the liver and stomach, and one end is closely applied to the top end of the small intestine, known as the duodenum. Most of the pancreas consists of the enzyme-producing acinar cells. These cells are clustered around small ducts which join to form the single large pancreatic duct (see Figure 9.2). Just before the pancreatic duct enters the duodenum it joins the bile duct so that the pancreatic juice is mixed with bile as it enters the small intestine. The endocrine cells of the pancreas are dispersed around the organ in clusters of cells known as the islets of Langerhans. Each group of cells appears to be responsible for the synthesis of a single hormone. The α-cells form glucagon and the β-cells produce insulin. A third type of islet cell, the γ-cells, are responsible for the

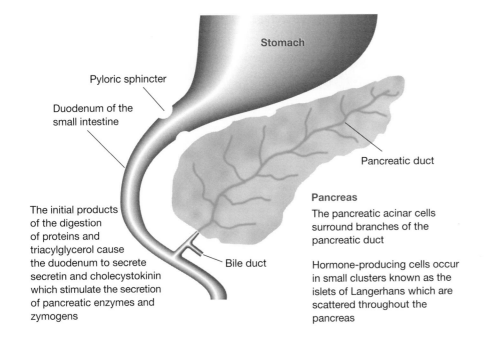

Stomach

Pyloric sphincter

Duodenum of the
small intestine

The initial products
of the digestion
of proteins and
triacylglycerol cause
the duodenum to secrete
secretin and cholecystokinin
which stimulate the secretion
of pancreatic enzymes and
zymogens

Bile duct

Pancreatic duct

Pancreas

The pancreatic acinar cells
surround branches of the
pancreatic duct

Hormone-producing cells occur
in small clusters known as the
islets of Langerhans which are
scattered throughout the
pancreas

Figure 9.2
Schematic diagram of the pancreas
showing its relationship to the top of
the small intestine.

formation of somatostatin, which stimulates pancreatic growth and appears to suppress the secretion of insulin and glucagon.

9.3 Production of digestive enzymes by the acinar cells

The pancreas synthesizes a wide range of enzymes which are involved in the digestion of all the major dietary constituents. Table 9.1 lists the digestive enzymes produced by the pancreatic acinar cells together with their substrates and products. Because the optimal activity of pancreatic digestive enzymes is pH 7.4, the proteolytic enzymes, such as trypsin and chymotrypsin, could destroy the secretory cells that are forming them. In order to prevent this from occurring the proteolytic enzymes are synthesized as proenzymes or zymogens, which are inactive forms of the enzymes. The proteolytic enzymes are activated by the removal of short peptide segments.

Because the presence of food in the digestive tract is episodic, secretion of the enzymes must be controlled so that they are released when they are required. Figure 9.3 indicates that this is achieved by the accumulation of membrane-bound secretory vesicles or granules at the apex of the acinar cells. When the cells receive an appropriate signal, either a nerve impulse or a hormone binding to a specific receptor, the secretory vesicles empty their contents into the pancreatic duct.

The proteolytic enzymes are secreted in an inactive form

Table 9.1 indicates that it is only the proteolytic enzymes which are released from the pancreas as proenzymes. Trypsin turns out to be a special case. Because trypsinogen can be activated by a very small amount of active trypsin, the pancreatic cells also synthesize a specific protein inhibitor which binds very

Table 9.1 Digestive enzymes synthesized by the pancreatic acinar cells together with their substrates and products

Enzyme (zymogen)	Substrate	Products
Amylase	Starch	Maltose
Isomaltase	Starch	Glucose, maltose
Trypsin (trypsinogen)	Protein	Oligopeptides
Chymotrypsin (chymotrypsinogen)	Protein	Oligopeptides
Elastase (proelastase)	Protein	Oligopeptides
Carboxypeptidases (procarboxypeptidases)	Proteins, peptides	Amino acids
Lipase	Triacylglycerol	Fatty acids, monoglycerides
Phospholipase	Phospholipids	Lysophospholipids
Cholesterylester hydrolase	Cholesteryl esters	Fatty acids, cholesterol

Pancreas

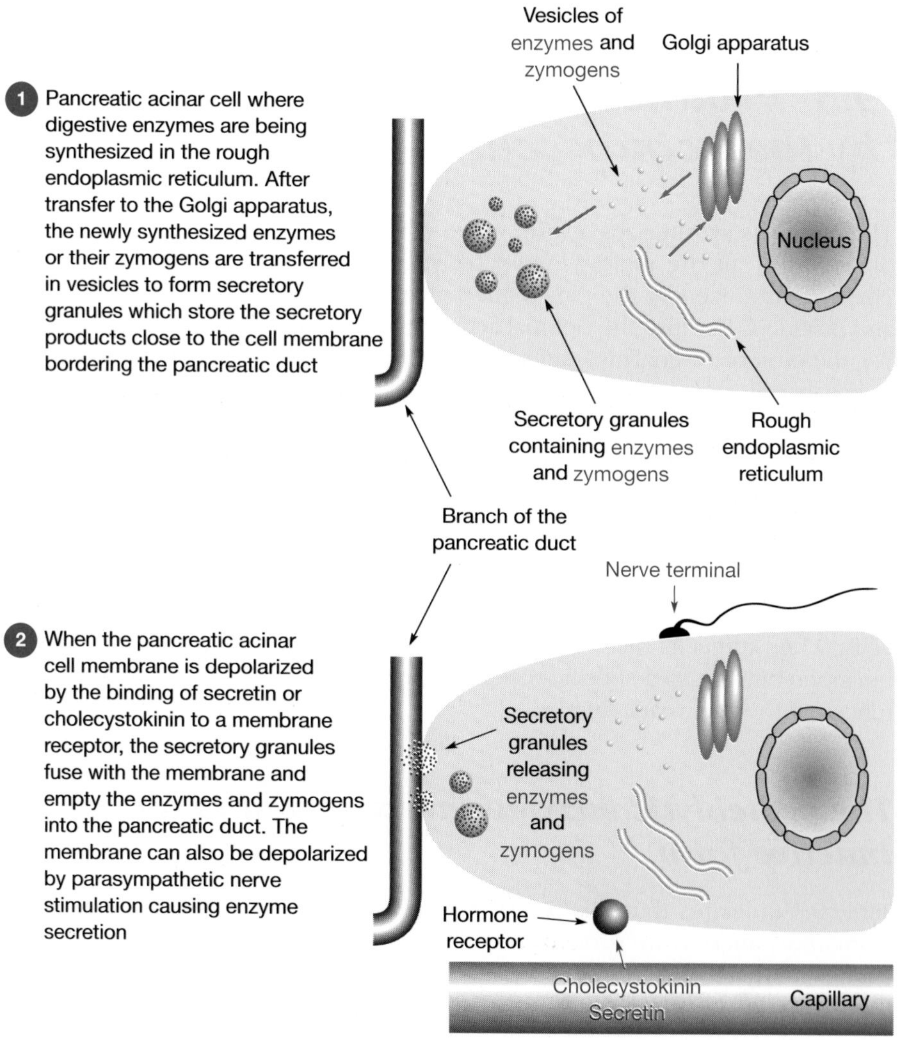

1 Pancreatic acinar cell where digestive enzymes are being synthesized in the rough endoplasmic reticulum. After transfer to the Golgi apparatus, the newly synthesized enzymes or their zymogens are transferred in vesicles to form secretory granules which store the secretory products close to the cell membrane bordering the pancreatic duct

Vesicles of enzymes and zymogens   Golgi apparatus

Nucleus

Secretory granules containing enzymes and zymogens

Rough endoplasmic reticulum

Branch of the pancreatic duct

Nerve terminal

2 When the pancreatic acinar cell membrane is depolarized by the binding of secretin or cholecystokinin to a membrane receptor, the secretory granules fuse with the membrane and empty the enzymes and zymogens into the pancreatic duct. The membrane can also be depolarized by parasympathetic nerve stimulation causing enzyme secretion

Secretory granules releasing enzymes and zymogens

Hormone receptor

Cholecystokinin Secretin

Capillary

Figure 9.3
Steps involved in the biosynthesis and release of digestive enzymes by the pancreatic acinar cells.

tightly to the active site of trypsin. This inhibitor prevents the activation of the trypsin until it reaches the lumen of the intestine. Trypsin itself, as soon as it is active, also converts chymotrypsinogen, proelastase and the procarboxypeptidases into their active forms. The most active of the proteases are the endopeptidases trypsin and chymotrypsin which split proteins into oligopeptides. C-terminal amino acids are removed from these protein fragments by the two carboxypeptidase enzymes. Many of the dipeptides and tripeptides produced by the pancreatic enzymes are absorbed intact by the intestinal epithelium with hydrolysis taking place inside the mucosal epithelial cells (see section 10.5).

Pancreatic enzymes are responsible for the hydrolysis of starch, lipids and nucleic acids

Amylase, isomaltase, ribonuclease and the pancreatic lipases are secreted in their active forms by the pancreas. Amylase is responsible for splitting the α–1, 4-glycosidic bonds in starch and the isomaltase is required to split the α–1, 6-glycosidic bonds. The principal dietary nucleic acid is RNA, which is converted into 3'-nucleotides by the pancreatic ribonuclease.

In addition to the triacylglycerol lipase the pancreas also secretes a phospholipase and a cholesterylester hydrolase. As indicated in Table 9.1 the pancreatic lipase converts triacylglycerol into a mixture of fatty acids and monoglycerides. The pancreatic phospholipase only removes the fatty acid from carbon 2 of the glycerol-producing lysophospholipids as the product for absorption. Cholesterylester hydrolase splits the cholesteryl esters to yield cholesterol and a free fatty acid.

Digestion of dietary lipids would be very slow without the presence of the bile salts secreted by the liver. As indicated above, the pancreatic juice enters the intestine together with the bile salts and the detergent effects of the bile salts emulsify the dietary lipid. This increases the surface area available for the action of the three pancreatic lipases (see section 10.4).

9.4 Hormonal and nervous control of the release of pancreatic digestive enzymes

Two peptide hormones, secretin and cholecystokinin, which are responsible for stimulating the release of the pancreatic enzymes, are formed by cells at the upper end of the small intestine. Secretin, which also stimulates the secretion of bicarbonate by both the pancreas and the liver, is probably produced in response to acid entering the duodenum. The main stimulus for cholecystokinin secretion is the presence of the products of protein and triacylglycerol digestion.

Food at the upper end of the small intestine also provides sensory input to the CNS. As a consequence the parasympathetic neurones which innervate the pancreas are probably stimulated. This could depolarize the acinar cell membranes, causing the release of the pancreatic enzymes from the zymogen granules at the apical surface of the cell (see Figure 9.3).

9.5 Biosynthesis of insulin by pancreatic β-cells: control of insulin release

Although mature insulin molecules have two polypeptide chains, insulin is synthesized as a single polypeptide, proinsulin. In order to convert proinsulin into the active hormone a connecting peptide must be removed. This process is completed before the hormone is released into the vascular system.

The main control of insulin release is the concentration of glucose reaching the β-cells. Because the GLUT 2 transporter on the β-cells has a high K_m the glucose content of the cells will reflect that in the blood. As the glucose level rises it is metabolized more rapidly by glucokinase and, as indicated in Figure 9.4, this increases the concentration of glucose-6-phosphate and stimulates glycolysis. The resulting rise in the ATP/ADP ratio inhibits the ATP-sensitive K^+ channels. This inhibition depolarizes the β-cell membrane causing voltage-dependent Ca^{2+} channels to open. The rise in cytoplasmic Ca^{2+} causes the release of insulin from the storage granules by facilitating their fusion with the plasma membrane. The increase in cytoplasmic glucose and the decline in the level of stored insulin stimulate additional insulin biosynthesis. Increased levels of circulating amino acids also stimulate the release of insulin and, although the mechanism responsible for this effect is not clearly understood, it seems probable that this stimulation is a consequence of an elevation in the ATP/ADP ratio because of increased amino acid metabolism. It is also possible that the higher amino acid levels stimulate insulin synthesis in the β-cells.

The other way in which the release of insulin from the pancreatic β-cells can be controlled is through the autonomic nervous system (see section 11.2). During the digestion of food the parasympathetic pathways are stimulated and the resulting release of acetylcholine stimulates the β-cells to release stored insulin. The β-cells are also innervated by neurones from the sympathetic nervous system, and these are stimulated during strenuous activity or when the individual is experiencing stress or excitement. The sympathetic nerve terminals release noradrenaline and the receptor for this neurotransmitter inhibits insulin release.

9.6 Synthesis of glucagon by the α-cells: regulation of glucagon secretion

The polypeptide hormone glucagon has 29 amino acids and is synthesized by the pancreatic α-cells. Like insulin, it is stored in vesicles near the cell membrane and released into the blood in response to changes in the circulating glucose concentration. However, in this case a rise in glucose concentration inhibits release of glucagon, and a drop in blood glucose stimulates its secretion. Because of the close link between the pancreas and the liver through the hepatic portal vein, glucagon secretion will cause a rapid rise in cyclic AMP in the liver. This stimulates glycogenolysis and gluconeogenesis, thus limiting the potential harm to the body of a sudden drop in blood glucose.

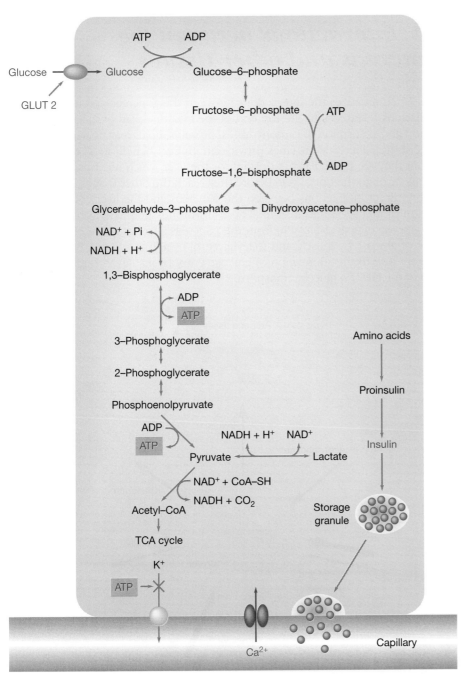

Pancreas

The GLUT 2 transporter has a high K_m so that increases in blood glucose concentration will increase the cytoplasmic glucose concentration in the β-cells. As a consequence the rate of glycolysis will rise and increase the ATP/ADP ratio. This inhibits K^+ channels and the resulting fall in membrane potential opens Ca^{2+} channels, stimulating insulin release.

Figure 9.4

The synthesis, storage and controlled release of insulin by pancreatic β-cells.

9.7 Interactions between the pancreas and other tissues

Figure 9.5 summarizes the interactions between the pancreas and other tissues. The enzymes released into the top end of the intestine play a crucial role in the digestion and absorption of carbohydrates, proteins, lipids and nucleic acids. The actions of the pancreatic enzymes provide an indirect benefit to all the other tissues, but they are particularly important for the liver which receives many of the nutrients through the portal vein before they reach the other tissues.

More direct interactions between the pancreas and the liver come from the secretion of glucagon and insulin. These hormones help the liver to regulate blood glucose effectively. Insulin from the pancreas also has major effects on the storage of glucose by muscle and triacylglycerol by adipose tissue. Both of these effects are due to the stimulation of glucose entry by insulin through the mobilization of the GLUT 4 glucose transporter.

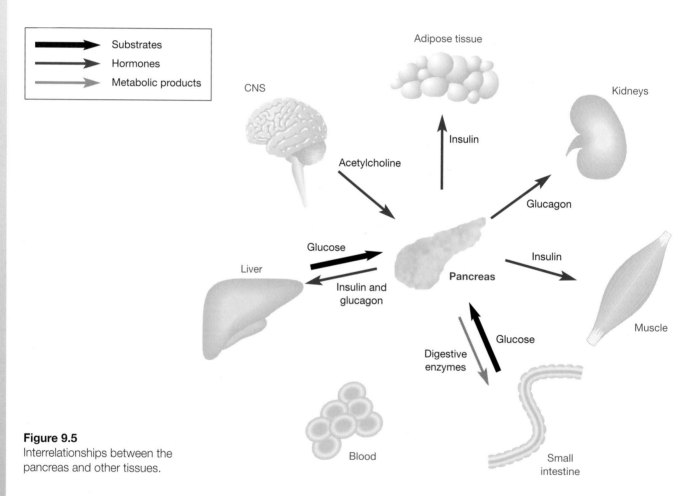

Figure 9.5
Interrelationships between the pancreas and other tissues.

EXERCISES

1. Why are the pancreatic proteases secreted in the form of inactive zymogens?

2. Describe the signals that cause the pancreatic acinar cells to secrete enzymes and zymogens.

3. How do rising vascular glucose levels stimulate the release of insulin by the pancreas?

4. Give the names and functions of the pancreatic enzymes responsible for the digestion of dietary lipids.

5. What is the role of isomaltase secreted by the pancreas?

Further reading

Frayn, K.N. (1996) *Metabolic Regulation: A Human Perspective*, Portland Press, Chapter 4.

Holz, G.G. & Habner, J.F. (1992) Signal transduction crosstalk in the endocrine system: β-cells and the glucose competence concept, *Trends in Biochemical Sciences* **17**, 388–393.

Neurath, H. (1989) Proteolytic processing and physiological regulation, *Trends in Biochemical Sciences* **14**, 268–271.

Newgard, C.B. & McGarry, J.D. (1995) Metabolic coupling factors in pancreatic β-cell signal transduction, *Annual Review of Biochemistry* **64**, 689–719.

White, D.A. & Baxter, M., eds (1994) *Hormones and Metabolic Control*, 2nd edition, Arnold, Chapter 6.

Intestinal metabolism and nutrient absorption

The small intestine is responsible for the absorption of nutrients and its metabolism helps to moderate the distortion of metabolite levels that results from feeding.
The intestine helps to protect the body from harmful agents ingested with food.

10.1 Summary of the functions of the small intestine

At first sight the function of the small intestine is self-evident: the digestion and absorption of food. However, careful consideration reveals that the intestine has two other important functions. It plays a significant role in nutrient homeostasis, and it also helps to protect the body from harmful agents ingested with food. There are important differences in the time scale over which these three functions operate. The digestion and absorption of food is obviously only important after a meal, but the homeostatic and protective functions operate continuously.

The basic structure of the small intestine with its great length and large surface area is designed to promote absorption. However, some of the detailed features of intestinal structure such as the tight junctions between cells, the mucous layer on the surface and the close packing of the microvilli aid the barrier function and serve to reduce the rate of nutrient absorption and increase its selectivity.

Figure 10.1 summarizes the main features of metabolism carried out by the enterocytes. It is important to recognize that these intestinal epithelial cells have a high rate of metabolism in order to support the transport processes associated with nutrient absorption. These cells also have a high rate of protein synthesis during the two to three days from their formation in the crypt region until they are sloughed off from the villus tips. The digestion, absorption and subsequent metabolism of carbohydrates, proteins, lipids and nucleic acids by the small

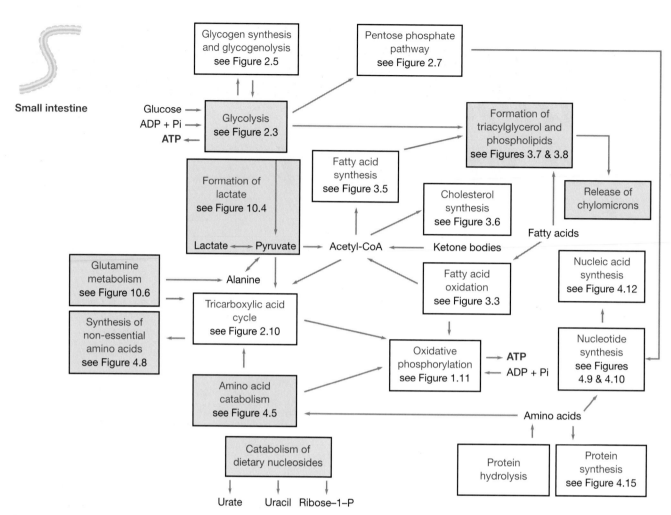

Figure 10.1 Summary of metabolism in the small intestine. The blue areas indicate those pathways that are particular features of intestinal metabolism.

intestine are handled in different ways as shown in Table 10.1. The differences are a consequence of the physical characteristics of each nutrient or its constituents, as well as their eventual fate and their metabolic roles.

Absorption of nutrients

For sugars and amino acids the rate of absorption is increased by the location of the final stages of digestion on the mucosal surface of the epithelial cells or within these absorptive cells, called enterocytes. Locating the final stage of digestion on the surface of the enterocytes or in the cytoplasm serves to increase the speed of absorption by raising the inwardly directed gradient of solute concentration. In the case of vitamins, which may only be present in the diet in minute concentrations, conversion to a coenzyme or its precursor within the enterocyte also helps to increase the rate of entry by keeping down the vitamin concentration in the cytoplasm.

Phospholipids and triacylglycerols are at least partially degraded in the intestinal lumen by the pancreatic lipases. Metabolism within the mucosal cells converts these molecules back into phospholipids and triacylglycerols for transport in the form of chylomicrons through the lymph to join the general circulation beyond the liver.

Table 10.1 Digestion and absorption of carbohydrates, lipids, proteins and nucleic acids in the small intestine

Nutrient	Intestinal lumen	Brush border membrane	Cytosol	Basolateral membrane
Starch	Amylase splits starch to maltose; isomaltase splits 1,6 branches	Maltase splits maltose to glucose (transported by Na^+-dependent SGLT1)	Some metabolism of glucose to lactate	Facilitative exit of glucose by GLUT 2
Sucrose	Sucrose	Sucrase splits it to glucose (SGLT1) + fructose (transported by GLUT 5)	Some glucose and most fructose converted to lactate	Facilitative exit of glucose and fructose by GLUT 2
Lactose	Lactose	Lactase splits lactose to glucose (SGLT1) + galactose (transported by SGLT1)	Some lactate from glucose; galactose unchanged	Facilitative exit of glucose and galactose by GLUT 2
Protein	Trypsin and chymotrypsin split proteins to dipeptides and tripeptides plus amino acids	Na^+-dependent amino acid transport; peptides transported by PepT1 with protons to give a net charge of +1	Some amino acids converted into protein or to other amino acids; peptides split to amino acids	Exit of amino acids by amino acid transport or exchange
Nucleic acids (mainly RNA)	Ribonuclease splits RNA to 3'-nucleotides	Split to nucleosides by phosphatase; Na^+-dependent nucleoside uptake	Phosphorolysis to bases + ribose-P; purines to urate, pyrimidines to uracil	Facilitative exit of urate and uracil
Triacylglycerol (TAG)	Bile salts help lipase to split TAG to free fatty acids (FFA) and monoacylglycerol	Uptake of monoacyl-glycerol and FFA leaving bile salts to be absorbed in the ileum	Reconversion of monoacylglycerol and FFA to TAG	Exit of TAG into lymph as chylomicrons
Phospholipids and cholesterol	Phospholipase converts phospholipids to monoacylphospholipids and FFA	Uptake of monoacyl-phospholipids and cholesterol	Reconversion of monoacylphospholipids to phospholipids	Phospholipids and cholesterol exit in chylomicrons

SGLT1 = Na^+–glucose cotransporter; PepT1 = intestinal peptide transporter; GLUT 2 = high K_m hexose transporter; GLUT 5 = fructose transporter.

In the case of the 3'-nucleotides released from nucleic acids by the pancreatic nucleases, metabolism within the enterocyte prevents most of the nucleobases from entering the bloodstream. This protects the intercellular messenger role of nucleosides such as adenosine, and also prevents the incorporation of modified dietary purines and pyrimidines into nucleic acids.

Homeostasis

The contribution of the intestine to nutrient homeostasis is carried out in collaboration with the liver. During feeding the intestine eases the nutrient load on the liver in three ways. A proportion of the glucose and fructose intake is converted into lactate which allows some of the carbohydrate to enter the metabolic pathways in the liver at the level of the TCA cycle rather than through glycolysis. Most dietary lipids are released into the lymph as chylomicrons after they are absorbed, and this enables them to bypass the liver so that the constituent fatty acids are delivered directly to adipose tissue or muscle. The peptides formed from dietary protein by pancreatic proteases are completely converted to amino acids during passage from the lumen to the hepatic portal circulation. However, during this transfer amino acid metabolism in the intestine brings the composition of the amino acid mixture closer to that of the physiological mixture present in blood plasma. Even when food is not being absorbed the intestine continues to generate lactate and alanine plus ammonia (from glucose and glutamine, respectively) to serve as substrates for the synthesis of glucose and urea by the liver. It also removes purines and pyrimidines from the blood and converts them to uric acid and uracil, respectively.

The barrier function

Protection of the body against pathogens and foreign antigens by the digestive tract is provided by acid secretion in the stomach and enzymatic hydrolysis of proteins and nucleic acids in the small intestine. The small intestine also has a highly developed system for the production of antibodies to foreign antigens ingested with food. The secretion of mucus and the effectiveness of the junctions between the epithelial cells also contribute to the barrier function of the intestine. The lower end of the digestive tract, particularly the large intestine, is colonized by benign bacteria such as *Escherichia coli*.

10.2 Structural organization of the small intestine

The small intestine begins at the pyloric sphincter which controls the movement of food out of the stomach. There are three distinct sections of the intestine starting with the duodenum, followed by the jejunum and ending with the ileum which joins the large intestine at the ileo-caecal junction. The duodenum is responsible for the secretion of cholecystokinin and secretin that control pancreatic secretions, and this is where the pancreatic juice and the bile enter the intestine. Most of the absorption of the constituents of dietary carbohydrates, lipids and proteins occurs in the jejunum. The remaining products of the various digestive enzymes and surplus bile salts are absorbed in the ileum.

The structure of the mammalian small intestine is illustrated by the scanning electron micrographs of rat intestine shown in Figure 10.2. Fundamentally the small intestine can be considered as two concentric tubes. The outer one consists of three layers of muscle each of which is oriented in a different direction so that contraction causes the tube to writhe about, a process known as peristalsis. The inner tube consists of a single layer of epithelial cells, with a surface area several times that of the outer tube. As a consequence the inner layer is thrown into folds which start in the crypt region and extend into the interior, or lumen, of the tube as villi. The space between the two layers is filled with connective tissue, blood vessels, lymph ducts, nerve cell processes and lymphocytes.

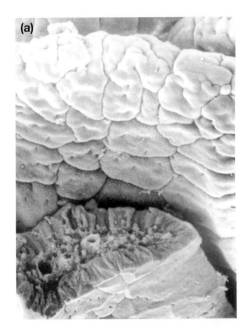

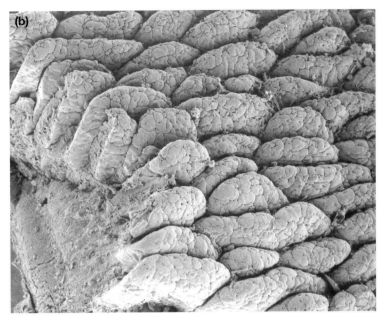

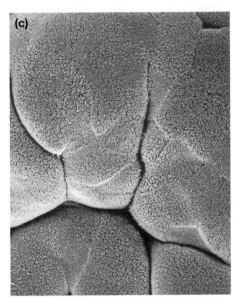

Figure 10.2
Scanning electron micrographs
of the small intestine.
(a) Cross-section of a villus
showing the epithelial layer and
submucosal tissue × 400.
(b) Low power view of the luminal
surface showing the ranks of villi
and underlying muscle layers × 112.
(c) High power view of the brush
border surface of a villus × 2200.
(Micrographs supplied by P.G.
Humpherson.)

Enterocytes are formed in the crypt region

The crypt region of the epithelium contains undifferentiated stem cells which
have a rapid rate of cell division. After new cells are formed, they migrate up the
villi and differentiate rapidly into mature enterocytes. Maturation of the enterocytes produces both structural and functional changes. The apical surface of each
cell proliferates to form tightly packed microvilli, the brush border, which mas-
sively increases the cell surface area. The microvilli retain their regular shape
because they contain actin filaments. Movement of the cells up the villi occurs
along the connective tissue layer at the base of the cells. Each cell is linked to the
four or five adjacent cells by spot desmosomes around the lateral membranes.
Most of the luminal surface of the small intestine consists of the absorptive cells,
or enterocytes. However, two other cell types are scattered among the enterocytes: goblet cells and M cells. The goblet cells are responsible for the mucous
secretion which lubricates the passage of food down the intestine, and also cre-

ates an unstirred layer over the surface of the microvilli. The thin M cells lack microvilli, and they can take in large foreign antigens by endocytosis and deliver them to antibody-producing cells immediately below the epithelial layer.

Functional differentiation of the enterocytes also occurs as the cells migrate up the villi. One of the most impressive examples is the Na^+-dependent glucose transporter (SGLT1, see section 10.3). This transporter is not present on the apical membranes of the enterocytes as they leave the crypts, and it only reaches its maximal expression per unit of membrane area when the cells reach the upper half of the villus. A number of other transporters and membrane-bound enzymes show a similar pattern of expression as the enterocytes mature.

Tight junctions link the enterocytes together

The other link between each enterocyte and its neighbours is provided by tight junctions which divide the lateral membranes from the microvilli on the apical face of each cell. Membrane constituents found in the apical membrane do not mix with those in the basolateral membrane below the tight junctions. As their name implies, the tight junctions provide an effective barrier to the movement of most ions and substances with a molecular weight of 100 or more. The tight junctions consist of five to seven rows of protein dimers (one protein monomer from each cell), and the tightness of the junction depends on the number of protein rows.

Small intestine

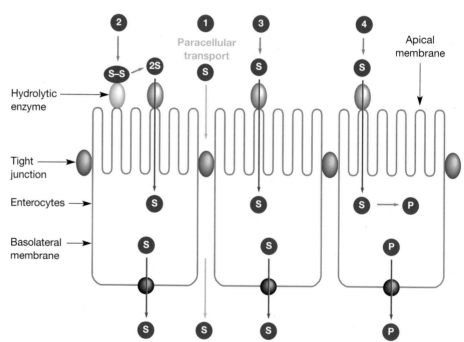

S Solute

S–S Solute with two or more transportable units

P Metabolic product produced from the solute

Apical membrane transporter

Basolateral membrane transporter

Types of transepithelial transport

1 In paracellular transport the solute passes between the cells without entering the enterocytes so that no metabolism can take place in the epithelial layer.

2 Some multiple unit substrates are hydrolysed on the apical membrane and then the solute is immediately transported into the enterocyte cytoplasm.

3 A solute that is transported through the enterocyte unchanged may have to enter against a gradient if its concentration on the basolateral side is high.

4 If a solute is immediately converted to a product when it enters the cell, it will be transported into the enterocyte down a concentration gradient.

Figure 10.3(a)
Examples of paracellular transport, transcellular transport and the link between absorption and metabolism.

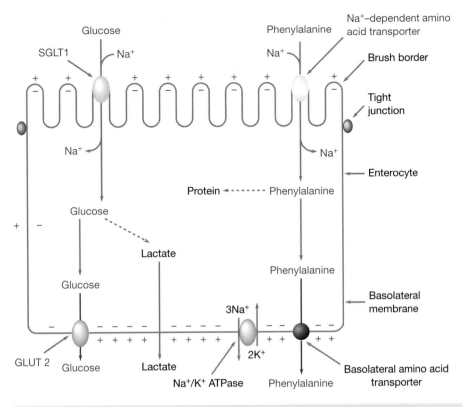

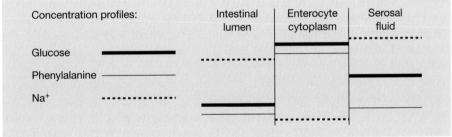

Small intestine

Figure 10.3(b)
Absorption of glucose and
phenylalanine against a
concentration gradient.

In mammalian intestine the tight junctions normally allow the transfer of water and some ions, including chloride and Na$^+$ by the paracellular route (Figure 10.3a). The fact that the tight junctions are permeable to water means that the direction and rate at which water moves across the epithelial layer will be determined by the difference in osmolarity across the tight junctions. Normally, as the result of solute uptake across the brush border and its subsequent transfer out of the enterocytes across the basolateral membrane, the osmolarity on the inside of the epithelial layer will be higher than that in the lumen so that water will be absorbed. The absorption of water will be increased if the intestinal contents are diluted by the consumption of water. Some intestinal diseases, such as cholera, result in the secretion of solutes into the lumen of the intestine, increasing the luminal osmolarity. This results in the loss of body fluids into the intestine causing diarrhoea. Any breakdown in the effectiveness of the tight junctions has serious consequences, if it permits the entry of foreign antigens into the blood.

The core of the villus

Each villus is served by an arteriole which feeds into the capillary bed. The capillaries are drained by a venule which empties into the hepatic portal vein leading to the liver. As a complement to its vascular supply each villus is drained by a lymph vessel which feeds into the main lymphatic system. The lymph fluid leaving the villi carries the chylomicrons formed by the enterocytes from dietary lipids. The lymph bypasses the liver and empties into the vascular system in the thoracic region. In addition, villi are well supplied with the axons and dendrites of motor and sensory neurones.

10.3 Digestion, absorption and metabolism of carbohydrate by the intestine

The principal dietary carbohydrate is starch

Starch is degraded to water-soluble glucose molecules prior to absorption by the enterocytes. This occurs in two steps: first the starch is degraded to maltose by pancreatic amylase, and to a mixture of glucose plus maltose by isomaltase. Then maltase, which is a membrane-bound enzyme on the luminal face of the enterocyte, converts the disaccharide into glucose. Since glucose is one of the major substrates used by intestinal cells, as well as most others in the body, it would seem reasonable that it should be phosphorylated immediately by ATP upon entry into the mucosal cells (as is the case in muscle). However, the eventual destination of much of the dietary glucose is the blood, where the glucose concentration is maintained at about 5 mM. Consequently, when glucose is being absorbed, the mucosal cells maintain an intracellular glucose concentration above 5 mM so that the sugar can be moved out into the circulatory system across the basolateral membrane by facilitated transport using the GLUT 2 transporter. This, in turn, necessitates an active Na^+-dependent transporter on the luminal surface of the enterocytes, known as SGLT1, which enables glucose to be accumulated by the enterocytes against a concentration gradient. This type of transport process is known as secondary active transport because, as Figure 10.3(b) shows, the driving force for glucose entry is provided by the movement of Na^+ ions down a concentration gradient into the cell. ATP supplies the energy for glucose transport indirectly through the Na^+/K^+ ATPase which pumps the Na^+ out across the basolateral membrane.

The fact that glucose is an important energy-providing substrate for the intestinal cells allows a second route for the assimilation of glucose carbons, as indicated in Figure 10.3(b). Most of the glucose metabolized by the intestine is converted into lactate (Figure 10.4) even though there is no shortage of oxygen in the small intestine. The lactate then passes directly via the hepatic portal vein to the liver where it can be converted into glycogen or glucose. In this way the intestine is able to obtain much of the ATP it needs without oxidizing any of the glucose carbons. Another consequence of this aerobic glycolysis is to keep down the intracellular glucose concentration, thereby increasing the rate of glucose uptake from the lumen by reducing the concentration gradient against which it must be accumulated.

Absorption of disaccharides

The other two major carbohydrates present in the diet are the disaccharides lactose and sucrose, and these are initially handled in the same way as maltose. The disaccharidases lactase and sucrase, like maltase, are anchored to the brush border membrane projecting into the lumen. The glucose derived from both

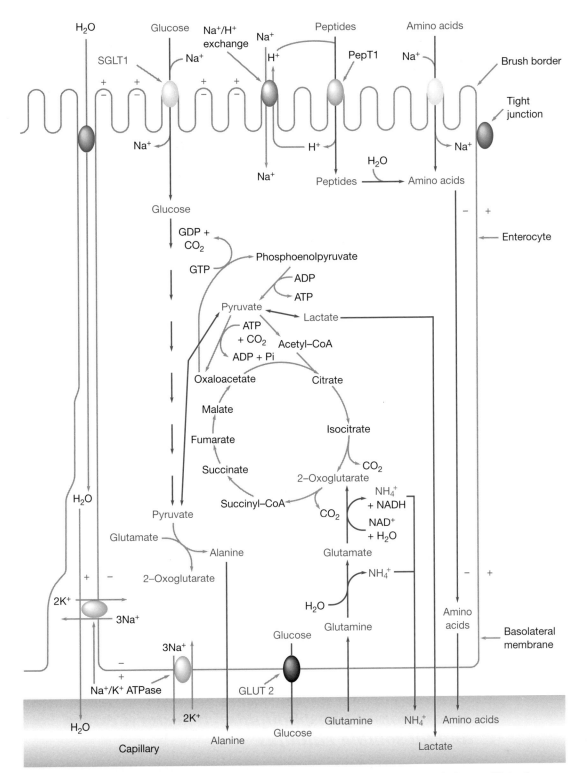

Figure 10.4 The relationship between absorption of nutrients and their metabolism in the small intestine.

lactose and sucrose is, of course, handled in exactly the same way as that from maltose. However, the other two hexoses, galactose and fructose, are treated differently. This is possible because neither of these hexoses is present in the blood at a controlled concentration. Galactose is transported into the entero-cytes by the SGLT1 transporter used by glucose, but because the galactose concentration in the blood is close to zero, it is not necessary for the enterocytes to accumulate this hexose to a high concentration or to metabolize it. Fructose, on the other hand, enters the mucosa by a separate facilitative transporter (GLUT 5) and much of it is metabolized to lactate. The remaining free fructose and the galactose move down a concentration gradient from the enterocytes into the blood by the GLUT 2 facilitative hexose transporter used by glucose. Galactose is then removed from the portal blood by the liver where it is phosphorylated by galactokinase and enters the glycolytic pathway at the glucose-1-phosphate level. When fructose enters the liver it is phosphorylated by fructokinase, bypassing the control point in the glycolytic pathway. Fructose can also be removed by adipose tissue where the facilitative fructose transporter found in intestine is also expressed.

10.4 Digestion and absorption of lipids

Triacylglycerol absorption

The principal dietary lipid is triacylglycerol which is only slightly soluble in water and must be absorbed by a different technique from that used for carbohydrates. The first step in the digestion and absorption of triacylglycerol is partial hydrolysis to monoacylglycerol plus free fatty acids (Table 10.1). The hydrolysis is due to the action of pancreatic lipase secreted into the duodenum, but it would be very slow except for the presence of the bile salts which serve to emulsify the triacylglycerol so that the surface available for lipase action is much increased. The bile salts also combine with the hydrolysis products forming small mixed micelles. When the micelles reach the surface of the enterocytes in the jejunum the absorption of free fatty acids and monoacylglycerol occurs leaving the bile salts to be absorbed in the ileum. Uptake of the free fatty acids is promoted by the presence of a fatty acid-binding protein in the enterocyte cytoplasm, which effectively keeps the cytosolic fatty acid concentration very low, as does the conversion of free fatty acids into fatty acyl-CoA at the expense of ATP (Eqs 3.1 and 3.2). Entry of the hydrolysis products is also promoted by the rapid reconversion of the monoacylglycerol and fatty acids into triacylglycerol. The triacylglycerol then leaves the enterocytes, in association with phospholipid and cholesterol, in the form of the large lipoprotein complexes called chylomicrons (Figure 10.5). In effect, the overall mechanism of triacylglycerol transfer from the intestinal lumen to the blood can be summarized as a rapid partial hydrolysis, transfer into the enterocyte, resynthesis and release as a lipoprotein complex.

Absorption of phospholipids, cholesteryl esters and fat-soluble vitamins

The processes responsible for the digestion and absorption of phospholipids are similar to those for triacylglycerol. Only one of the fatty acids is removed by the pancreatic phospholipase and the resulting lysophosphatidic acid is then reabsorbed and converted back into phospholipid for the formation of chylomicrons. Cholesteryl esters are hydrolysed in the lumen and the free cholesterol and fatty acids are absorbed. Although some free cholesterol is released in the chylomicrons, most is converted back into cholesteryl esters.

The uptake of the fat-soluble vitamins (A, D, E and K) also occurs in the mixed micelles responsible for monoacylglycerol uptake. Furthermore, it is likely

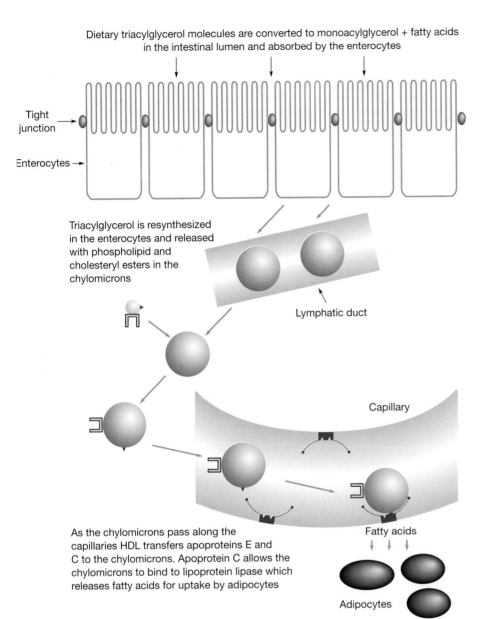

Dietary triacylglycerol molecules are converted to monoacylglycerol + fatty acids in the intestinal lumen and absorbed by the enterocytes

Tight junction →

Enterocytes →

Triacylglycerol is resynthesized in the enterocytes and released with phospholipid and cholesteryl esters in the chylomicrons

Lymphatic duct

Capillary

As the chylomicrons pass along the capillaries HDL transfers apoproteins E and C to the chylomicrons. Apoprotein C allows the chylomicrons to bind to lipoprotein lipase which releases fatty acids for uptake by adipocytes

Fatty acids

Adipocytes

Small intestine

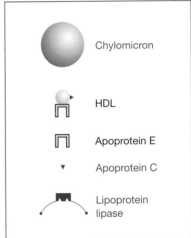

Chylomicron

HDL

Apoprotein E

Apoprotein C

Lipoprotein lipase

Figure 10.5
The steps involved in the absorption of triacylglycerol by the intestine and its transfer to adipose tissue in chylomicrons.

that the transfer of most of these minor constituents into the bloodstream is by way of the chylomicrons entering the lymph circulation.

10.5 Peptide absorption is the major route for amino acid uptake

The mechanism responsible for protein absorption is different from that for the absorption of carbohydrates and lipids. The ultimate aim is to supply the body with the constituent amino acids and to ensure that complete proteins are not absorbed, since they would have serious immunological consequences. Because of the presence in the intestinal lumen of vicious proteases, it might be reasonable to expect that proteins were completely degraded to amino acids before absorption. However, enterocytes have a high rate of protein synthesis so that they must maintain relatively high cytosolic amino acid levels. As a consequence,

243

uptake of amino acids would have to occur against large concentration gradients. This problem is overcome by partial hydrolysis of the proteins to dipeptides and tripeptides. This process is much more rapid than full hydrolysis, and is followed by absorption of the peptides. Once inside the cytosol the peptides are immediately hydrolysed to free amino acids, ensuring that the peptides are always entering the mucosa down a concentration gradient (Figure 10.6). The fact that the bulk of amino acid uptake occurs in the form of peptides also means that it is not influenced by the intracellular concentrations of individual amino acids, ensuring that all 20 amino acids will be taken up in proportion to their prevalence in dietary proteins. Exit of the amino acids from the mucosal cells into the blood is also down a concentration gradient.

The initial recognition that peptide uptake was likely to be an important route for the uptake of amino acids by the mammalian small intestine came from the observation that the amino acids from orally ingested protein appeared in the blood more quickly than the time required for complete protein hydrolysis by the principal pancreatic proteases, trypsin and chymotrypsin. Since the enterocyte cytosol contains a range of peptidases, peptide uptake is normally followed by rapid hydrolysis. However, the presence of peptidases on the luminal face of the enterocytes means that the hydrolysis of some peptides prior to uptake remains probable.

Small intestine

This example shows the transport of a neutrally charged dipeptide which requires the cotransport of a single proton. For a peptide with a net charge of −1 the cotransport of two protons occurs. No proton cotransport is needed for a peptide with a net charge of +1.

Transporters:

Na⁺/H⁺ exchange

Na⁺/K⁺ ATPase

Peptide transporter (PepT1)

Basolateral amino acid transporter

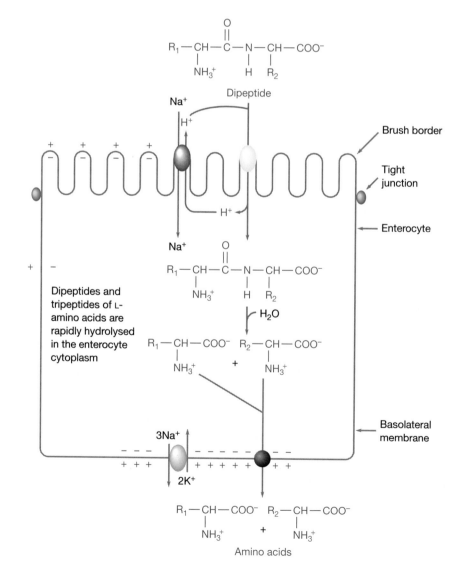

Figure 10.6
Peptide transport and hydrolysis in the small intestine.

Characteristics of the peptide transporter

The identification and expression cloning of the PepT1 transporter from rabbit, rat and human small intestine has demonstrated unequivocally that dipeptides and tripeptides can be transported into enterocytes prior to hydrolysis. Uptake experiments with hydrolysis-resistant dipeptides has shown that transport of all peptides by the intact intestinal epithelium, and by the cloned transporter expressed in oocytes, is associated with the entry of positive charges (i.e. it is electrogenic). For neutral dipeptides the dipeptide uptake requires the cotransport of one proton, and for dipeptides with a net negative charge there is cotransport of two protons. On the other hand, a dipeptide with a net positive charge may not require any proton cotransport. These observations indicate that the uptake of short peptides by the peptide transporter requires the combination of peptide and transport protein to have a net charge of $+1$. The fact that proton cotransport is required for the uptake of most dipeptides and tripeptides indicates that the rate of absorption will be increased by a decrease in luminal pH. It was pointed out in the last chapter that the pancreatic juice neutralizes the acid coming from the stomach. However, it has been shown that the pH of the unstirred layer that covers the microvilli in the intestine is about 6. This reduction in pH is the result of the exit of protons from the enterocytes in exchange for the entry of Na^+ ions as indicated in Figure 10.6.

The absorption of intact peptides provides a number of advantages as a method of amino acid uptake. As pointed out above, it avoids the absorption of the amino acids against large concentration gradients. This is particularly important in the case of the two acidic amino acids, aspartate and glutamate, which are present in the enterocytes at concentrations in the range of 3–5 mM. Secondly, the fact that some of the less common essential amino acids, such as tryptophan or methionine, are absent from many dietary proteins means that they would also have to be absorbed against a relatively large concentration gradient, if they were not absorbed as peptides. In effect the absorption of amino acids from dietary proteins in peptide form means that uptake of the various amino acids is not controlled by the free amino acid concentrations in the enterocytes.

Amino acid absorption

Despite the strong evidence that peptide transport provides the major route for amino acid absorption by the small intestine, it is clear that the enterocytes have amino acid transporters on the brush border and the basolateral membranes that enable the cells to accumulate amino acids against a concentration gradient. Table 10.2 lists the amino acid transporters that have been identified on the plasma membranes of most mammalian cells. These transporters are present on the basolateral membranes of the enterocytes, and it seems likely that most are also expressed on the brush border. Transport studies in the small intestine have shown that the uptake of most individual amino acids against a concentration gradient requires the cotransport of Na^+ ions, and follows the pattern shown for phenylalanine in Figure 10.3(b). The other point which has important implications for amino acid absorption is the length of the small intestine. Most of the sugars and short peptides are absorbed in the jejunum, and as the longer peptides move down the intestine they come in continual contact with the peptidases on the brush border surface. Thus it is probable that much of the Na^+-dependent amino acid absorption will take place in the ileum.

Table 10.2 Amino acid transporters

Name	Amino acid type	Substrate	Na$^+$-dependent
System Gly	Neutral	Gly, sarcosine	Yes
System A	Neutral	Most neutral amino acids	Yes
System ASC	Neutral	Most amino acids	Yes
System N	Neutral	His, Gln, Asn	Yes
System L	Neutral	Leu, Ile, Met, Trp, Val	No
System y$^+$	Positively charged	Arg, Lys, His	No
System X	Negatively charged	Asp, Glu	Yes
System β	Neutral	β-Ala, taurine	Yes

10.6 Amino acid absorption and metabolism

Amino acid metabolism in the small intestine serves two main purposes: adjustment of the composition of the amino acid mixture released into the hepatic portal vein, and the metabolism of glutamine.

Glutamine metabolism

Perhaps the most crucial feature of intestinal amino acid metabolism is the conversion of glutamine into alanine (Figure 10.7). It was pointed out in Chapter 8 that substantial amounts of glutamine are formed in muscle, partly as a consequence of the metabolism of the branched chain amino acids. Increased muscular activity also results in the production of additional glutamine in order to detoxify the NH$_3$ released by the purine nucleotide cycle. It will be shown in Chapter 11 that the CNS also releases substantial amounts of glutamine in order to rid itself of potentially toxic NH$_4^+$ ions.

Amino acid homeostasis

The alterations in the composition of the amino acid mixture released by the small intestine can occur in several ways. If there are deficiencies in the levels of the more common non-essential amino acids, these are synthesized by the pathways shown in Figure 4.8. This is particularly likely to occur in the case of the two acidic amino acids that can be synthesized from glutamine (Figure 10.7) or any of the other amino acids that contribute TCA cycle intermediates. On the other hand, if any of the non-essential amino acids are present in excess they will be converted into alanine for export to the liver. Most of the essential amino acids are not catabolized by the intestine so that increased absorption of these amino acids would be balanced by further synthesis of the common non-essential amino acids. However, a shortage of absorbed essential amino acids is likely to result in a reduction in the rate of protein synthesis and additional catabolism of non-essential amino acids so that a reasonably normal mixture of amino acids enters the portal vein.

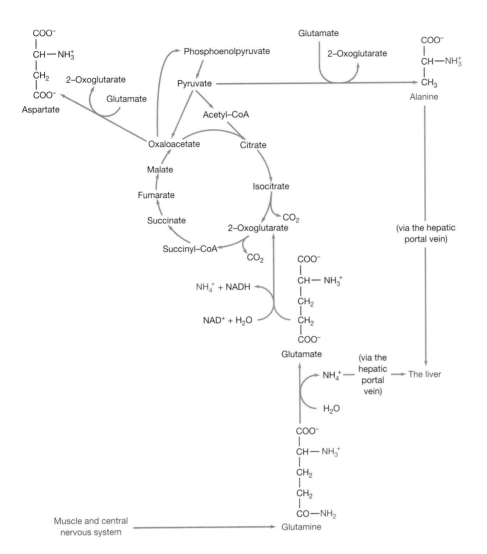

Small intestine

Figure 10.7
Special features of amino acid metabolism in the small intestine including the metabolism of glutamine as a major energy source.

10.7 Digestion and absorption of nucleic acids

Nucleic acids, chiefly RNA molecules, form another significant constituent of the diet, and again a different strategy is employed for their digestion and absorption. The complete hydrolysis of RNA to 3'-nucleotides occurs in the lumen through the action of pancreatic ribonuclease. This is followed by removal of the phosphate from the nucleotides by a brush border phosphatase to form the four ribonucleosides. As with peptide absorption, uptake of the nucleosides is rapidly followed by their catabolism within the enterocytes. This involves phosphorolysis within the cytosol to form the nucleobases plus ribose-1-phosphate (Figure 10.8). All mammalian cells except red blood cells can synthesize their own nucleotides, and the dietary nucleobases are largely degraded rather than made available to the body for RNA synthesis. This probably helps to ensure that no modified bases are incorporated into nucleic acids. Figure 10.8 shows that adenosine and guanosine, the two purines, are degraded to urate by the enterocytes, whereas the pyrimidines are converted into uracil which is then degraded to β-alanine in the liver. Cytidine, one of the two main pyrimidine nucleosides, is poorly absorbed by the intestine. Thus, the general strategy for digestion and absorption of the

Small intestine

Basolateral anion transporter

Nucleoside transporter

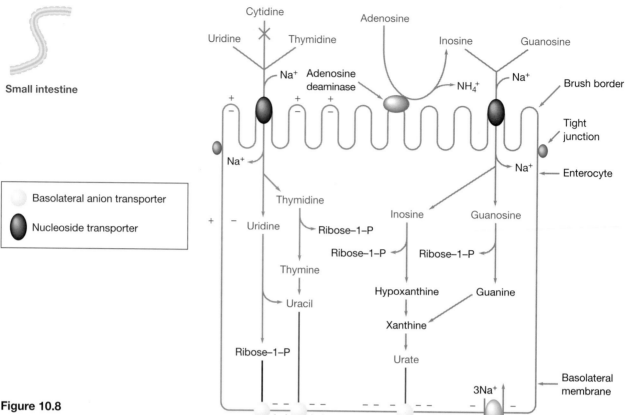

Figure 10.8
Intestinal absorption and metabolism of nucleosides.

nucleic acids is hydrolysis followed by metabolic degradation to ensure that the dietary nucleotides, nucleosides or nucleobases (except uracil) do not enter the general circulation.

10.8 Uptake of B vitamins

Specific transporters have been identified in the apical membrane for the uptake of many of the water-soluble B vitamins. The main difficulty with the absorption of these important coenzyme precursors is that the capacity of these transporters is very low. As a consequence, it is important that the intestine should receive low levels of the B vitamins on a regular basis. This does not present a problem for individuals whose diet contains substantial amounts of fresh vegetables.

Uptake of many of the B vitamins is helped by their rapid conversion into metabolites after uptake, since this prevents absorption occurring against a concentration gradient. Figure 10.9 shows that thiamine, nicotinic acid and folate are all converted into derivatives after absorption. It is clear, however, that in these three cases only the free vitamin can be transferred out of the enterocyte across the basolateral membrane. Once the vitamin structure has been modified to form a coenzyme it remains trapped within the enterocyte. It is important that the coenzymes are prevented from leaving the enterocytes because they are essential for the metabolic pathways.

Small intestine

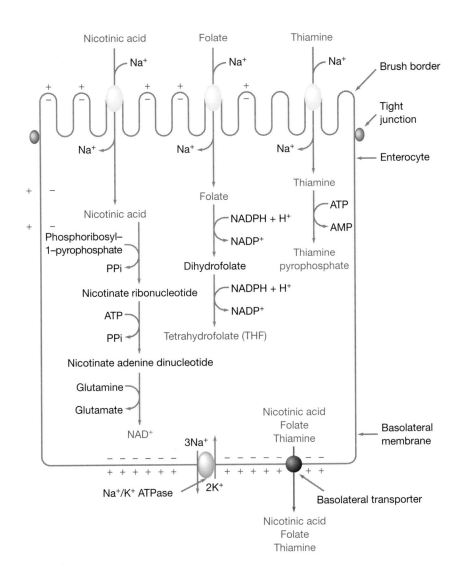

Figure 10.9
Absorption and metabolism of B vitamins in the small intestine.

10.9 The small intestine's contribution to nutrient homeostasis

The intestine makes a number of contributions to nutrient homeostasis during the absorption of food. The most important of these changes are the conversion of glucose and fructose into lactate, and the conversion of excess non-essential amino acids (especially glutamine) into alanine. These changes simplify the metabolic burden imposed on the liver during nutrient absorption by supplying it with lactate and alanine from which pyruvate can easily be formed. Pyruvate is the liver's most versatile metabolite because it can be used to satisfy almost any of the metabolic demands which the body is making on the liver. Thus, it can serve as the substrate for the TCA cycle, for the synthesis of glucose or glycogen, for the formation of fatty acids, ketone bodies or cholesterol and for the formation of all but two of the non-essential amino acids.

The conversions of glucose to lactate and glutamine to alanine by the intestine continue even when the absorption of food is no longer taking place. These processes allow the intestine to obtain its supply of ATP while at the same time feeding the liver with versatile substrates. In order to permit the liver to convert the excess nitrogen released from amino acids and nucleotides into urea it is essential for the nitrogen present in glutamine to be converted into a form that can enter the urea cycle. By converting it into alanine plus ammonia the intestine provides the substrates for the synthesis of carbamoyl-phosphate and for the transamination of oxaloacetate to aspartate. It is important that the liver should not receive excessive levels of glutamine because it synthesizes glutamine from glutamate whenever the cytoplasmic NH_3 level in hepatocytes begins to reach toxic levels.

The barrier function of the small intestine continues to operate at all times to protect the body from the uptake of pathogens and foreign antigens. In part this function is provided by the integrity of the epithelial layer and its mucous covering. However, the thin-walled M cells help the intestine to produce and secrete immunoglobulin A (IgA) to deal with potentially harmful bacteria and other foreign antigens.

10.10 Interactions between the small intestine and other tissues during and after feeding

Figure 10.10 summarizes the relationship between the intestine and the other tissues. It is important to note that these interactions are most important during and immediately after feeding, although many of them continue between meals. Thus, the intestine always maintains a close association with the liver, by convert-

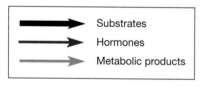

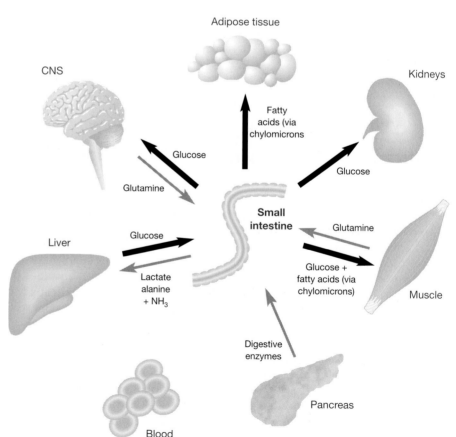

Figure 10.10

Interactions between the small intestine and other tissues.

ing glutamine into alanine plus ammonia, and glucose into lactate. It also continually recovers the bile salts from the lumen and returns them to the liver.

The absorption of food results in the transfer of glucose and chylomicrons to both muscle and adipose tissue. Also during carbohydrate absorption the intestine will transfer glucose to the pancreas signalling that insulin must be secreted. Despite these interactions with other tissues the intestine retains its close relationship to the liver during feeding by sending it the hexoses, amino acids and short-chain fatty acids that have been absorbed from the lumen.

EXERCISES

1. Compare the ways in which the intestine absorbs and metabolizes the three main dietary hexoses, galactose, glucose and fructose.

2. What is the driving force for water absorption by the intestine?

3. Since the absorption of most short peptides by the intestine is a proton-dependent process, explain what is responsible for the proton gradient across the luminal membrane of the enterocytes.

4. What is the role of bile salts in the digestion and absorption of dietary lipids?

5. What is the fate of dietary RNA in the small intestine?

6. How does the metabolism of glutamine by the intestine aid liver metabolism even when food is not being absorbed?

7. Show how the intestine forms ATP from ADP during the metabolism of glutamine to alanine.

8. What do the characteristics of B vitamin absorption tell us about the best way to acquire them from the diet?

9. List the principal ways in which the intestine helps to protect the body.

10. What is the fate of chylomicrons formed by the intestine?

Further reading

Bronk, J.R. & Hastewell, J.G. (1988) The transport of naturally occurring pyrimidine nucleosides by isolated rat jejunum, *Journal of Physiology* **395**, 349–361.

Bronk, J.R. & Hastewell, J.G. (1989) The transport and metabolism of the uridine mononucleotides by rat jejunum *in vitro*, *Journal of Physiology* **408**, 129–135.

Bronk, J.R. & Hastewell, J.G. (1989) The specificity of pyrimidine nucleoside transport and metabolism by rat jejunum *in vitro*, *Journal of Physiology* **408**, 405–411.

Deves, R. & Boyd, C.A.R. (1998) Transporters for cationic amino acids in animal cells: discovery, structure and function *Physiological Reviews* **78**, 487–545.

Ferraris, R.P. & Diamond, J. (1997) Regulation of intestinal sugar transport. *Physiological Reviews* **77**, 257–302.

Hediger, M.A. & Rhoads, D.B. (1994) Molecular physiology of sodium-glucose cotransporters. *Physiological Reviews* **74**, 993–1026.

Lister, N., Bailey, P.D., Collier, I.D., Boyd, C.A.R. & Bronk, J.R. (1997) The influence of luminal pH on transport of neutral and charged dipeptides by rat small intestine, *in vitro*, *Biochimica et Biophysica Acta* **1324**, 245–250.

Lister, N., Sykes, A.P., Bailey, P.D., Boyd, C.A.R. & Bronk, J.R. (1995) Dipeptide transport and hydrolysis in isolated loops of rat small intestine: effects of sterospecificity, *Journal of Physiology* **484**, 173–182.

Madara, J.L. (1998) Regulation of the movement of solutes across tight junctions. *Annual Review of Physiology* **60**, 143–159.

Malandro, M.S. & Kilberg, M.S. (1996) Molecular biology of mammalian amino acid transporters, *Annual Review of Biochemistry* **65**, 305–336.

Matthews, D.M. (1991) *Protein Absorption. Development and Present State of the Subject*, Wiley-Liss.

Meredith, D. & Boyd, C.A.R. (1995) Oligopeptide transport by epithelial cells, *Journal of Membrane Biology* **145**, 1–12.

Nicholls, T.J., Leese, H.J. & Bronk, J.R. (1983) Transport and metabolism of glucose by rat small intestine, *Biochemical Journal* **212**, 183–187.

Parsons, D.S. (1979) Fuels of the small intestinal mucosa, *Topics in Gastroenterology* **7**, 253–271.

Spring, K.R. (1998) Routes and mechanisms of fluid transport by epithelia. *Annual Review of Physiology* **60**, 105–119.

Stow, R.A. & Bronk, J.R. (1993) Purine nucleotide transport and metabolism in isolated rat jejunum, *Journal of Physiology* **468**, 311–324.

Temple, C.S., Bailey, P.D., Bronk, J.R. & Boyd, C.A.R. (1996) A model for the kinetics of neutral and ionic dipeptide–proton cotransport by the apical membrane of rat kidney cortex, *Journal of Physiology* **494**, 795–808.

Temple, C.S., Bronk, J.R., Bailey, P.D. & Boyd, C.A.R. (1995) Stoichiometry of proton:peptide co-transport depends on the substrate charge in the mammalian epithelial peptide transporter, *Pflugers Archiv* **430**, 825–829.

Metabolism and the central nervous system

Metabolically the CNS is one of the most active tissues in the body, although it is isolated from the vascular system by the blood–brain barrier.

The CNS regulates metabolism in the remainder of the body in three ways: (a) it stimulates hormone secretion as a result of monitoring circulating metabolite levels; (b) it can stimulate internal organs directly in response to changes in activity; (c) it can initiate an increase in the levels of energy-supplying substrates in anticipation of future activity.

11.1 Summary of the metabolism and functions of the central nervous system

At the most basic level the CNS can be considered as a communication centre which receives and evaluates sensory information from inside and outside the body, and which formulates and executes a response to this input through peripheral nerves. In mammals, however, the operation of the CNS is very complex. As a simple example, the brain can devise and hold in memory a complicated response to an anticipated event. This plan can be put into action and then rapidly altered on the basis of new information which may not have been anticipated. The CNS also regulates the metabolism and functions of internal organs through its control of the endocrine system.

Cell types in the central nervous system

From a metabolic point of view the cells in the CNS are of two main types: neurones, which are concerned with receiving and transmitting impulses, and glial cells, which are responsible for a wide range of metabolic processes necessary to support the neurones within the CNS. In order to transmit impulses neurones must maintain the Na$^+$ and K$^+$ gradients across their extensive membrane areas. This requires continual ion pumping and is largely responsible for the high metabolic rate of the brain shown in Table 5.1. Although the brain is only 2% of the body weight, it uses about 20% of the total oxygen consumed by the body at rest. The brain is richly supplied with arteries which branch from the carotid artery on each side of the head and these vessels provide the brain with the necessary oxygen and glucose to support its requirement for ATP. Figure 11.1 shows that the pathways responsible for supplying ATP are particularly important in the CNS, although specialized pathways are also required for the synthesis of neurotransmitters in order to transmit impulses from one neurone to another across a small gap called a synapse. In addition neurones must synthesize specific membrane receptors to bind incoming signal molecules. Like all other cells, those in the CNS are also continually renewing their membranes and other cell constituents.

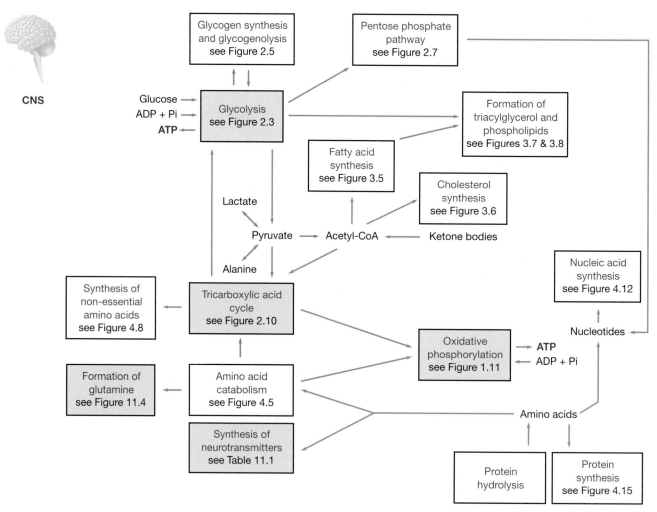

Figure 11.1 Summary of metabolism in the CNS. The blue areas show the pathways that are particularly important within the CNS.

Regulation of the endocrine system

The CNS also regulates metabolism through its neuronal connections to the endocrine system. For example, the secretion of adrenaline and noradrenaline occurs when the cells in the adrenal medulla are stimulated by neurones from the CNS. The neurones in the hypothalamus secrete a range of neuropeptides, some of which travel to the anterior pituitary by a small portal system, which begins with the capillaries in the hypothalamus, forms a single vessel and divides into a second capillary bed in the anterior pituitary. These neuropeptides stimulate the release of pituitary hormones that control a range of other endocrine glands and internal organs. In the posterior pituitary the nerve endings of other hypothalamic neurones secrete the peptide vasopressin which controls water reabsorption in the kidneys (see section 13.9).

Neuroglial cells

In addition to the impulse-transmitting neurones the CNS has large numbers of neuroglial support cells. Astrocytes help to supply substrates and remove waste products from the CNS. They also help to remove excess neurotransmitters and their breakdown products from the extracellular spaces around the neurones. This helps to maintain the high sensitivity of CNS neurones to incoming signals. Oligodendrocytes are responsible for synthesizing the myelin sheath that surrounds nerve axons and increases the speed at which nerve impulses travel along the axons.

The blood–brain barrier

The CNS is also protected from potentially harmful molecules circulating in the blood by the blood–brain barrier, a layer of endothelial cells joined by tight junctions. This barrier effectively prevents the entry of proteins and long-chain fatty acids unless they are transferred by endocytosis or specific transport mechanisms. Consequently the CNS cannot use fatty acids as a source of energy and must rely on blood glucose as its main energy-supplying substrate. The formation of ketone bodies in the liver from excess fatty acids protects the energy supply of the CNS during starvation. Ketone bodies can cross the blood–brain barrier and are readily metabolized by the mitochondria in nervous tissue. Some glucose is still required in order to maintain ATP levels by glycolysis in long axons and dendrites where mitochondria may be sparse. Amino acid metabolism in the CNS can also provide an energy source, but the utilization of amino acids in this way appears to be limited. This is probably because of the importance of many easily metabolized amino acids, such as glutamate, glycine and tyrosine, as neurotransmitters or their precursors.

Although the blood–brain barrier prevents the use of long-chain fatty acids as an energy source in the CNS, it is important to note that the formation and maintenance of neuronal and glial cell membranes and the insulating myelin sheath does require a supply of fatty acids and cholesterol. The cells of the CNS can synthesize cholesterol and most fatty acids from glucose and this explains why the composition of dietary fatty acids has no effect on the fatty acid composition of lipids in the CNS. However, in order to form membrane phospholipids a supply of essential fatty acids is still necessary. This is particularly important in the developing foetus and newborn child where rapid development of the CNS is occurring. Consequently it is probable that the blood–brain barrier has specific transport mechanisms for the delivery of essential fatty acids to the CNS.

11.2 Structure of the central nervous system and communication with other tissues

It is beyond the scope of this book to describe in any detail the structural organization of the CNS and its links to the rest of the body. The aim of this section is merely to give a brief overview of the organization of the brain and the remainder of the CNS in order to explain the purpose of the sections on neurone function and metabolism that follow. The brain controls the nervous system and the apex of this control is provided by the cerebral cortex. During neurosurgery it has been possible to identify particular areas of the cortex with the control of the muscles that move various parts of the body. Other areas of the cortex receive sensory input from the eyes and ears as well as from different areas of the skin and internal organs. However, there are also large parts of the cerebral cortex that have not been identified with particular sensory or motor activities and these are probably concerned with integration, evaluation, planning, memory, etc.

The brain

Figure 11.2 shows a cross-section of the human brain and the upper end of the spinal cord. The cerebral cortex of the brain is composed of a large number of different regions, and it is clear that the various areas of the cerebral cortex have a large number of neuronal interconnections. These interactions between the cortical areas are probably responsible for the intelligence of humans and their capacity to plan complicated future activities, rather than merely responding to sensory input. It seems likely that the more complex functions of the brain which are concerned with thoughts, emotion and memory are also a consequence of the vast numbers of interconnections between different areas of the brain. The loss of memory that occurs in Alzheimer's disease is probably associated with a reduction in the number of neurones in the hippocampus as well as in the cerebral cortex.

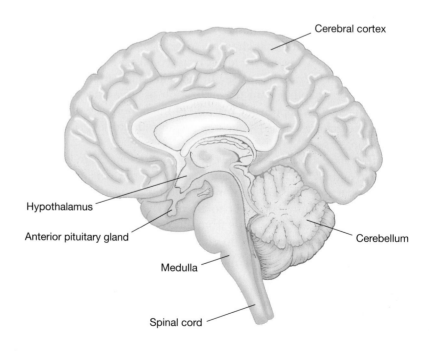

Figure 11.2
Diagram showing a cross-section of the brain and the top of the spinal cord. (Courtesy of Dr P.G. Strange.)

Other areas of the brain are concerned with the integration of impulses originating in the cortex. The cerebellum is responsible for the coordination of muscular activity but, with the exception of simple reflexes, the initiation of this activity comes from the cerebral cortex. The medulla is an enlarged area at the top of the spinal column and this is responsible for a number of simple reflexes. The axons of neurones which innervate muscles and internal organs travel down the spinal cord until they reach the appropriate level where they connect with the cell bodies of motor neurones that send their axons out of the spinal column to the muscles. Sensory neurones have their cell bodies in ganglia outside the CNS and send their axons into the spinal cord to connect with neurones of the CNS. Nervous control of the metabolism and functions of internal organs is achieved by two antagonistic groups of neuronal pathways originating in the CNS, the **sympathetic** and **parasympathetic** nervous systems.

The neuronal control of hormone secretion is organized by the hypothalamus. Secretion of neuropeptides by the hypothalamus occurs in response to the input from sensory neurones at various locations around the body. For example, if the salt content of the blood rises, this is detected by neurones which signal to the hypothalamus to secrete vasopressin into the bloodstream from the posterior region of the pituitary which increases reabsorption of water by the collecting ducts in the kidney.

The brain and the spinal cord are not in direct contact with the vascular system. They are suspended in a separate compartment filled with cerebrospinal fluid which provides the CNS with a stable extracellular fluid environment. This fluid surrounds the spinal cord, fills the brain cavities or ventricles, and separates the brain from the skull and protects it from physical damage. The cerebrospinal fluid is essentially an ultrafiltrate of blood plasma with no erythrocytes and little protein. In the brain this fluid is supplied with oxygen and nutrients by bundles of capillaries known as the choroid plexus. The tight junctions between the endothelial cells separating the capillaries from the cerebrospinal fluid form the blood–brain barrier and prevent the movement of solutes between the cells. Since these endothelial cells have a limited range of transport systems they restrict the range of substances that can pass from the blood to the cerebrospinal fluid. Below the blood–brain barrier there is a high concentration of neuroglial cells called astrocytes which act as a second barrier monitoring the composition of the cerebrospinal fluid to protect the neurones from changes in their extracellular environment.

Functions of the neuroglial cells

The large number of neuroglial support cells, which include astrocytes, outnumber the neurones in the CNS and perform a wide range of functions. There are two types of astrocytes. The fibrous astrocytes are largely found near the white myelinated axons. Protoplasmic astrocytes are packed around the neuronal cell bodies, or grey matter, and have fewer internal filaments. Since the astrocytes are often seen to have contacts with both the neurones and the endothelial cells forming the blood–brain barrier, they may help to supply them with nutrients. In any case the astrocytes are clearly involved in removing excess neurotransmitters and maintaining the ion composition of the extracellular fluid. The other major class of neuroglial cells are the oligodendrocytes which are responsible for myelinating the axons in the CNS. The myelin sheath is formed from the plasma membrane of the oligodendrocytes which these cells wrap around the axon many times. Myelin contains two specific proteins, myelin basic protein and myelin proteolipid. Because of its high proportion of lipid myelin provides an effective insulation for the axons. The myelin sheath is interrupted at intervals known as the nodes of Ranvier. Two minor groups of glial cells are also found in the CNS.

They are the microglia, which act as phagocytes, and the ependymal cells that line the ventricles and probably help to maintain the composition of the cerebrospinal fluid.

The peripheral nervous system

The CNS is connected to the rest of the body by peripheral neurones. The sensory neurones send their axons into the spinal cord where there are connections to the brain, and there may also be direct connections to motor neurones forming a reflex arc. The cell bodies of the motor neurones in the spinal column have axons extending either directly to the motor end plate on a muscle fibre or to synapses in ganglia outside the CNS. The axon terminals of postsynaptic neurones are in direct contact with muscles or internal organs. Axons of peripheral motor neurones can transmit impulses rapidly because they are insulated from the surrounding extracellular matrix by a myelin sheath formed by Schwann cells.

The parasympathetic nervous system

The efferent nerve pathways which connect the CNS to the circulatory system and internal organs form the **autonomic nervous system**. This consists of two sets of pathways, which produce opposite effects, the parasympathetic and sympathetic systems. The parasympathetic neurones have their cell bodies in the medulla and sarcal regions of the spinal cord. The axons of the parasympathetic neurones go to the respiratory system, heart, liver, pancreas, stomach, small intestine and kidneys by way of the vagus nerve. These neurones stimulate the blood supply to the liver, pancreas, kidneys and digestive system during nutrient absorption as well as stimulating the activity of smooth muscles in the digestive tract. Parasympathetic neurones also slow the heart rate, constrict the airways and reduce the blood supply to skeletal muscles. The postsynaptic neurones in the parasympathetic pathway have their cell bodies in small ganglia on or near the organs that they are innervating and their axon terminals produce acetylcholine. The general effects of stimulation by the parasympathetic nervous system is to promote the activity of internal organs responsible for digestion and the absorption of food, and to reduce the blood supply to the muscles and skin.

The sympathetic nervous system

The presynaptic neurones of the sympathetic nervous system have their cell bodies in the thoracic and lumbar regions of the spinal cord. Their axons extend to sympathetic ganglia lying just outside the spinal column. The postsynaptic neurones from these ganglia innervate the blood vessels supplying the main groups of striated muscles. In addition there are a number of specialized sympathetic ganglia at a distance from the spinal column. The postsynaptic sympathetic neurones serving the pancreas, liver, kidneys and small intestine have their cell bodies in the coeliac ganglion. The postsynaptic neurones of the sympathetic nervous system secrete noradrenaline at their axon terminals. One exception to the normal pattern of sympathetic nerve pathways are the neurones serving the adrenal medulla. In this case endocrine cells secreting adrenaline and noradrenaline take the place of the postsynaptic neurones. The most important function of the sympathetic nervous system is to respond to emergencies by increasing the blood supply to muscles, stimulating the heart rate and dilating the respiratory pathways. In addition the blood supply to internal organs is restricted and the muscular activity in the digestive system is inhibited. The sympathetic nervous system achieves these effects by the secretion of adrenaline and noradrenaline into the vascular system from the adrenal medulla as well as by releasing noradrenaline at the nerve endings.

11.3 Structural and functional features of neurones

Figure 11.3 gives a schematic representation of the general features of neurone structure in the CNS. However, it is important to recognize that neurones display an enormous variation in the pattern of dendrites and the length and degree of branching of the axon. The various parts of the neurone are shown diagrammatically in Figure 11.3(a), but they are not drawn to scale. Figure 11.3(b), (c), (d) and (e) provides more detail about the structure of the axon, the myelin sheath and the special features of the axon terminal. Two features of neurone structure that are difficult to illustrate are the extensive cytoskeletal network of neurofilaments and microtubules that is present and the vast number of axon terminals from other neurones that interact with each neurone in the CNS.

Transport of organelles and vesicles along the axon

Figure 11.3(b) and (c) illustrates another characteristic feature of neurones, the transport of vesicles and cell organelles in both directions along the axon. The fast axonal transport of these structures (up to 400 mm/day) is an active process in both directions which requires ATP and appears to depend on the actin filaments present in the axon as well as the microtubules and neurofilaments. Disruption of the actin filaments or the microtubules stops transport in both directions. Outward transport from the cell body toward the axon terminal is termed anterograde and is driven by the molecular motor protein kinesin. Movement back to the cell body, termed retrograde, requires a different motor protein, dynein. The axonal transport from the cell body is very important for neuronal metabolism since it includes enzymes, a range of different sized vesicles and tubular structures. The retrograde transport consists of somewhat larger vesicles containing cell debris from organelles in the axon terminal and molecules taken up by endocytosis in the terminal. These vesicles are carrying the material from the axon terminal back to lysosomes in the cell body where it is degraded.

In addition to the fast axonal transport described above there is also a much slower flow of material along the axon at about 1% of the fast transport rate. This axoplasmic flow from the cell body consists of the cytoskeletal elements as well as structural proteins and cytoplasmic enzymes. This slow transport has the effect of recycling the structural and metabolic components of the axon and its terminal. Although there is no direct evidence for this type of slow transport in dendrites, it seems reasonable to suggest that a similar process must be responsible for the maintenance of the dendrite structure as well as for that in the axon. After the human brain matures in the first few years of life no new neurones are formed. Consequently, the total number of nerve cells in the brain steadily decreases during an individual's lifetime, although the rate of loss varies from one individual to another. It seems reasonable to suggest that reducing the rate of cell loss may depend on how effectively the neuronal constituents are recycled.

CNS

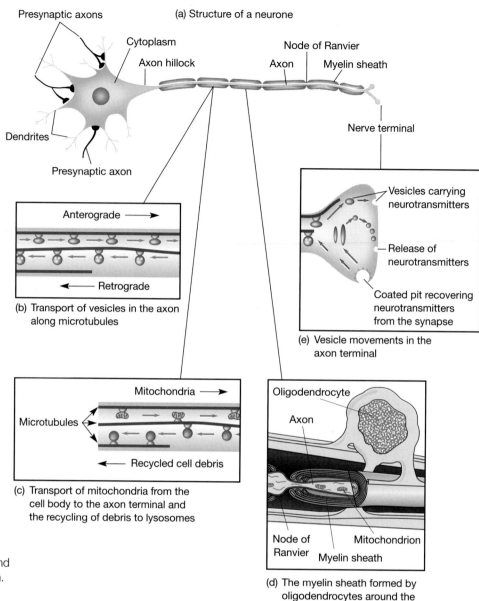

Figure 11.3
Structural features of a neurone and organelle transport along the axon. (Inserts reproduced courtesy of Dr P.G. Strange.)

11.4 Energy supply and nitrogen metabolism in the central nervous system

The function of a neurone is to transmit impulses along its axon after it has been stimulated either through one of its dendrites or by the axon terminal of another neurone on its cell body. As shown below, impulse transmission requires strict maintenance of the Na^+ and K^+ gradients across the cell membrane and the release of a neurotransmitter at the axon terminal. From a metabolic point of view the maintenance of the ion gradients across the extensive area of membrane covering the axon, dendrites and cell body of the neurones provides the major demand for ATP in the neurone. Because of the substrate supply limitations imposed by the blood–brain barrier, the principal energy-supplying substrate for the CNS is glucose as shown in Figure 11.4.

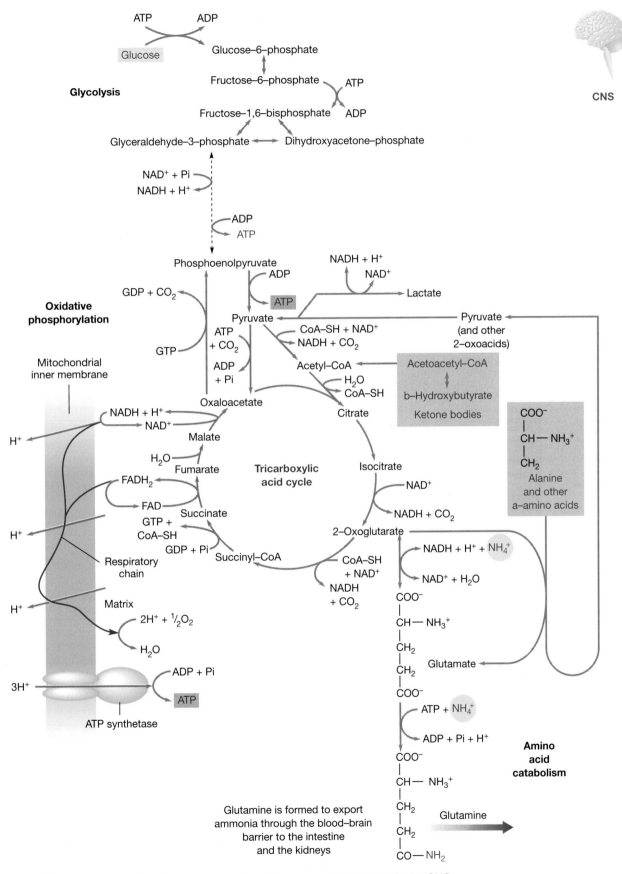

Figure 11.4 Pathways responsible for energy supply and the removal of ammonia in the CNS.

Glucose is the main energy-supplying substrate

The high demand for oxygen in the brain underlines the importance of its blood supply, and explains the serious consequences of asphyxia or the blockage of any of the arteries by a clot. Each day the human brain uses about 100 g of glucose which is completely metabolized to CO_2 and H_2O through the glycolytic pathway, the TCA cycle and oxidative phosphorylation to yield ATP. Approximately 20% of the total oxygen consumption and glucose utilization in a resting individual is accounted for by the brain. When fatty acids are plentiful, either because of dietary intake or release from adipocytes, most other tissues will switch from glucose to fatty acids as their major fuel. However, this cannot occur in the CNS because long-chain fatty acids do not cross the blood–brain barrier at a rate sufficient to make a significant contribution to the energy supply.

As a consequence of the blood–brain barrier, the brain remains dependent on glucose as its main energy-supplying substrate when liver glycogen has been exhausted. The liver continues to supply glucose by gluconeogenesis, but there is a limit to the amount of glucose that can be provided in this way. This explains the importance of switching other tissues to the use of fatty acids when glucose is in short supply. During starvation, as we shall see in Chapter 15, ketone body levels rise sharply and it has been shown that in severe starvation up to 60% of the energy requirements of the CNS can be met by the oxidation of ketone bodies. It is important to note that although the blood–brain barrier permits the entry of ketone bodies, they cannot serve as an alternative fuel for the CNS under fed conditions because ketone body concentrations in the blood are very low. It has been shown that cells within the CNS are capable of oxidizing fatty acids so that fatty acids released as a consequence of the recycling of membranes and other cell constituents can be metabolized in the normal way.

Amino acids are used to form neurotransmitters

In principle amino acids can also provide the brain with an alternative to glucose as energy-supplying substrates. As we shall see in section 11.7, a number of amino acids are needed as substrates for the synthesis of neurotransmitters (see Figure 11.7), and both glutamate and glycine serve as neurotransmitters (see Table 11.1). Therefore it is essential for the neurones that the cytoplasmic concentrations of neurotransmitter precursors are not prejudiced by the energy requirements of the cells. However, an even more important reason for not relying on amino acids as energy-supplying substrates for the CNS is the problem caused by the large amount of NH_4^+ which would be released during amino acid catabolism. A considerable amount of NH_4^+ is released within the CNS by the degradation of neurotransmitters and the purine nucleotide cycle. This is dealt with by the conversion of 2-oxoglutarate into glutamine (see Figure 8.5, Box 1 for the details) which is then exported across the blood–brain barrier into the vascular system to be dealt with by the intestine and kidneys. Large increases in NH_4^+ production could depress TCA cycle activity by withdrawing 2-oxoglutarate for the formation of glutamine.

Recycling of membranes requires the central nervous system to synthesize lipids

The other major metabolic requirements of the neurones and glial cells in the CNS are concerned with the recycling of cell constituents. These processes involve protein synthesis and the formation of membrane constituents. The blood–brain barrier permits the uptake of amino acids, inorganic ions and the vitamin structures required for coenzymes. However, membrane synthesis in the CNS requires the neurones and glial cells to use glucose to synthesize cholesterol and most of the fatty acids needed for the membrane phospholipids. This further increases the demand for glucose.

11.5 Action potentials and their propagation along the axon

The resting potential in neurones, like that in most other cells, is generated by the action of the Na^+/K^+ ATPase together with the presence of passive K^+ channels which result in K^+ leakage out of the cell down its concentration gradient until the potential difference balances K^+ movement through the passive K^+ channel. Neurones also have a passive Na^+ channel which reduces the membrane potential slightly and requires continual operation of the Na^+/K^+ ATPase to maintain the membrane potential. Three Na^+ ions are pumped out of the cell and two K^+ ions are pumped in for each ATP hydrolysed.

Propagation of the action potential along the axon

The transmission of a nerve impulse along an axon involves the movement of a wave of depolarization, known as an action potential. Figure 11.5(a) shows the ion concentrations inside and outside of the neurone and the classical trace of an action potential recorded from a squid giant axon. It is now clear that the shape of the trace can be explained in terms of the local disturbance of the membrane potential caused by the successive opening and closing of Na^+ and K^+ channels in the axon membrane. The action potential is triggered by a small initial depolarization of the membrane which opens the voltage-sensitive Na^+ channels. The resulting Na^+ movement into the axon completely depolarizes a small section of the membrane inactivating the Na^+ channels and these channels remain inactive until the membrane repolarizes. The repolarization of the squid axon is due to the somewhat slower opening of voltage-sensitive K^+ channels. The resulting outward movement of K^+ permits the rapid restoration of the membrane potential. In mammalian myelinated axons there are no voltage-sensitive K^+ channels so that repolarization occurs as a result of the movement of K^+ through the passive K^+ channel responsible for the resting potential. This means that the repolarization phase of the action potential in a myelinated mammalian axon is slower.

Because the action potential causes an outward movement of K^+ ions these will diffuse along the axon and cause a mild depolarization of the adjacent area by reducing the passive outward movement of K^+. As a consequence, voltage-sensitive Na^+ channels will open and this completely depolarizes the adjacent section of the axon, inactivating the Na^+ channels and increasing the passive outward flow of K^+ ions. In this way the action potential is propagated along the axon as indicated in Figure 11.5(b). Since the action potential is initially set off by the axon hillock at the cell body it progresses in one direction along the axon from the cell body to the axon terminal.

CNS

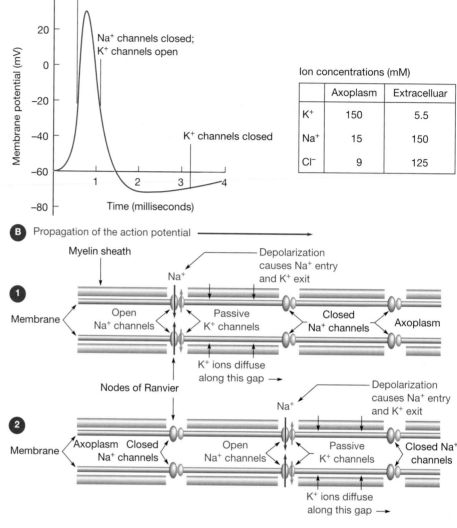

A Action potential recorded from a squid giant axon

Na⁺ channels open

Na⁺ channels closed; K⁺ channels open

K⁺ channels closed

Ion concentrations (mM)

	Axoplasm	Extracelluar
K⁺	150	5.5
Na⁺	15	150
Cl⁻	9	125

Membrane potential (mV)

Time (milliseconds)

B Propagation of the action potential

Myelin sheath

Depolarization causes Na⁺ entry and K⁺ exit

Na⁺

1

Membrane

Open Na⁺ channels — Passive K⁺ channels — Closed Na⁺ channels — Axoplasm

Nodes of Ranvier

K⁺ ions diffuse along this gap →

Depolarization causes Na⁺ entry and K⁺ exit

Na⁺

2

Membrane

Axoplasm Closed Na⁺ channels — Open Na⁺ channels — Passive K⁺ channels — Closed Na⁺ channels

K⁺ ions diffuse along this gap →

Figure 11.5

(a) Ion concentrations inside and outside an axon and the action potential recorded from a squid axon. (b) Diagrams illustrating the propagation of an action potential along a myelinated axon from panel 1 to panel 2.

The myelin sheath increases the rate at which the impulse travels

Myelination of the axon by oligodendrocytes increases the rate at which the action potential is propagated. The myelin sheath insulates the axon in sections separated by the nodes of Ranvier at intervals of 1 mm. This insulation reduces the space into which K⁺ ions can exit so that the small depolarization they cause spreads further along the axon from one node to the next. As a consequence in myelinated axons the voltage-sensitive Na⁺ channels are clustered at the nodes and the action potential jumps from one node to the next increasing the rate of propagation of the action potential by five times or more. The other factor in determining the rate of propagation of the action potential is the diameter of the axon. The squid axon achieves a high rate of propagation without myelination because of its large diameter, but in the mammalian nervous system myelination allows a rapid rate of propagation without increasing axon diameter.

11.6 Summary of the metabolic processes responsible for the transmission of impulses across a synapse

There are also a number of different mechanisms for the transmission of impulses from one neurone to the next across the small gap, or synapse. The basic principle of synaptic transmission is fairly simple. When an impulse reaches the end of the axon a neurotransmitter which has been stored in a vesicle just below the membrane is released into the space between the neurones. The neurotransmitter then binds to a receptor on the surface of the postsynaptic neurone and initiates a response. These events are summarized in Figure 11.6.

A As the action potential reaches the nerve terminal Ca^{2+} channels are opened by depolarization

The influx of Ca^{2+} stimulates exocytosis of neurotransmitter from synaptic vesicles

Neurotransmitter diffuses across the synaptic gap and binds to receptors on the postsynaptic membrane

Action potential

Ca^{2+}

Ca^{2+}

Ca^{2+}

Vesicles carrying neurotransmitter from the cell body

Axon terminal of presynaptic neurone

Synaptic gap

Neurotransmitter

Postsynaptic neurone

Receptors

CNS

B Following transmission of a nerve impulse across a synapse the excess neurotransmitter is removed by one of the following mechanisms:

1   Reabsorption by coated pits on the presynaptic neurone. The reabsorbed neurotransmitter is either recycled for future synaptic transmissions or broken down

2   Hydrolysis by enzymes in the synaptic gap followed by reabsorption of the products of hydrolysis (e.g. acetylcholinesterase splits acetylcholine; peptidases split neuropeptides)

3   Absorption of excess neurotransmitter by astrocytes

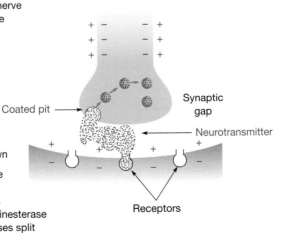

Coated pit

Synaptic gap

Neurotransmitter

Receptors

Figure 11.6

(a) The role of neurotransmitters in synaptic transmission. (b) The fate of excess neurotransmitters remaining in the synaptic gap after an impulse has been transmitted across the synapse.

265

Neurotransmitters can produce a variety of effects

The pattern of synaptic transmission can vary because there are considerable differences in the responses caused by the various neurotransmitters. In addition there are some neurones in which more than one transmitter is available for

Table 11.1 List of neurotransmitters showing their precursors, receptors, the types of response they evoke in postsynaptic neurones and their metabolic fate

Neurotransmitter	Precursors	Receptor	Type	Response	Metabolic fate
Acetylcholine	Choline, acetate	Nicotinic	Fast	Opens Na^+/K^+ channels	Hydrolysis by acetylcholinesterase
		Muscarinic 1,3 Muscarinic 2	Slow Slow	Phospholipase C Adenyl cyclase$\downarrow$ opens K^+ channels	
Adenosine	5'-AMP	A_1	Slow	Adenyl cyclase$\downarrow$ $K^+\uparrow$, $Ca^{2+}\downarrow$	Uptake and phosphorolysis
		A_2	Slow	Adenyl cyclase$\uparrow$	
Adrenaline (and noradrenaline)	Tyrosine	α_1 α_2	Slow Slow	Phospholipase C Adenyl cyclase$\downarrow$ $K^+\uparrow$, $Ca^{2+}\downarrow$	Uptake and oxidation by monoamine oxidase
		β_1,β_2	Slow	Adenyl cyclase$\uparrow$	
Dopamine	Tyrosine	D_1	Slow	Adenyl cyclase$\uparrow$ phospholipase C	Uptake and oxidation by monoamine oxidase
		D_2	Slow	Adenyl cyclase$\downarrow$ $K^+\uparrow$, $Ca^{2+}\downarrow$	
GABA	Glutamate	$GABA_A$	Fast	Opens Cl^- channels	Uptake and GABA aminotransferase, etc.
		$GABA_B$	Slow	Adenyl cyclase$\downarrow$ $K^+\uparrow$, $Ca^{2+}\downarrow$	
Glutamate	Glutamine or 2-oxoglutarate	*N*-methyl-D-aspartate	Fast	Opens Na^+/K^+ channels	Conversion to glutamine (glial), oxidation to 2-oxoglutarate (neurones)
Glycine	Serine	Glycine	Fast	Opens Cl^- channels	Uptake
Histamine	Histidine	H_1 H_2	Slow Slow	Phospholipase C, Adenyl cyclase$\uparrow$	Uptake and oxidation by monoamine oxidase
5-Hydroxy-tryptamine	Tryptophan	$5\text{-}HT_3$	Fast	Opens Na^+/K^+ channels	Uptake and oxidation by monoamine oxidase
		$5\text{-}HT_{1A,1B}$ $5\text{-}HT_{1C}$	Slow Slow	Adenyl cyclase$\downarrow$ Phospholipase C	
Neuropeptides	Amino acids	Various	Slow	Phospholipase C, adenyl cyclase$\downarrow$	Hydrolysis by neuropeptidases

Note: For adenyl cyclase $\uparrow$ = stimulation, $\downarrow$ = inhibition; for ion channels $\uparrow$ = open, $\downarrow$ = inhibition.

release, and in some cases transmitter release is controlled by a third neurone. The neurotransmitters can produce a fast or a slow response, and their effects on the postsynaptic neurone may be either excitatory or inhibitory. There are also differences in the speed with which the transmitters can be degraded or reabsorbed. Table 11.1 shows that a particular neurotransmitter can produce a range of different responses. These differences are mainly due to the specific characteristics of the postsynaptic receptor which binds the neurotransmitter.

Drugs can alter the action of postsynaptic receptors

In addition to the characteristics of the postsynaptic receptor its activity can be varied in several ways. The receptor can be desensitized, so that it requires a larger concentration of neurotransmitter to produce a response, or it can be down-regulated by reducing the receptor density on the postsynaptic membrane. Furthermore, external compounds can modulate the activity of the receptor, either positively or negatively. This type of modulation explains the mechanism of action of many drugs that are used to treat various medical and psychological disorders of the CNS. Potential, but often unknown, interactions between mood-enhancing drugs and the neurotransmitter receptors underline the serious hazards that accompany the use of such drugs, particularly by the young. It is clear that there is enough individual variation in the regulation of receptor function and in the interconnections between neurones in the CNS to make it difficult, and possibly hazardous, to use the past experience of others to predict the effects that antidepressants, tranquillizers and mood-enhancing drugs will have on a particular individual.

11.7 Metabolic processes responsible for the synthesis and release of neurotransmitters

In order to transmit an impulse across a synapse every neurone must synthesize neurotransmitter molecules. These are stored in the axon terminal and released when the nerve impulse reaches the end of the axon. Table 11.1 lists a range of neurotransmitter molecules and their precursors. Most of these molecules are synthesized from amino acids or central pathway constituents by fairly simple routes.

Synthesis of neurotransmitters

The structures of four neurotransmitters are shown in Figure 11.7 together with the steps responsible for their synthesis. GABA (γ-aminobutyric acid) is a neurotransmitter formed by the decarboxylation of glutamate and its catabolism involves deamination to succinic semialdehyde followed by entry into the TCA cycle as succinate (see Figure 11.7b). The conversion of tyrosine into noradrenaline and adrenaline involves a more complex pathway (see Figure 11.7a). Hydroxylation of the tyrosine ring yields L-DOPA and this is decarboxylated by a pyridoxal phosphate-dependent reaction to produce dopamine which is an important neurotransmitter in the brain. Hydroxylation of the side chain by an ascorbate-dependent monooxygenase reaction produces noradrenaline and the addition of a methyl group by the *S*-adenosylmethionine cycle (see Figure 6.5) completes the synthesis of adrenaline. After they are synthesized the neurotransmitters are transferred along the axon and stored in vesicles in the axon terminal just below the membrane facing the synapse. Adrenaline and noradrenaline are synthesized by the cells of the adrenal medulla and secreted into the vascular system when stimulated by neurones of the sympathetic nervous system. However, postsynaptic neurones of the sympathetic nervous system also synthesize noradrenaline which is released from their axon terminals when the nerves are stimulated.

Ca²⁺ causes the release of neurotransmitters from the axon terminal

When the action potential which is initiated in the axon hillock reaches the axon terminal, depolarization of the terminal membrane opens Ca^{2+} channels. The rise in the Ca^{2+} concentration in the terminal region causes the synaptic vesicles located immediately below the membrane facing the synaptic gap to release their neurotransmitters by exocytosis. In order to prevent the exocytosis process from increasing the membrane area of the axon terminus, it is necessary for the axon to recover the vesicle membrane and it does this by the endocytosis of coated pits. In some cases this endocytosis is associated with the uptake of surplus neurotransmitter by the axon terminal where it can either be packaged in new vesicles for future release or sent back to the cell body and degraded.

CNS

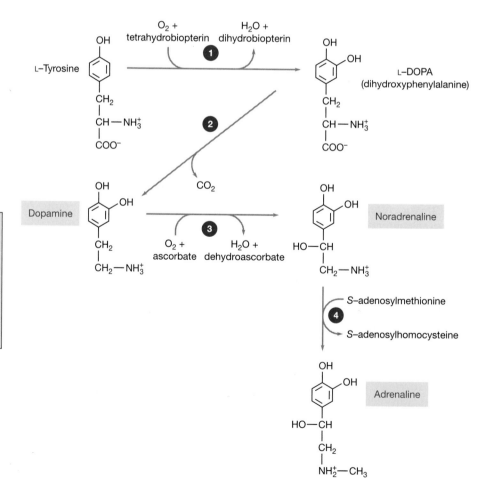

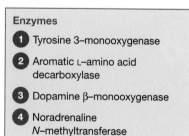

Enzymes

1. Tyrosine 3–monooxygenase
2. Aromatic ʟ–amino acid decarboxylase
3. Dopamine β–monooxygenase
4. Noradrenaline *N*–methyltransferase

Figure 11.7(a)
Synthetic pathways for the formation of dopamine, adrenaline and noradrenaline.

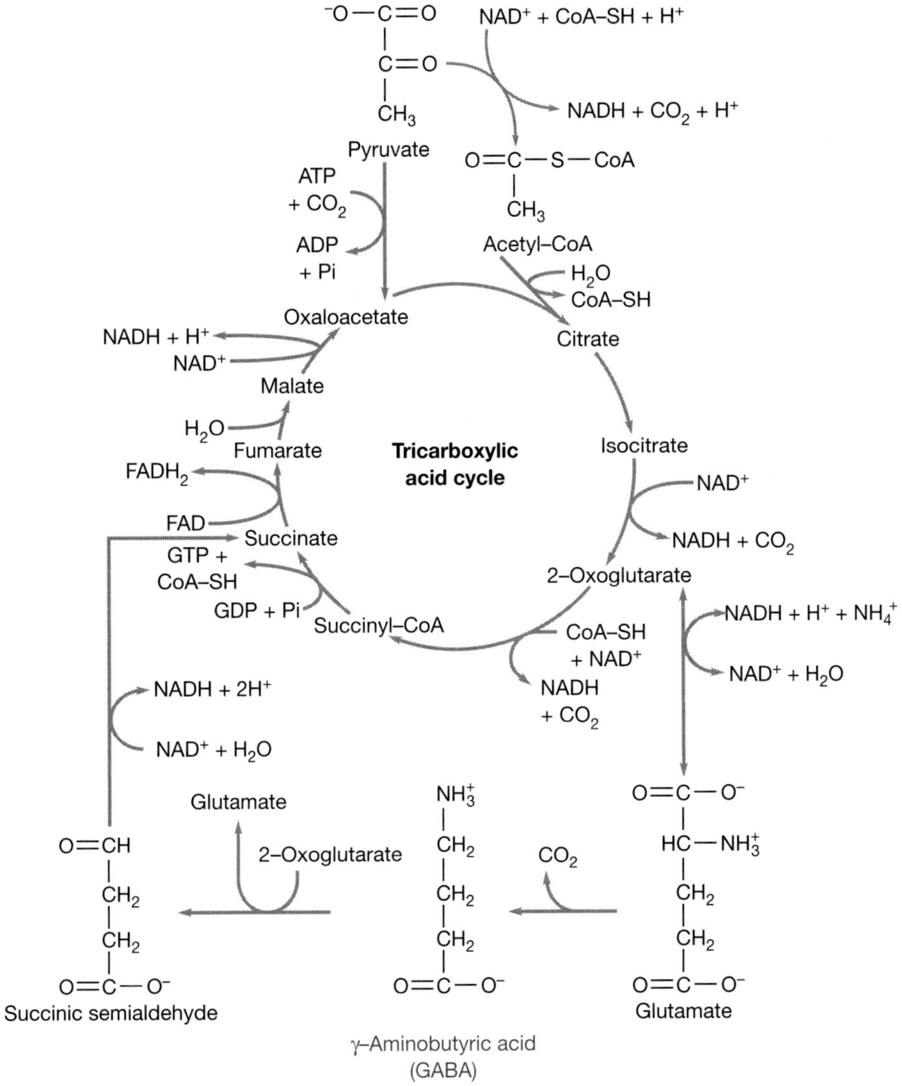

CNS

Figure 11.7(b)
Pathways for the synthesis and
catabolism of γ-aminobutyric
acid (GABA).

11.8 Postsynaptic response to the binding of neurotransmitters

Table 11.1 shows that many neurotransmitters produce quite different effects depending on the particular postsynaptic receptor to which they bind. In order to understand the diversity of these effects it is important to look at the relationship between the receptor protein and the membrane constituents with which it interacts. All specific receptors for a particular neurotransmitter are integral membrane proteins. Molecular biological techniques are providing information about the expression of a wide range of different receptors in the neurones of the CNS, and it is beyond the scope of this book to provide a detailed description of their characteristics. However, there are two main classes of receptor in the CNS and a brief description of each type will illustrate the extent of the differences in receptor mechanisms.

Fast postsynaptic receptors

Fast ion receptors have an integral ion channel in addition to the neurotransmitter binding site as shown in Figure 11.8a. This association enables the receptor to depolarize the postsynaptic membrane as soon as the transmitter binds. The second type, which operates more slowly, is simply a membrane protein with a binding site for the neurotransmitter. In order to produce a response after the transmitter has bound, as illustrated in Figure 11.8(b), this type of receptor must move along the membrane until it comes in contact with a G protein which will then dissociate one of its subunits to activate an effector. This type of receptor acts in an analogous way to the adrenaline receptor in muscle and liver described in Figure 1.12.

It is important to recognize that the interaction of the neurotransmitter with the postsynaptic neurone can have either a stimulatory or inhibitory effect on the neurone depending on the type of receptor to which it binds. Glutamate, which is an example of a fast-acting neurotransmitter (Figure 11.8a), depolarizes the postsynaptic neurone because its receptor is linked to a Na^+ channel. The same postsynaptic effect is caused by acetylcholine, although it is a less important neurotransmitter in the CNS than it is for peripheral nerves. GABA, which is also a fast-acting neurotransmitter, hyperpolarizes the postsynaptic neurone if it combines with the $GABA_A$ receptor by opening a chloride channel. This permits the entry of Cl^-, increasing the membrane potential and producing an inhibitory effect on the postsynaptic neurone by making it less easily excitable. A similar inhibitory effect is also produced by glycine as a neurotransmitter.

Slow postsynaptic receptors

Either stimulatory or inhibitory effects can also be evoked by the slow-acting neurotransmitters (Figure 11.8b). When dopamine binds to a D_1 receptor this acts through a G protein to stimulate adenyl cyclase to raise the level of cyclic AMP. However, when dopamine binds to a D_2 receptor the G protein interaction

CNS

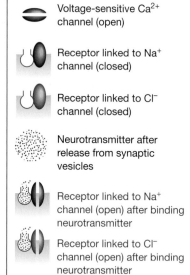

Figure 11.8(a)
Examples of the actions of neurotransmitters binding to fast-acting postsynaptic receptors.

Legend:
- Voltage-sensitive Ca^{2+} channel (open)
- Receptor linked to Na^+ channel (closed)
- Receptor linked to Cl^- channel (closed)
- Neurotransmitter after release from synaptic vesicles
- Receptor linked to Na^+ channel (open) after binding neurotransmitter
- Receptor linked to Cl^- channel (open) after binding neurotransmitter

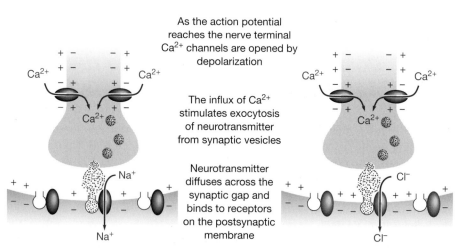

As the action potential reaches the nerve terminal Ca^{2+} channels are opened by depolarization

The influx of Ca^{2+} stimulates exocytosis of neurotransmitter from synaptic vesicles

Neurotransmitter diffuses across the synaptic gap and binds to receptors on the postsynaptic membrane

If the receptor is linked to a Na^+ channel, the postsynaptic neurone is stimulated because the membrane is depolarized. Examples of neurotransmitters that fulfil this role are glutamate and acetylcholine (when bound to a nicotinic receptor).

If the receptor is linked to a Cl^- channel, the postsynaptic neurone is inhibited by the hyperpolarization. Examples of neurotransmitters that act in this way are GABA (bound to the $GABA_A$ receptor) and glycine.

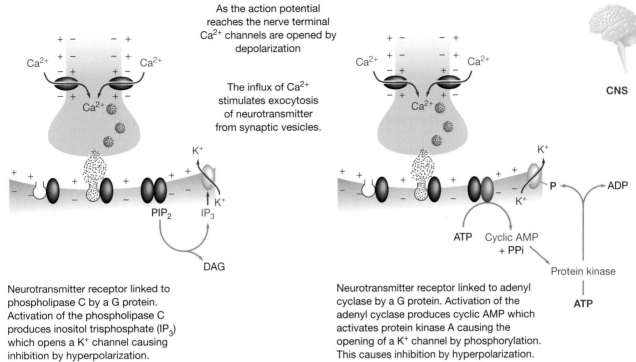

As the action potential reaches the nerve terminal Ca^{2+} channels are opened by depolarization

The influx of Ca^{2+} stimulates exocytosis of neurotransmitter from synaptic vesicles.

CNS

Neurotransmitter receptor linked to phospholipase C by a G protein. Activation of the phospholipase C produces inositol trisphosphate (IP$_3$) which opens a K$^+$ channel causing inhibition by hyperpolarization.

Neurotransmitter receptor linked to adenyl cyclase by a G protein. Activation of the adenyl cyclase produces cyclic AMP which activates protein kinase A causing the opening of a K$^+$ channel by phosphorylation. This causes inhibition by hyperpolarization.

Figure 11.8(b) Examples of the effects of neurotransmitters binding to slow postsynaptic receptors acting through a G protein. PIP$_2$ = phosphatidylinositol bisphosphate; DAG = diacylglycerol

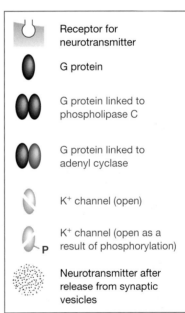

Receptor for neurotransmitter

G protein

G protein linked to phospholipase C

G protein linked to adenyl cyclase

K$^+$ channel (open)

K$^+$ channel (open as a result of phosphorylation)

Neurotransmitter after release from synaptic vesicles

results in the inhibition of adenyl cyclase reducing the cyclic AMP levels. Similar differences are also observed for the neurotransmitter adenosine which stimulates adenyl cyclase when bound to the A$_2$ receptor but inhibits when bound to the A$_1$ receptor.

Removal of excess neurotransmitters from the synapse

There are only a small number of receptor molecules on the postsynaptic membrane, so that most of the neurotransmitter molecules released by the axon terminal will remain unbound in the synapse. Since the transmitter is being used as a signal, it is vital that excess transmitter molecules should be rapidly removed from the synapse so that the postsynaptic receptors no longer have neurotransmitter molecules bound to them. This is essential in order to permit transmission of the next action potential when it arrives. There are two main mechanisms for removing the neurotransmitter: uptake into the presynaptic nerve terminal and inactivation by metabolism. An example of the latter process is the hydrolysis of acetylcholine by acetylcholinesterase, which is normally followed by recovery of the choline by the terminal region of the axon. Other neurotransmitters such as glutamate, glycine and dopamine are removed from the synapse by uptake into the axon terminal where they are usually repackaged into the synaptic vesicles. After uptake the dopamine can also be metabolically inactivated by monoamine oxidase which is present in the outer mitochondrial membrane. Peptide neurotransmitters are inactivated by the action of neuropeptidases on the membrane of the axon terminal, and the amino acid products can be recovered by transporters in the axon terminal or by glial cells.

Because of the importance of the removal of neurotransmitter molecules for the continuing function of the synapse, inhibitors of this process will effectively block transmission across the synapse. This is the basis of the action of some antidepressant drugs, which can inhibit the uptake of the neurotransmitter or its subsequent metabolism within the axon.

Recycling of postsynaptic receptors

It is also necessary to remove the neurotransmitter from the receptor on the postsynaptic neurone, and this is accomplished by recycling of the receptor within the neurone. Sections of the membrane-containing receptor bound to neurotransmitter are internalized by endocytosis of coated pits. Once inside the cell vesicles containing the receptors are either completely degraded by lysosomes or, after detachment of the neurotransmitter, the receptor molecules may be recycled to the membrane.

11.9 Changes in brain function associated with some brain disorders

The recent advances in our knowledge of the ways in which neurotransmitters and their receptors operate in the brain has improved our understanding of the causes of serious brain disorders. Sadly the increased knowledge about the way the brain functions has not yet been able to provide much improvement in the medical treatment of these conditions. The paragraphs that follow provide a brief description of four conditions and the ways in which they are treated.

Parkinson's disease

In many ways the most thoroughly studied condition is Parkinson's disease which was first described by J. Parkinson in 1817. The condition is characterized by tremor, rigidity and lack of movement. There is extensive degeneration of the substantia nigra region of the brain and the levels of dopamine and its metabolite homovallinic acid in the striatum region decline by as much as 80%. For this reason treatment with dopamine was tried, but since this does not cross the blood–brain barrier, the precursor L-DOPA (see Figure 11.7) is used instead with reasonable success, at least in the early stages. Eventually this form of treatment probably fails because of the continued loss of neurones.

Huntington's chorea

Huntington's chorea, which was first described by G. Huntington more than 100 years ago, is a rare disease inherited as an autosomal dominant. Its mean age of onset is at 35 to 40 and the symptoms are jerky, involuntary movements and difficulties in thinking and learning. The disease is invariably fatal and is characterized by a general shrinkage of the brain by up to 20%. In the striatum up to 95% of the neurones may be lost. No successful treatment for this condition has been found.

Alzheimer's disease

Recently Alzheimer's disease has achieved a high profile because about 30% of elderly people with senile dementia can be confirmed at autopsy as suffering from this condition. An autopsy confirms that the individual was suffering from Alzheimer's disease when degenerative amyloid plaques are found in the brain. This condition was named for A. Alzheimer who first described the results of such a post-mortem in 1907. Again there is considerable shrinkage of the brain with up to 30% of the cerebral cortex neurones being lost. It has been shown that the activity of choline acetyltransferase in the brain of patients with Alzheimer's disease is low and there are also reductions in the levels of a number of neurotransmitters. Attempts to treat the disease with precursors of acetylcholine or inhibitors of cholinesterase have provided some short-term relief. Recent studies indicate that a rise in the plasma concetration of homocysteine may be associated with the development of Alzheimer's disease. This suggests that the disease could be linked to a reduction in the activity of the S-adenosylmethionine cycle (see Figure 6.5).

Schizophrenia

Schizophrenia has been shown to be linked to enlargement of the brain ventricles, often as a result of trauma. This causes severe psychosis and the loss of rational behaviour. However, it can be treated successfully with a wide range of drugs. Although it is not really clear how the drugs act, they are probably producing their effects by inhibiting dopamine D_2 receptors as well as the receptors for adrenergic neurotransmitters and histamine.

11.10 Metabolic interrelationships between the central nervous system and other tissues

The CNS has a unique relationship with the other tissues in the body. It depends on the liver for its essential supplies of glucose, and must rely on the proper functioning of the heart and the circulatory system to provide a steady supply of substrate and oxygen and to remove the waste products of carbon dioxide and glutamine. But as long as these basic requirements are provided, the CNS is able to exercise reasonably effective control over the metabolism of the remaining tissues by stimulating the appropriate neural pathways or by controlling the secretion of appropriate hormones.

Figure 11.9 illustrates some of the interrelationships between the CNS and the other seven tissues we are considering in this book. Energy-supplying substrates for the CNS come from the liver in the form of glucose, or ketone bodies in starvation. During the absorption of nutrients the intestine will also be able to contribute some glucose directly. Apart from the transfer of carbon dioxide to the lungs by the blood, the major metabolic waste product involved is glutamine. This will either be converted to alanine by the intestine or used by the kidneys to adjust the pH of the urine. Although the principal relationship between the CNS and the muscles is through the motor neurones, the brain also has the capacity to prepare the body for activity by causing the secretion of adrenaline from the adrenal medulla and glucagon from the pancreas. These hormones will increase glycogenolysis in muscle and the release of glucose from the liver. At the same time the noradrenaline, which will also be released on stimulation of the adrenal medulla and the

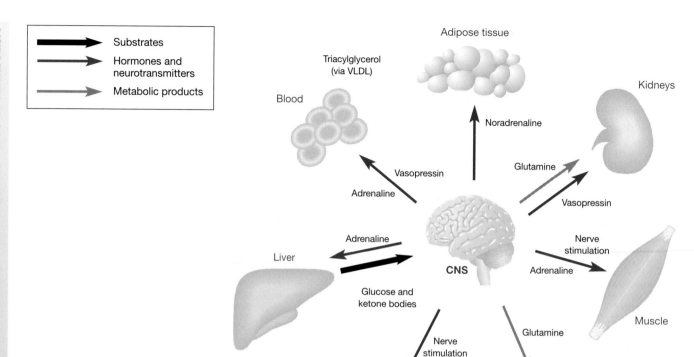

Figure 11.9
Summary of the metabolic
interrelationships between the CNS
and other tissues.

sympathetic neurones, will stimulate the hormone-sensitive lipase in adipose tissue to release fatty acids into the blood. In this way the CNS helps to preserve the supplies of glucose for its own metabolism and for red blood cells.

Another level of control operated by the CNS is the autonomic regulation of the activity of internal organs and their blood supply. Thus, the parasympathetic nervous system reduces the blood supply to muscles during the digestion of food. These autonomic controls can be overridden by higher centres in the CNS in an emergency or when the individual is excited. During exercise the circulation to the digestive tract and other internal organs is restricted whereas the blood supply to the muscles, the lungs and the brain is increased.

EXERCISES

1. What are the effects on the activity of the digestive tract of stimulation of the parasympathetic and the sympathetic nervous systems?

2. Since the CNS can use ketone bodies as an energy source, why does this only occur during periods of starvation?

3. Explain the basis of an action potential.

4. Why does a myelin sheath increase the rate at which impulses are transmitted along an axon?

5. What is the effect of the blood–brain barrier on metabolism in the CNS?

6. How does a neurotransmitter transmit impulses across a synapse?

7. Why is it necessary to remove excess neurotransmitters from the synaptic gap?

8. What is the molecular basis for the difference between a fast and slow postsynaptic response?

9. Why is the release of glutamine as a metabolic waste product vital for the CNS?

10. Summarize the relationship between the CNS and the endocrine system.

Further reading

Alberts, B., Bray, D., Lewis, J., Raff, M., Roberts, K. & Watson, J.D. (1989) *Molecular Biology of the cell*, 2nd edition, Garland.

Bradford, H.F. (1986) *Chemical Neurobiology*, W.H. Freeman.

Catterall, W.A. (1995) Structure and function of voltage-gated ion channels, *Annual Review of Biochemistry* **64**, 493–531.

Neer, E.J. & Clapman, D.E. (1988) Roles of G protein subunits in transmembrane signalling, *Nature* **333**, 129–134.

Huang, C-L, Feng, S. & Hilgemann, D.W. (1998) Direct activation of inward rectifier potassium channels by PIP_2 and its stabilization by $G_{\beta\gamma}$. *Nature* **391**, 803–806

Jen, L.S., Hart, A.J., Jen, A., Relvas, J.B., Gentleman, S.M., Garey, L.J. & Patel, A.J. (1998) Alzheimer's peptide kills cells of the retina *in vivo*. *Nature* **392**, 140–141.

Kaczmarek, L., Kossut, M. & Skangiel-Kramska, J. (1997) Glutamate receptors in cortical plasticity: molecular and cellular biology. *Physiological Reviews* **77**, 215–255.

Missale, C., Nach, R., Robinson, S.W., Jaber, M. & Caron, M.G. (1998) Dopamine receptors: from structure to function. *Physiological Reviews* **78**, 189–225.

Nicoll, R.A. (1988) The coupling of neurotransmitter receptors to ion channels in the brain, *Science* **241**, 545–551.

Strange, P.G. (1988) The structure and mechanism of neurotransmitter receptors. Implications for the structure and function of the central nervous system, *Biochemical Journal* **249**, 309–318.

Strange, P.G. (1992) *Brain Biochemistry and Brain Disorders*, Oxford University Press.

Watson, S. & Abbott, A. (1992) Receptor nomenclature supplement, *Trends in Pharmacological Sciences* **12**, 1–36.

Blood

Nutrient transport and protection of the body are the major functions of the blood.
A range of hormones and local messengers are responsible for controlling blood pressure and volume.

12.1 Summary of the composition of the blood and its role in metabolite transport and protection

The blood has two major functions: transport of nutrients, oxygen and waste products between tissues, and protection of the body against infection and the loss of blood. The composition of blood plasma is important for the health of the whole body because it provides the external medium for all cells, with the exception of those in the CNS. The composition of the plasma must also provide an appropriate environment for the erythrocytes and leucocytes which are responsible, respectively, for transport of oxygen and protection from infection. The metabolism of erythrocytes and leucocytes is summarized in Figure 12.1. The blood clotting mechanism provides emergency protection against blood loss as a result of damage caused to blood vessels due to injury. In order to ensure that the blood is circulated to all cells in the body without endangering the structure of the vessels it is essential that the composition, volume and pressure of the blood be maintained within fairly narrow limits, and this control is mainly executed by the kidneys responding to nervous and hormonal signals from sensors in the brain.

A feature of the metabolism of blood cells is their marked dependence on glycolysis for their energy supply despite the fact that plenty of oxygen is present. Erythrocytes, of course, must rely on glycolysis since they contain no mitochondria. However, high rates of lactate formation are also found in leucocytes, particularly when their activity is stimulated, even though the full complement of TCA cycle enzymes are present. This may indicate a lack of the normal glycolytic pathway controls and could provide the metabolic basis for the development of leucocyte tumours in leukaemia.

Oxygen is transported around the body by the haemoglobin carried in the erythrocytes. Haemoglobin has a natural affinity for oxygen, but transport of oxygen from the lungs to the tissues requires that the haemoglobin binds the oxygen in the lungs and gives it up in the tissues where the oxygen tension is lower. The presence of the haemoglobin within the red cell cytoplasm enables the oxygen binding to be increased in the lungs and decreased in the tissues. These effects are largely due to the formation of 2,3-bisphosphoglycerate in the

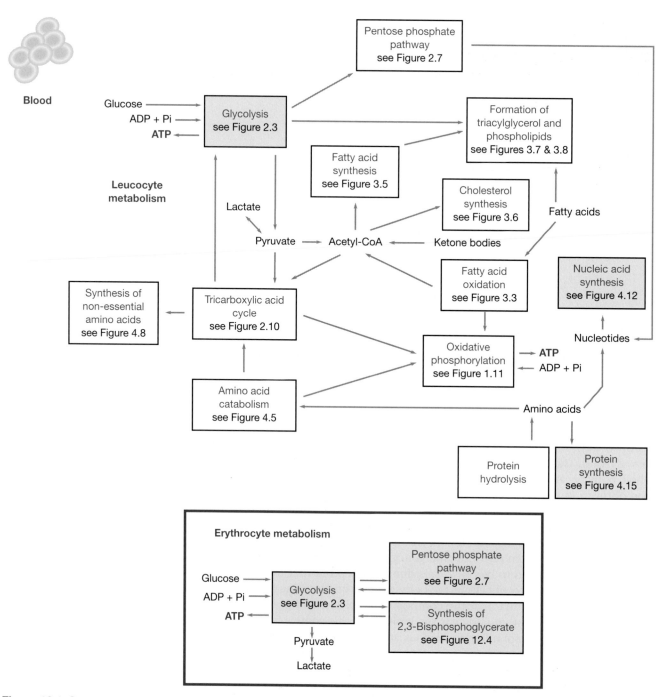

Figure 12.1 Summary of the metabolism in leucocytes and erythrocytes. The blue areas show the important pathways.

red blood cells. Because red cells have no mitochondria their metabolism is very restricted as shown in Figure 12.1.

Protection from infection is achieved in a number of ways by the leucocytes which have the normal range of metabolic pathways (see Figure 12.1). A basic level of protection is provided by a number of phagocytic cell types (macrophages, monocytes and granulocytes) which engulf and destroy foreign particles and bacteria (Table 12.1). Macrophages are present in the extracellular fluid that fills the spaces between the capillaries and the tissue cells as well as in the lymph. Monocytes and the various types of granulocytes are responsible for phagocytosis within the bloodstream. However, phagocytosis fails to protect the

Table 12.1 Principal functions of major blood constituents

Constituents	Functions
Erythrocytes (red cells)	Transport of oxygen and carbon dioxide
Leucocytes (white cells)	
Granulocytes	
Basophils	Secretion of histamine and platelet-activating factor
Eosinophils	Destroy parasites and provide allergic responses
Neutrophils	Phagocytosis of small foreign organisms particularly at sites of inflammation
Monocytes	Develop into macrophages
Macrophages	Phagocytosis of cell debris and foreign organisms; endocytosis of particles coated with antibodies
Lymphocytes	
B lymphocytes	Synthesize antibodies
T lymphocytes	Stimulate B lymphocytes and destroy virus-infected cells
Platelets (formed by megakaryocytes)	Release clotting factors
Plasma proteins	
Albumin	Important for osmoregulation and the transport of fatty acids, copper and zinc ions, bilirubin and non-polar drugs
Globulins	
α and β	Three large groups of different proteins which include fibrinogen and a range of specific binding proteins
γ	Soluble antibodies produced by B lymphocytes
Lipoproteins	
Chylomicrons	Transport of lipids from intestine to adipocytes
VLDL	Transport of lipids from the liver to adipocytes
IDL	Formed from VLDL after triacylglycerol removal
LDL	Formed from IDL; delivers cholesterol to peripheral tissues
HDL	Removal of cholesterol from peripheral tissues to return it to the liver

body from most pathogens so that the lymphocytes responsible for the adaptive immune system must respond by synthesizing specific immunoglobulins. The two classes of lymphocytes, B cells and T cells, operate in different ways. Soluble antigens, such as foreign proteins, are bound by specific antibodies. These proteins are synthesized by plasma cells which are differentiated from B lymphocytes. After the antigen–antibody complex is formed, it is taken up by the phagocytic cells. The T lymphocytes respond to invading organisms or viruses in a more complex manner. They are able to stimulate the B cells to generate specific soluble antibodies, and they are also able to detect and destroy cells infected with viruses.

Nutrients and waste products are transported between the various tissues in the blood plasma. Ions and small water-soluble compounds are simply carried in solution, but there are also a number of plasma proteins with specialized transport functions. Albumin, for example, which is the most common of the plasma proteins, is the vehicle for transport of free fatty acids. It also transports zinc and copper ions, non-polar drugs and the haem waste product bilirubin. For iron and the thyroid hormones there are specific binding proteins (transferrin and thyroid hormone-binding protein, respectively). Table 12.1 indicates that apart from fatty acids the transport of lipids occurs in the five lipoprotein types, chylomicrons, VLDL, IDL, LDL and HDL, which differ chiefly in their apoproteins and the relative proportions of triacylglycerol and cholesterol.

Because the blood transports nutrients and waste products around the body, measurements of the concentrations of key compounds in the blood are often used to monitor the health of the individual. However, it is important to recognize that for a normal constituent such as a metabolite a rise in the blood level can signal either a decrease in its metabolism or an increase in its production. For example, if a rise in the blood glutamine concentration were detected, it could be due to increased production by muscle or to an increase in ammonia levels in peripheral tissues; but equally it could be due to a decreased rate of metabolism of glutamine by the intestine, or failure of the liver to maintain an adequate rate of urea synthesis. Thus, the interpretation of changes in blood concentrations of metabolites is not simple. On the other hand, detection of components which are not normally present in the blood can be an excellent guide to potential problems. Transaminase enzymes are normally intracellular so that the detection of sharply elevated blood transaminase levels is an indication of tissue damage, usually either to the liver or the heart.

An excellent example of the usefulness of detecting the increased levels of compounds which are generally present in the blood at low concentrations is a recently published study showing the relationship between serum homocysteine concentrations and cardiovascular disease in middle-aged males. Those in the 40–60 year age group with a homocysteine concentration in the blood 10% above normal are more than three times as likely to have coronary heart disease or a stroke. Although the reasons are not entirely clear, a diet supplement with the three B vitamins, pyridoxine, folate and B_{12}, has been shown to reduce the vascular homocysteine concentrations and the risk of cardiovascular disease.

12.2 Structural characteristics and functions of the various blood cell types

Erythrocytes and leucocytes are all derived from the same haemopoietic stem cells in the bone marrow, although they have very different structures and functions (see Table 12.1). Some of the stem cells are released into the general circulation and settle in other tissues such as the spleen where they become colony-forming units. It is not clear at exactly what point in their differentiation that the stem cells become committed to form a particular cell type. In addition to erythrocytes, the stem cells can form granulocytes (neutrophils, eosinophils and basophils), lymphocytes and monocytes. Monocytes give rise to macrophages that are located in various tissues as well as in the blood. The stem cells also form megakaryocytes in the bone marrow, which produce the platelets, and mast cells which are found in the connective tissue associated with a number of internal organs and secrete histamine.

The formation of red blood cells

The stem cells in the bone marrow which are committed to the formation of erythrocytes are stimulated by a specific glycoprotein growth factor, erythropoietin, which is formed by the kidneys in response to a shortage of red cells. The erythropoietin binds to a specific receptor on the surface of the erythrocyte colony forming cells stimulating their development into mature erythrocytes. The size of the colony and the number of red cells produced from each precursor cell depend on the extent of their exposure to erythropoietin. The maturation of the erythrocytes is linked to the production of haemoglobin and is described in the next section.

Growth and differentiation of leucocytes

It seems likely that production of the various types of leucocytes is controlled by hormonal growth factors after the stem cells have become committed to form a particular cell type. There is evidence that a glycoprotein is secreted by a variety of tissues in response to infection, and this stimulates the growth of colonies producing granulocytes and macrophages. Presumably additional growth factors are needed to control the differentiation of granulocyte precursors into neutrophils, eosinophils and basophils which are formed in different proportions as a result of inflammation or infection. The differentiation of monocytes into macrophages also requires a growth factor.

The three major types of granulocytes differ in their functions (see Table 12.1), and their relative proportions are often used as an indication of a particular type of infection. Neutrophils are particularly concerned with the phagocytosis of small organisms, and eosinophils are responsible for the destruction of parasites and for allergic reactions. The basophils secrete histamine in response to a local inflammation, and they also secrete the platelet-activating factor.

Macrophages have a generalized scavenging function and are responsible for clearing up the remnants of dying cells. This role is particularly important for dealing with the erythrocytes which are constantly being replaced because of their limited life. Despite that fact that the removal of cell debris is a major function of macrophages it is not clear exactly how this particular form of endocytosis is initiated. More is known about the ingestion of foreign organisms and particles that have been targeted by specific antibodies. The macrophages have specific cell-surface receptors which recognize and engulf antibody-coated particles and bacteria. They can degrade a protein antigen into peptide fragments which are posted on the surface in conjunction with its special major histocompatibility complex (MHC) class II proteins.

Lymphocytes are derived from stem cells which differentiate initially in the bone marrow and migrate to lymphoid tissue where they form small clones of T cells and B cells, which can recognize a specific antigen. When this recognition occurs the B cells divide rapidly, forming memory cells, which retain the capacity to recognize the antigen, and plasma cells, which secrete large amounts of specific immunoglobulins. T cells do not secrete antibodies but can recognize and bind to B cells which have detected and bound a specific antigen. This interaction by the helper T cell subset stimulates the B cell to proliferate by the release of cytokines. The cytotoxic T cells have the specialized function of recognizing foreign peptides posted on the surface of infected cells in association with the normal cell-surface protein marker, the class I MHC. When this recognition occurs the cytotoxic T cells destroy the infected cell by making its membrane leaky.

Platelet formation

The megakaryocytes differentiate from stem cells without leaving the bone marrow. These large cells have polyploid nuclei and are filled with secretory granules which contain platelet precursors. A single cell can produce as many as 1000 platelets. Platelets are membrane-bound structures that have no nucleus or cytoplasmic organelles but do have granules containing blood clotting factors. These factors are released when the platelets are stimulated by a plasmalogen, the platelet-activating factor, which is released by basophils at sites of endothelial cell damage.

12.3 The formation and degradation of red blood cells

Haemopoietic stem cells in the bone marrow can form both erythrocytes and leucocytes. Interleukin 3, a cytokine, is responsible for stimulating the differentiation of these stem cells into an erythrocyte burst-forming cell. The actual formation of an erythrocyte colony-producing cell also requires the binding of erythropoietin, a glycoprotein produced by the kidney. The erythropoietin stimulates the production and release of mature erythrocytes.

Erythrocyte maturation

Figure 12.2 shows the stages in the maturation of the erythrocytes. The first stage is the formation of erythroblasts, which begin the synthesis of haemoglobin as well as spectrin and other characteristic red cell membrane proteins. The next stage is the loss of the nucleus which is pinched off. The surviving part of the cell is called a reticulocyte. When the nucleus is lost, most of the cell-surface glycoproteins disappear with the nucleus except for the band 3 anion exchange protein and glycophorin. At the reticulocyte stage, synthesis of haemoglobin and the other erythrocyte proteins continues, but gradually the mitochondria and ribosomes are lost so that protein synthesis stops and the reticulocyte develops into a mature erythrocyte.

Erythrocyte degradation

Human erythrocytes have a life span of approximately 120 days, and then they are degraded by the spleen. The polypeptide part of the haemoglobin is degraded to amino acids, but the haem is converted to biliverdin, a linear tetrapyrrole, by haem oxygenase, a P-450 monooxygenase (see Figure 12.3). The central methylene carbon in biliverdin is then reduced by biliverdin reductase in the presence of NADPH to form bilirubin which is transported to the liver by

Blood

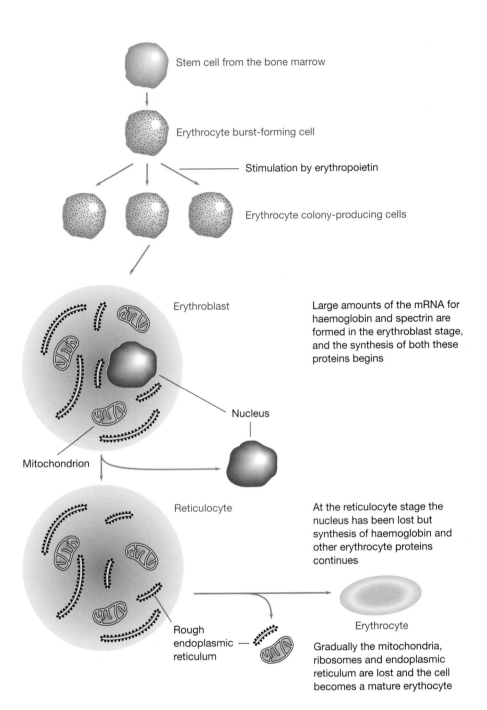

Stem cell from the bone marrow

Erythrocyte burst-forming cell

Stimulation by erythropoietin

Erythrocyte colony-producing cells

Erythroblast

Large amounts of the mRNA for haemoglobin and spectrin are formed in the erythroblast stage, and the synthesis of both these proteins begins

Nucleus

Mitochondrion

Reticulocyte

At the reticulocyte stage the nucleus has been lost but synthesis of haemoglobin and other erythrocyte proteins continues

Erythrocyte

Rough endoplasmic reticulum

Gradually the mitochondria, ribosomes and endoplasmic reticulum are lost and the cell becomes a mature erythocyte

Figure 12.2
Steps involved in the maturation of erythrocytes.

serum albumin. In the liver bilirubin is solubilized by conjugation with two gluc-uronate molecules and excreted into the bile.

The other interesting point about the conversion of biliverdin into bilirubin is that bilirubin can act as a very effective antioxidant. When it reacts with oxygen free radicals bilirubin reverts to biliverdin. In this way bilirubin joins with ascorbate and urate as valuable antioxidants circulating in the blood. It is also interesting to note that bilirubin, because of its limited aqueous solubility, is an effective antioxidant in membranes together with vitamin E.

Blood

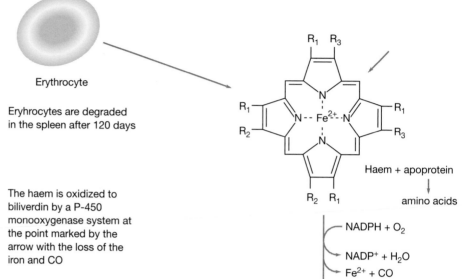

Erythrocyte

Eryhrocytes are degraded in the spleen after 120 days

Haem + apoprotein

amino acids

The haem is oxidized to biliverdin by a P-450 monooxygenase system at the point marked by the arrow with the loss of the iron and CO

NADPH + O_2

NADP$^+$ + H_2O

Fe^{2+} + CO

Biliverdin is then reduced to bilirubin which is transported to the liver by serum albumin. In the liver it is conjugated with glucuronate and excreted in the bile

Biliverdin

NADPH + H$^+$

NADP$^+$

H_2O_2

$O_2^{-\cdot}$

Since bilirubin can be converted back to biliverdin by oxygen free radicals ($O_2^{-\cdot}$) it serves as a valuable antioxidant

Bilirubin

$R_1 = -CH_3$

$R_2 = -CH_2-CH_2-COO^-$

$R_3 = -CH=CH_2$

Figure 12.3
Bilirubin formation during erythrocyte degradation.

12.4 The transport of oxygen and carbon dioxide

Haemoglobin is responsible for oxygen transfer from the lungs to the tissues. This process is a consequence of the quaternary structure of the haemoglobin molecule which is constructed from two α chains and two β chains. If haemoglobin were a monomer, or a polymer of one type of polypeptide chain, the molecule would have a high affinity for oxygen in common with that exhibited by myoglobin in muscle. However, the combination of two pairs of α plus two pairs of β chains produces a molecule which has a much lower initial affinity for oxygen in red blood cells and binds oxygen in a cooperative manner. The reason for the difference in oxygen-binding affinity is the presence in the red cells of a three-carbon compound, 2,3-bisphosphoglycerate (BPG), formed from one of the intermediates in the glycolytic pathway (see Figure 12.4). One molecule of BPG binds to the two β chains in the central cavity of the haemoglobin molecule and stabilizes the deoxygenated form of the molecule. When oxygen binds to haemoglobin the BPG is extruded from the haemoglobin, but the BPG re-enters the protein when the oxygen dissociates. The concentration of BPG in red blood cells is about the same as that of haemoglobin and the effect of the presence of BPG is to give the haemoglobin a low affinity for oxygen at the P_{O_2} found in tissues and a relatively high affinity at the P_{O_2} in the lungs.

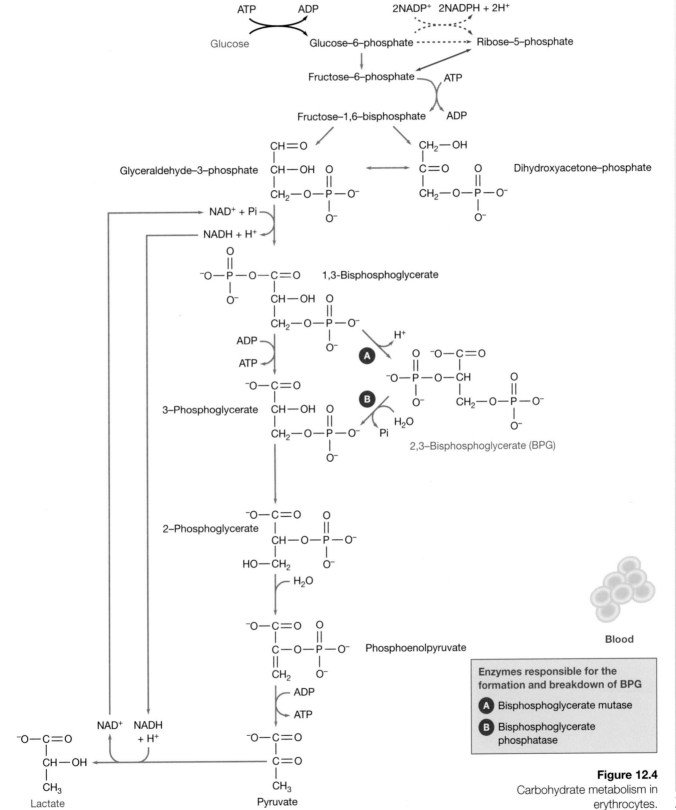

Figure 12.4
Carbohydrate metabolism in erythrocytes.

The effect of pH on haemoglobin in erythrocytes

The other factor that influences the oxygen-binding affinity of haemoglobin is the pH inside the red blood cells. As the pH is reduced the affinity of haemoglobin for oxygen decreases. As indicated in Figure 12.5(a) this has important implications for the transport of CO_2 from the tissues back to the lungs. When the red cells arrive in the tissue capillaries with oxygenated haemoglobin there is a relatively high CO_2 concentration, as a result of substrate oxidation. This diffuses into the red cells where carbonic anhydrase rapidly converts it into carbonic acid which immediately dissociates into HCO_3^- and H^+. The protons decrease the affinity of the haemoglobin for O_2, increasing its release into the tissues where the oxygen level is low. The deoxygenated haemoglobin is stabilized by BPG binding. The bicarbonate ions diffuse out into the plasma in exchange for chloride so that most of the CO_2 is transported back to the lungs in the plasma as HCO_3^-. In the lungs, where the O_2 concentration is relatively high, the O_2 binds to haemoglobin displacing the BPG and releasing protons. The H^+ combines with HCO_3^- which has diffused in from the plasma and carbonic anhydrase converts H_2CO_3 into $H_2O + CO_2$ which is released into the air spaces in the lung. About 15% of the CO_2 is also carried from the tissues to the lung by haemoglobin by the reversible formation of carbaminohaemoglobin through the addition of CO_2 to the N-terminal groups on the protein (see Figure 12.5a).

Because erythrocytes have no mitochondria they have only a limited set of metabolic pathways and the only source of ATP is the conversion of glucose to lactate by the glycolytic pathway. The absence of a nucleus also means that there is no protein synthesis so that most of the ATP produced will be required for the operation of the Na^+/K^+ ATPase. This ion pumping is essential to permit red cells to retain their doughnut shape.

The formation of 2,3-bisphosphoglycerate

As shown in Figure 12.4 the glycolysis pathway provides the BPG which is important for oxygen transport in addition to supplying the erythrocytes with ATP. BPG is formed from 1,3-bisphosphoglycerate by bisphosphoglycerate mutase, and converted back to 3-phosphoglycerate by a phosphatase. As described in section 2.3 trace amounts of BPG are necessary for the conversion of 3-phosphoglycerate to 2-phosphoglycerate in the glycolytic pathway. However, erythrocytes differ from other cells in that they contain about 4 mM BPG so the activity of the bisphosphoglycerate mutase and the bisphosphoglycerate phosphatase must be maintained at a high level. It is also important for BPG formation to be carefully regulated for two reasons. First of all, as mentioned above, the concentration of BPG must be maintained in order to ensure the unloading of O_2 from haemoglobin in the tissues where the Po_2 is low. Secondly, the reactions for the formation and degradation of BPG are essentially irreversible, and it is also important to prevent an excessive operation of this shunt around 3-phosphoglycerate because it sharply reduces the ATP yield from glycolysis. The pyruvate produced in glycolysis must be converted into lactate in order to regenerate the NAD^+ needed for the glyceraldehyde-3-phosphate dehydrogenase step. The lactate returns to the liver where it can serve as a substrate for gluconeogenesis.

BPG itself inhibits the bisphosphoglycerate mutase reaction so that when the O_2 concentration is high in the lung, and BPG is released from most haemoglobin molecules because of O_2 binding, the high concentration of free BPG will inhibit its synthesis. When the erythrocytes are in the tissues, on the other hand, most of the haemoglobin molecules will have BPG bound to them and the reduction in the concentration of unbound BPG will stimulate its synthesis and reinforce the release of O_2 from the haemoglobin.

1 Gas exchange in the lungs

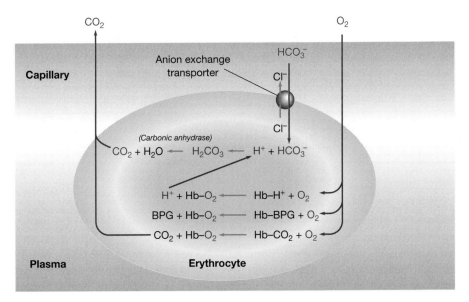

2 Gas exchange in the tissues

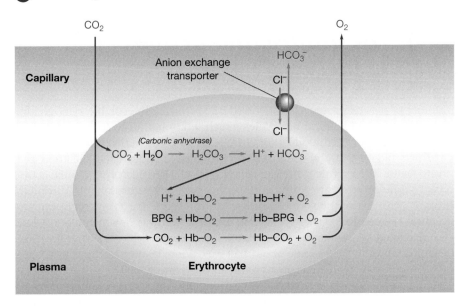

Figure 12.5(a)
Transport of oxygen and carbon dioxide by erythrocytes.

The protective role of NADPH in erythrocytes

Figure 12.5(b) indicates that the other metabolic pathway which is important in red blood cells is the pentose phosphate pathway which oxidizes glucose-6-phosphate and produces NADPH. This reduced coenzyme is important to protect the erythrocytes from the superoxide free radicals that are generated by the high concentration of oxygen. Deoxyhaemoglobin can be oxidized to methaemoglobin by free O_2 and this reaction produces a superoxide radical. The methaemoglobin cannot bind O_2 because the iron is in the Fe^{3+} state, but it can be reduced back to the normal deoxyhaemoglobin form by NADPH in the presence of methaemoglobin reductase. The NADPH is also important for the elimination of the superoxide radical, where the initial step is the conversion of two superoxide radicals into hydrogen peroxide and oxygen by superoxide dismutase (see Figure 4.11). The hydrogen peroxide is converted to water by glutathione peroxidase,

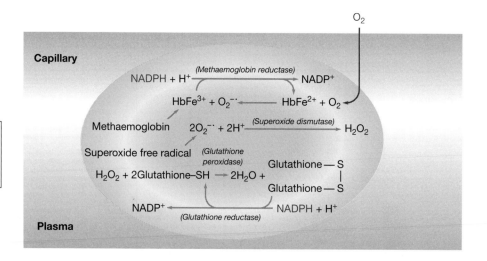

Hb, HbFe^{+2} = haemoglobin
HbFe^{+3} = methaemoglobin
O$_2^{-\cdot}$ = oxygen free radical
H$_2$O$_2$ = hydrogen peroxide

Figure 12.5(b)
The protective effects of NADPH
in erythrocytes.

and the resulting oxidized glutathione must be reduced by NADPH. Removal of the superoxide radicals and hydrogen peroxide is crucial for the survival of red blood cells because these cells cannot regenerate their proteins or membrane components, and oxidation by the superoxides would damage these constituents.

12.5 The nature and actions of clotting factors

A number of plasma proteins are involved in converting the soluble zymogen fibrinogen into insoluble fibrin molecules which link together to form blood clots. The initial signal for the blood-clotting process can come in two ways. The intrinsic pathway begins with the release of two proteins, kininogen and kallikrein, that activate factor XII, a serine protease, which sets off a cascade of sequential activations of serine proteases resulting in the conversion of prothrombin to thrombin. Thrombin, the last of the serine proteases in the sequence, converts fibrinogen into fibrin (Figure 12.6). There is also an extrinsic pathway in which blood vessel tissue damaged by trauma releases a tissue factor and activates a serine protease. These proteins join the cascade about half way along, leading to the activation of prothrombin and the formation of fibrin in the same way. The insoluble fibrin molecules associate loosely with each other. This soft clot is converted into a hard clot by a transglutaminase enzyme (factor XIII) which cross-links the fibrin molecules by the removal of short peptides. It is also important that the circulatory system should be protected from the presence of thrombin when it is not needed. This is achieved by the presence of another plasma protein, antithrombin, which binds excess thrombin.

The action of platelets in the clotting process

Another feature of the blood-clotting process is the involvement of platelets. Damage to endothelial cells exposes collagen fibres and stimulates basophils to secrete a plasmalogen called platelet-activating factor. As a consequence platelets begin to aggregate at the site of the damage, a process which is facilitated by the release of a large glycoprotein, known as the von Willebrand factor. This protein binds the platelets to the site of the injury, and it also helps to oper-

Blood

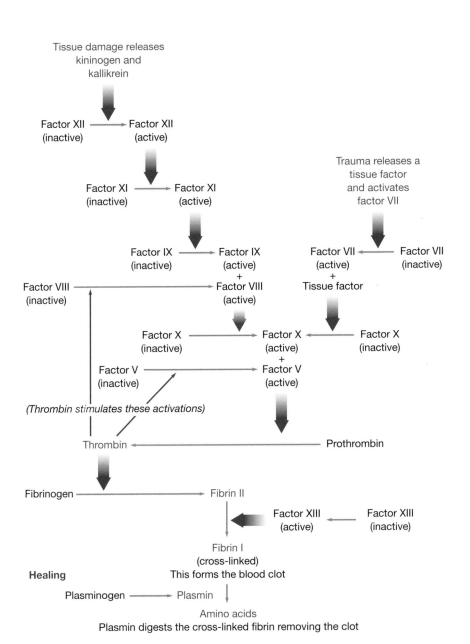

Figure 12.6
The cascade of proteolytic enzymes responsible for the formation of blood clots and the action of plasmin in the removal of clots.

ate the clotting cascade since it is complexed with the inactive form of factor VIII. When the platelets aggregate at the site of the damage they release a number of constituents by exocytosis including phospholipids and lipoproteins. This release is initiated by thrombin or adrenaline. As indicated in section 12.9 the release of a growth factor known as platelet-derived growth factor from the endothelial cells and macrophages as well as platelets may have an important role in the initiation of atherosclerosis. The release of material from the platelets by exocytosis is stimulated by a particular group of prostaglandins, the thromboxanes. The formation of prostaglandins is inhibited by aspirin and it is for this reason that individuals thought to be at risk because the blood-clotting mechanism has become too active are often treated with low doses of aspirin.

Once bleeding from a damaged vessel has been stopped, healing begins and the hard fibrin clot is digested by plasmin, another proteolytic enzyme which is activated by conversion from plasminogen. This removal of the clot is an important feature of the healing process.

12.6 Summary of the stages in the synthesis of antibodies by lymphocytes and plasma cells

The functions of B cells

In order to protect the body against infection two types of immune responses by lymphocytes have developed. The simpler approach, known as humoral immunity, involves the production and secretion of soluble antibody molecules. Each specific antibody protein has a unique amino acid sequence which binds to a particular antigenic determinant. In principle this implies that each of the millions of antibodies must have its own specific genetic information. However, it is now clear that the genes within a particular lymphocyte for the heavy and light chains of a specific antibody have been formed by combining base sequences from different segments of DNA. The genetic information for each chain is obtained from a constant region gene and segments of variable and joining region genes. The B lymphocytes arise from the bone marrow stem cells which enter the blood and lymph nodes. During the differentiation of the antibody-producing B lymphocytes the genetic information is formed for millions of distinct antibodies.

Each mature B cell will express only one binding specificity, and initially this specificity will be found in a small number of identical cells. The B cells can synthesize five different types of immunoglobulin with the same antigen-combining site. When a B cell first detects an antigen with its specific antigenic determinant, its primary response is to secrete the large pentameric IgM antibodies. In addition to secreting soluble antibodies, the B lymphocytes have cell-surface receptors that express the same binding specificity. When a foreign antigen appears it only binds to those B cells with the appropriate binding site for that antigenic determinant. This binding causes the cells to divide and produce a large clone of antibody-producing plasma cells. After a week or more the secretion of IgM declines and the smaller monomeric IgG molecule is secreted, reaching its maximal levels after about three weeks. Any subsequent exposure to the same antigen will result in the production of large amounts of IgG within a few hours. The other type of immunoglobulin secreted in significant amounts is IgA. This crosses epithelial layers as a dimer and its presence in the airways, saliva, tears and in the digestive and reproductive tracts helps to protect against pathogens entering the body.

As a consequence of the combination of the soluble antibodies with the antigenic determinant on a bacterium or a foreign protein, the antibody–antigen complex will be taken up by phagocytosis. Uptake by macrophages, neutrophils and eosinophils will be followed by the intracellular digestion of the foreign material. Combination of antigen and antibody can also trigger the complement cascade which results in the lysis of the bacterium (see section 12.7).

Cytotoxic T lymphocytes

The second and more complex type of immune response developed by lymphocytes is called cellular immunity. In this case no binding proteins are secreted. Instead the T lymphocytes express specific receptors on the surface of their cell membranes. Like the soluble antibodies these T cell receptors have a wide range of specificity as a consequence of forming the receptor genes by combining sequence information from constant, variable and joining region genes. There are two types of T cells with quite different functions. The function of one of the T cell types is to destroy cells which have become infected with a virus. These cytotoxic T cells are able to recognize the infected cell because fragments of the foreign antigen will appear on the surface of the cell in association with the normal cell-surface marker for that individual (MHC I).

The cell-surface markers that are crucial for the operation of the two types of T cells are produced by a large group of genes known as the MHC. For each individual differentiation leads to the expression of a specific MHC I glycoprotein on virtually all cells in the body. When a cell becomes infected by a virus, fragments of the virus proteins will appear on the surface of the infected cell in association with the MHC I glycoprotein. This combination is recognized as an abnormal antigen by cytotoxic T cells and as a result they secrete enzymes that cause the destruction of the infected cell.

Helper T cells

The second group of T cells are helper T cells. The B lymphocytes and macrophages have a different surface marker from all the other cells in the body. When these cells encounter a foreign antigen that binds to a receptor on their surface, the antigen plus receptor are internalized by endocytosis. Subsequently the antigen is digested by the combination of the endosome with a lysosome, producing peptide products which return to the cell surface. On the outside of the plasma membrane the peptides are displayed in association with the special surface marker MHC II, which is expressed only on the B cells of the immune system and macrophages. The helper T cell binds to this combination and secretes stimulatory lymphokines and chemotactic elements. If the helper T cell binds to a B cell, the lymphokines it secretes will stimulate the B cell to divide and differentiate into antibody-producing plasma cells. The binding of helper T cells to a macrophage expressing an antigenic fragment associated with its surface marker will result in the secretion of lymphokines and chemotactic secretions which initiate an inflammatory response.

Lymphocyte response to repeated infection

After the initial reaction to infection or the presence of a foreign antigen memory cells will be formed. If the body is then exposed to the same foreign antigen or infecting organism a second time the production of antibodies by B cells and the T cell response will be rapid. This protects against repeated infections unless the bacterium or virus is able to mutate so that it appears as a new antigen when it reinfects. This sort of genetic alteration is responsible for the recurrent infection by influenza viruses as well as the common cold.

The response of B cells and T cells to infection involves a rapid increase in the rate of cell division and protein synthesis. This increases the demand on the liver for glucose and amino acids. Because of the increased rate of nucleic acid synthesis there will also be a strong demand for glutamine to support the formation of additional nucleotides. Sections 14.9 and 14.10 indicate that this requirement may explain the increase in plasma glutamine concentration that is associated with infection and tumour growth.

12.7 Complement enzymes and their functions

The complement proteins are a group of about 20 enzymes present in the blood plasma in an inactive form. There are two pathways for activating the complement enzymes. The classical pathway is triggered by the binding of IgG or IgM to antigenic groups on a bacterium. Component C1, which has a number of globular heads, then becomes linked to the constant region of several antibody molecules bound to the antigens on the microorganism. This starts the cascade of proteolytic reactions. When the end of the sequence is reached, five activated complement proteins combine to form a lytic complex which can cause the lysis of bacteria by forming an aqueous channel through the cell membrane. An early component of the activation cascade can combine with specific macrophage receptors. Since this complement protein is bound to the bacterium it promotes the phagocytosis of the organism by the macrophage even if the lytic complex does not form. A number of the components of the complement cascade also produce protein fragments which activate mast cells to secrete histamine causing a local inflammation.

12.8 Distribution of cholesterol to peripheral tissues and its return to the liver

All cells require cholesterol for their membranes. Although many tissues, including the CNS, have the capacity to synthesize cholesterol from glucose, most cholesterol is either obtained from the diet or as a result of synthesis in the liver. In addition, the liver is the only quantitatively important site of cholesterol excretion in the body. Consequently it is necessary for the blood to transport cholesterol to the peripheral tissues and to return excess cholesterol or the cholesterol released from recycled membranes to the liver for excretion.

Cholesterol makes up about 50% of the LDL particles which are responsible for transporting most of the cholesterol from the liver to other tissues (see Figure 6.12b). However, more than half of the LDL is actually taken back into the liver. Uptake of LDL depends on the presence of the LDL receptor which binds the apoprotein B-100. The LDL receptor is a large glycoprotein anchored to the plasma membrane by a small membrane-spanning region near the C-terminus. Much of the LDL receptor has close sequence homology with epidermal growth factor, and the negatively charged N-terminal region binds the positively charged region of apoprotein B-100 on the LDL. Once it is attached to the receptor the LDL is taken up by endocytosis. Acidification of the endosome separates the LDL from the receptor. The lipoprotein is transferred to a lysosome and the LDL receptor is returned to the membrane. Hydrolysis of the lipoprotein constituents contributes free cholesterol and amino acids to the cell taking up the LDL particle. If the pool of free cholesterol exceeds the amount required for membrane synthesis, this will tend to restrict the acquisition of additional cholesterol in two ways. The cholesterol inhibits HMG-CoA reductase, the controlling enzyme for endogenous cholesterol synthesis, particularly in the liver. Synthesis of new LDL receptor molecules is also inhibited. The free cholesterol increases the activity of acyl-CoA cholesterol acyltransferase so that the excess cholesterol is stored in the cell as cholesteryl esters.

Since cholesterol transport by LDL is only from the liver to peripheral tissues, the return transport requires a different process. HDL particles secreted by the liver or the intestine contain about 20% cholesterol, partly in the free form, and a number of apoproteins. One of these proteins, apoprotein A1, binds the HDL to a specific receptor on the peripheral cell enabling it to take cholesterol from the plasma membrane of the cell (Figure 6.12b). It is also possible that in some cases the HDL can enter the cell and accept cholesterol from the intracellular stores, although to do this the cholesteryl esters would have to be hydrolysed. When the cholesterol has been taken up by the HDL particles it is esterified by lecithin cholesterol acyltransferase in order to keep the concentration of free cholesterol in the HDL particle low so that it can continue to receive the cholesterol down a concentration gradient.

Although it is the HDL particles that transfer the cholesterol back to the liver, they do not appear to deliver it directly to the hepatocytes (see Figure 6.12b). Instead a cholesteryl ester transfer enzyme which is synthesized in the liver transfers the cholesteryl esters from HDL to chylomicron remnants and IDL particles which are then taken up by the liver. In this way the HDL particles will return cholesterol to the liver from recycled membranes of peripheral cells and cells that are broken down. This free cholesterol entering the liver will enable it to regulate cholesterol levels by reducing synthesis or increasing excretion into the bile.

12.9 Atherosclerosis and its relationship to heart disease and stroke

Since cholesterol is essential for normal membrane structure, it is important to understand the evidence which has led to current theories about the link between elevated blood cholesterol levels and atherosclerosis. First of all it is worth describing briefly the pathological features of atherosclerosis. The initial event is thought to be due to a small injury or lesion in the endothelial lining of an artery that can easily occur even in relatively young people. This lesion can lead over a number of years to the formation of a fibrous plaque by one of three routes. If the injury increases the permeability of the vessel wall to plasma, there will be an increase in the LDL concentration in the interstitial fluid. The LDL concentration in the extracellular space outside the endothelial lining of the blood vessels is normally only about 10% of that in the plasma, and the rise in concentration can lead macrophages to form foam cells loaded with cholesteryl esters, as described below. A second route involves the presence of platelets at the site of the blood vessel lesion which leads to the release of cytokines that stimulate the proliferation of the smooth muscle cells, macrophages and extracellular deposits of lipid. Another variant has smooth muscle cells generating large amounts of connective tissue microfibrils and glycosaminoglycans together with lipid deposits.

The second phase of atherosclerosis involves the fibrous plaques enlarging and developing a complicated structure of smooth muscle and fibrous tissue with increasing amounts of extracellular lipid. In some cases the lipid core is covered by a thin cap consisting of muscle and fibrous tissue. As a result the lumen of the artery becomes seriously narrowed, increasing the possibility of a number of dangerous consequences. The narrowing of the arteries in the heart can give rise to angina because part of the heart muscle is deprived of adequate oxygen. A thrombosis or clot formation may occur at the lesion possibly as a result of the activation of one or more of the clotting factors by the cells in the plaque. The thrombosis may have no immediate effect except to extend the fibrous plaque, but it can lead to the complete occlusion of the artery causing a heart attack or a stroke. A third possibility is that the lesion may rupture, causing a haemorrhage, which can be extremely serious, particularly if it occurs in the brain.

Recent studies have provided a possible explanation for the manner in which the cholesterol-rich foam cells mentioned above are formed. It was pointed out in section 12.8 that the LDL uptake by peripheral cells not only controls the endogenous synthesis of cholesterol but also suppresses synthesis of the LDL receptor, thus limiting further LDL uptake. Unfortunately this control mechanism is only effective with low concentrations of circulating LDL. It appears that all cells are able to take up LDL particles by receptor-independent endocytosis if the LDL concentration is elevated. Under these conditions suppression by the accumulated cholesterol of endogenous cholesterol synthesis or formation of the LDL receptor would not prevent further uptake. The cholesterol taken up by cells is converted into cholesteryl esters which are deposited in the cytoplasm in a manner analogous to the storage of triacylglycerol. Furthermore, it is clear that the normal LDL levels in human blood in affluent countries are high enough to endanger arterial smooth muscle tissue and macrophages if plasma enters the extracellular spaces as a result of damage to the endothelial wall of the arteries.

Another dangerous consequence of the movement of LDL into the extracellular space is that the apoprotein B-100 may become oxidized so that it is no longer recognized by the LDL receptor but instead is taken up by a scavenger receptor on macrophages. It should be pointed out that oxidation of the LDL is much more likely outside the blood vessels because the lipoprotein is no longer protected by the antioxidants present in the blood. Figure 12.7 shows a possible way in which the oxidation of LDL can promote the formation of foam cells in atherosclerosis plaques. Despite the HDL particles and antioxidants present in the blood it is apparently possible for fatty acids in some of the phospholipids on the surface of LDL to be oxidized to aldehydes without any change in the apoprotein B-100. As a result the LDL receptor on circulating monocytes can recognize the mildly oxidized LDL and take it up. This promotes the adhesion of the monocytes to the endothelial cells and their migration between the cells into the extracellular space. The mildly oxidized LDL can also stimulate the endothelial cells to secrete cytokines into the extracellular space stimulating the development of the monocytes into a colony of macrophages with the scavenger receptor on their surface. These macrophages accumulate the fully oxidized LDL which loads them with cholesteryl esters, converting them into foam cells that fill the fibrous plaque. The presence of the fully oxidized LDL can further damage the endothelial lining of the vessel, increasing entry of monocytes and causing the adherence of platelets. In this way the initial lesion will be extended.

Although the scenario shown in Figure 12.7 is not necessarily the full explanation of the way that foam cells are produced, it does raise a number of important points in relation to diet. First, it is clear that a reduction in plasma LDL levels must be advantageous and this can result from reducing both the cholesterol and the long-chain saturated fatty acid content of the diet. Secondly, increased levels of antioxidants such as vitamins C and E and β-carotene should be helpful. Angiotensin II, which increases blood pressure, is also thought to increase the production of oxygen free radicals. Finally, it is possible that nitric oxide (NO) may exert a protective effect by stimulating superoxide dismutase. In any case, as pointed out in the next section, NO causes vasodilation which counteracts the vasoconstrictive effects of angiotensin II.

Blood

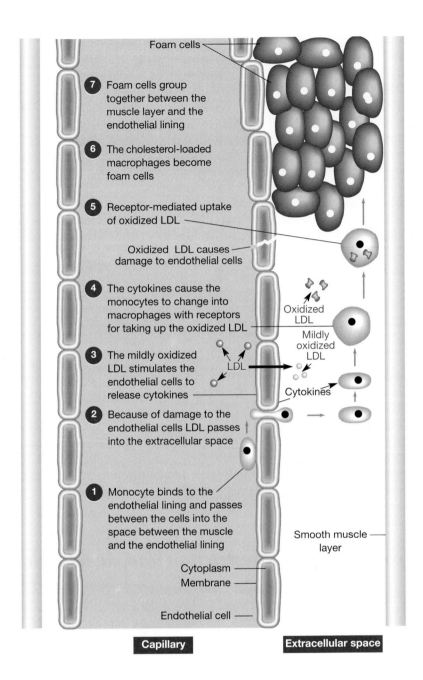

7 Foam cells group together between the muscle layer and the endothelial lining

6 The cholesterol-loaded macrophages become foam cells

5 Receptor-mediated uptake of oxidized LDL

Oxidized LDL causes damage to endothelial cells

4 The cytokines cause the monocytes to change into macrophages with receptors for taking up the oxidized LDL

3 The mildly oxidized LDL stimulates the endothelial cells to release cytokines

2 Because of damage to the endothelial cells LDL passes into the extracellular space

1 Monocyte binds to the endothelial lining and passes between the cells into the space between the muscle and the endothelial lining

Foam cells

Oxidized LDL

Mildly oxidized LDL

LDL

Cytokines

Smooth muscle layer

Cytoplasm

Membrane

Endothelial cell

Capillary

Extracellular space

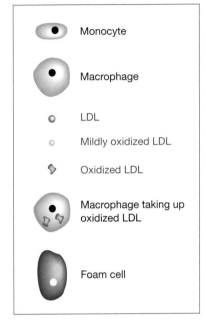

Monocyte

Macrophage

LDL

Mildly oxidized LDL

Oxidized LDL

Macrophage taking up oxidized LDL

Foam cell

Figure 12.7
Scheme indicating the role of monocytes and oxidized LDL in the formation of foam cells in atherogenesis. (Redrawn from Fig. 1 in an article by D. Steinberg in *Circulation* **84**, 1420–1425, 1991, with permission.)

12.10 Overview of the control of blood pressure

The maintenance of the blood volume and blood pressure is of vital importance for the supply of oxygen to the brain and other tissues. On the other hand, it is also essential that the pressure should not be allowed to rise too high because this can damage the endothelial lining of blood vessels, leading to the formation of blood clots that can block key arteries in the heart and brain causing heart attacks and strokes in individuals suffering from atherosclerosis. Blood pressure is monitored by pressure receptors, known as baroreceptors, in the arteries and this information is transmitted by neurones to the brain. The

Table 12.2 Mechanisms responsible for changes in blood volume (see sections 12.10 and 13.9 and Figure 13.8)

Processes that increase blood volume
- Vasopressin, produced in the hypothalamus and secreted in the posterior pituitary, increases water reabsorption by the kidney
- Aldosterone, secreted by the adrenal cortex as a result of stimulation by angiotensin II, increases the reabsorption of Na^+ and Cl^- by the kidneys and this increases water reabsorption

Processes that reduce blood volume
- Inhibition of vasopressin secretion reduces water reabsorption by the kidneys. This inhibition can be caused by alcohol or diuretics such as tea and coffee
- Inhibition of aldosterone secretion reduces water reabsorption by slowing the reabsorption of Na^+ and Cl^- by the kidneys
- Loss of blood. This can be caused by injury and would be made worse by a failure of the clotting mechanism

most important of these baroreceptors are in the carotid arteries supplying blood to the head, and in the aortic arch which monitors the output from the heart. The information from the baroreceptors about pressure changes is integrated with other information from chemoreceptors about the composition of the blood in a control centre in the medulla of the brain. The output from this cardiovascular control centre operates through the autonomic nervous system to regulate the heart rate and the degree of constriction of the peripheral blood vessels. Table 12.2 summarizes the mechanisms responsible for controlling the blood volume.

The control of vasoconstriction and vasodilation

Blood pressure is elevated as a result of stimulation of the heart through the sympathetic nerve pathways and by the secretion of adrenaline. Vasoconstriction, which also raises blood pressure, can be caused by the peptide hormones vasopressin and angiotensin. Vasopressin, which is produced in the hypothalamus and secreted into the blood in the posterior pituitary, acts on blood vessels in the kidney and also on a range of peripheral blood vessels. Figure 12.8(a) shows that angiotensin is formed from angiotensinogen synthesized in the liver and converted into the active form, angiotensin II, by a two-stage process. Renin in the blood converts the angiotensinogen into angiotensin I. The second stage of the activation is carried out by another enzyme, angiotensin I-converting enzyme which also inactivates the vasodilator bradykinin. The angiotensin II binds to specific receptors on the membrane of vascular cells causing vasoconstriction by opening Ca^{2+} channels in the underlying smooth muscle cells. Bradykinin and parasympathetic nerve stimulation cause vasodilation by relaxation of vascular smooth muscle. The mechanism responsible for this process involves the formation of the local effector NO from arginine in the endothelial lining of blood vessels. Figure 12.8(b) shows the process involved in the stimulation of NO synthesis and the subsequent effects of this signal molecule on the adjoining smooth muscle cells. NO-mediated smooth muscle relaxation is also important for erection of the penis.

Mechanisms responsible for vasoconstriction

(a) Stimulation of the sympathetic nervous system. This results in the secretion of adrenaline which increases the heart rate, and causes contraction of muscles surrounding blood vessels serving internal organs. Some sympathetic nerves cause direct vasoconstriction.

(b) Release of the enzyme renin from the juxtaglomerular cells of the arteries leading into the glomeruli in the kidney. Renin is released in response to a fall in blood pressure which may be detected by the CNS, leading to direct stimulation of β_2-adrenergic receptors. Alternatively, local changes in blood pressure may stimulate prostacyclin secretion by endothelial cells which directly causes renin release from the juxtaglomerular cells via cyclic AMP. Once it is released the renin activates the renin–angiotensin system, causing vasoconstriction by stimulating contraction of the smooth muscle surrounding the endothelial lining of the blood vessel.

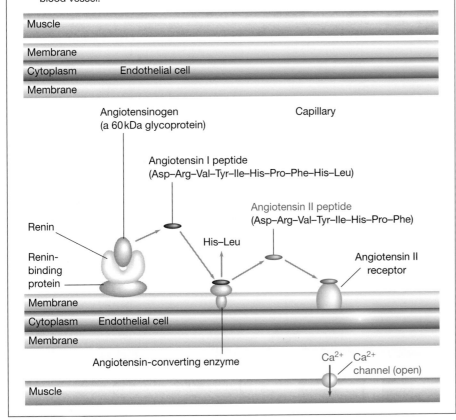

The binding of angiotensin II to its receptor on the endothelial cell causes the calcium channels in the adjacent smooth muscle to open, initiating contraction.

Figure 12.8(a)
Mechanisms responsible for vasoconstriction.

12.11 Summary of the role of the blood in the transport of nutrients, hormones and waste products between tissues

The blood interacts with all tissues, although it is isolated from the CNS by the blood–brain barrier. In addition to supplying oxygen and removing carbon dioxide from all tissues, blood, as shown in Figure 12.9, is responsible for the transport of hormones and other signal molecules. It also transports nutrients from the intestine and the liver to all the remaining tissues and removes meta-

Blood

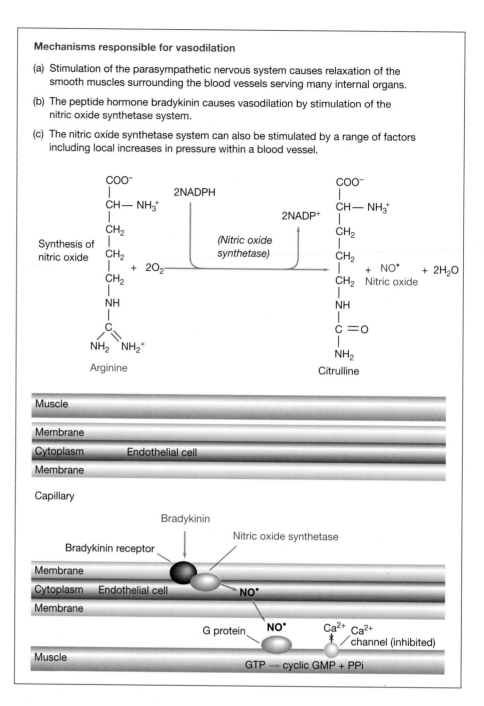

Mechanisms responsible for vasodilation

(a) Stimulation of the parasympathetic nervous system causes relaxation of the smooth muscles surrounding the blood vessels serving many internal organs.

(b) The peptide hormone bradykinin causes vasodilation by stimulation of the nitric oxide synthetase system.

(c) The nitric oxide synthetase system can also be stimulated by a range of factors including local increases in pressure within a blood vessel.

The release of NO$^•$ causes vasodilation by inhibiting muscle contraction.

Figure 12.8(b)
Mechanisms responsible for vasodilation.

bolic waste products formed in other tissues to the kidneys and the liver. The controlled operation of the heart and the kidneys is obviously crucial for the maintenance of the blood circulation.

The protective function of the blood has many facets. At the simplest level the phagocytes remove cell debris, and the clotting system prevents leaks. At the sophisticated end the immune system operates to protect the body against infective agents and other foreign antigens. Between these extremes there are a number of important protective processes such as the effects of the circulating antioxidants, and the role of the endothelial cells and their adjacent smooth muscle cells in regulating blood supply to specific areas in response to changes in conditions.

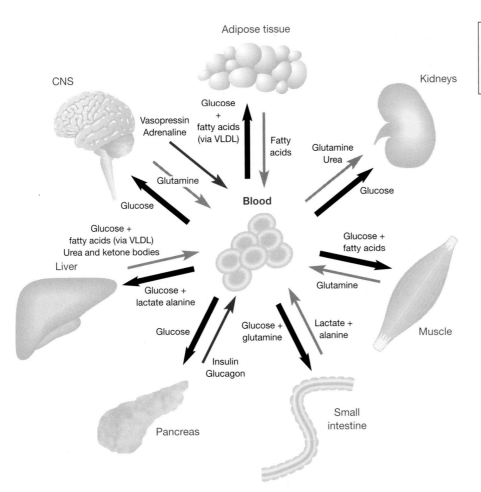

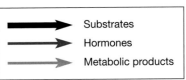

Figure 12.9
Summary of the role of the blood in transporting nutrients, waste products and hormones.

E X E R C I S E S

1. List the principal features that distinguish erythrocytes from leucocytes.

2. List the stages in erythrocyte formation.

3. What is the role of 2,3-bisphosphoglycerate in oxygen transport?

4. How does the transport of carbon dioxide as bicarbonate help the transfer of oxygen from the lungs to the tissues?

5. Why is NADPH production important for erythrocytes?

6. What is the role of platelets in the formation of blood clots?

7. Summarize the distinction between B and T lymphocytes.

8. How does HDL transfer cholesterol from peripheral cells to the liver?

9. What is a foam cell?

10. List the main antioxidants that are present in the blood.

Further reading

Austyn, J.M. and Wood, K.J. (1993) *Principles of Cellular and Molecular Immunology*, Oxford University Press.

Bussolino, F., Mantovani, A. & Persico, G. (1997) Molecular mechanisms of blood vessel formation, *Trends in Biochemical Sciences* **22**, 251–256.

Dow, J., Lindsay, G. & Morrison, J. (1996) *Biochemistry, Molecules, Cells and the Body*, Addison-Wesley, Chapter 12.

Matsusaka, T. & Ichikawa, I. (1997) Biological functions of angiotensin and its receptors. *Annual Review of Physiology* **59**, 395–412.

Meyer, B. & Hemmens, B. (1997) Biosynthesis and action of nitric oxide in mammalian cells, *Trends in Biochemical Sciences* **22**, 477–481.

Parham, P. (1996) Functions for MHC class I carbohydrates inside and outside the cell, *Trends in Biochemical Sciences* **21**, 427–433.

Smith, C.A. & Wood, E.J. (1996) *Cell Biology*, 2nd edition, Chapman & Hall.

Tall, A. (1995) Plasma lipid transfer proteins, *Annual Review of Biochemistry* **64**, 235–257.

The kidneys

Glomerular filtration allows waste products to be excreted and the reabsorption of solutes from the lumen of the kidney tubules is largely responsible for maintaining the concentrations of most low molecular weight constituents of the blood.

In the kidneys glutamine metabolism helps to regulate blood pH, and gluconeogenesis supports metabolism in the kidney medulla as well as maintaining blood glucose during starvation.

13.1 Elimination of waste products and control of blood volume and solute concentrations in plasma

The kidneys play a key role in the control of blood volume as well as the plasma concentrations of ions and most solutes with a molecular weight below 10,000. Human kidneys achieve this by the ultrafiltration of about 200 litres of blood plasma per day through the glomerulus into the top ends of the kidney tubules. As the filtrate passes down the tubules most of the water and solutes are reabsorbed by the epithelial lining so that only about 1.5 litres of urine are produced each day. The major nitrogen compounds in the urine which enter the kidney tubule through the glomerulus are urea (about 30 g/day), creatinine (1–4 g/day) and urate (1–2 g/day). In addition the tubule cells secrete ammonium ions (about 1 g/day) into the tubule, thus providing an active form of excretion of nitrogen to supplement the passive filtration by the glomerulus. The secretion of protons and ammonia also enables the kidneys to regulate the acid--base balance of the blood.

Metabolism in the kidneys

The kidney tubule cells are able to carry out their reabsorptive and secretory functions because they are highly polarized epithelial cells linked by tight junctions. As with the intestinal epithelium the presence of the tight junctions can restrict particular transport proteins to either the luminal or the basolateral membrane. This separation of luminal and basolateral transporters permits the flow of transported solutes from tubule lumen to the blood or, in the case of secreted solutes, from the blood to the lumen. The tight junctions do not prevent the paracellular movement of water across the tubule wall, and the uptake of water from the tubule lumen is a passive osmotically driven process resulting from the active reabsorption of ions and other solutes. The driving force for these transport processes is largely provided by the Na^+/K^+ ATPase on the basolateral membrane which maintains a low intracellular Na^+ concentration and a membrane potential of about $-80\,mV$ (negative intracellularly). As a consequence of their high level of transport activity the kidneys have the highest rate of oxidative metabolism/kg tissue in the body, and they use nearly 20% of the body's oxygen consumption at rest (see Table 5.1). Figure 13.1 shows that the kidneys are capable of metabolizing a wide range of substrates including glucose, fatty acids, amino acids and ketone bodies, when they are available.

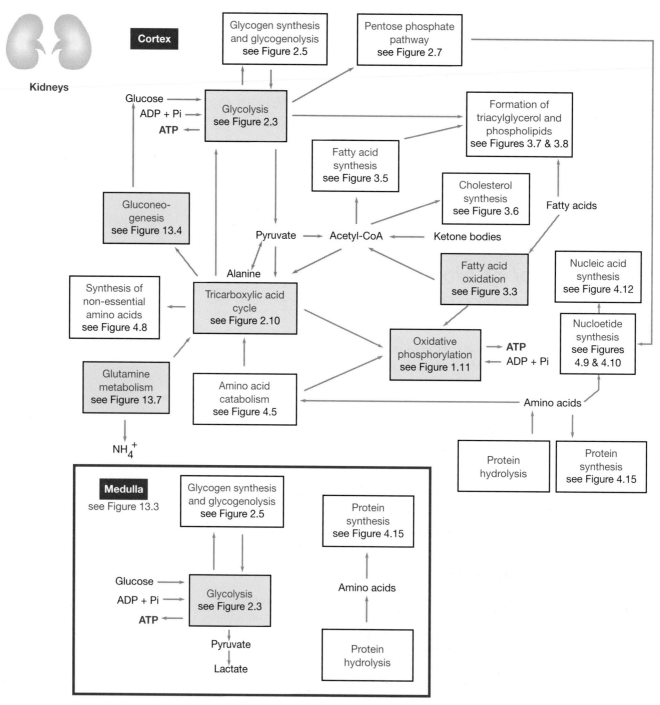

Figure 13.1 Summary of metabolic pathways in kidney cortex and medulla. The blue areas show the important pathways in the cortex and the medulla.

Excretion and reabsorption by the kidney tubules

As illustrated in Figure 13.2 each kidney tubule, or nephron, begins with the glomerulus in the cortex region, loops down into the medulla and back up to the cortex where it joins the collecting duct. This allows the glomerular filtrate to pass through both the cortex and medulla regions of the kidney twice before it leaves as urine. The first cortical section of the tubule, known as the proximal convoluted tubule, is where most of the glucose and amino acids are reabsorbed. The cortex is well vascularized so that all the metabolism in this region is aerobic. The next section of the tubule is the loop of Henle which extends down into the medulla where the oxygen supply is relatively poor so that in this section the energy for ion absorption comes largely from glycolysis (see Figure 13.1). The medulla does have reasonable supplies of glycogen, but it seems likely that the glucose from the tubule lumen provides much of the substrate for glycolysis in the medulla. The Na^+ and Cl^- absorption from the loop of Henle in the medulla provide a relatively high osmolarity in the interstitial fluid surrounding the collecting duct branches which also pass through the medulla region on the way to the renal pelvis. As a consequence of the high salt concentration, water moves rapidly out of the collecting ducts, increasing the osmolarity of the urine until it is three to four times that of the blood. At the end of the loop of Henle the tubule joins the distal convoluted tubule in the cortex where the remaining glucose and amino acids are reabsorbed. The distal section of the tubule ends where it joins a branch of the collecting duct in the cortical region. Only those substances that are reabsorbed are returned from the glomerular filtrate to the blood so that, in addition to the nitrogen-containing waste products such as creatinine, urea and urate, foreign molecules such as drugs will pass out in the urine. It should also be noted that since the osmolarity of the urine is about three times that of the blood, it contains relatively high concentrations of inorganic salts (e.g. NaCl, KCl, NaH_2PO_4, Na_2SO_4).

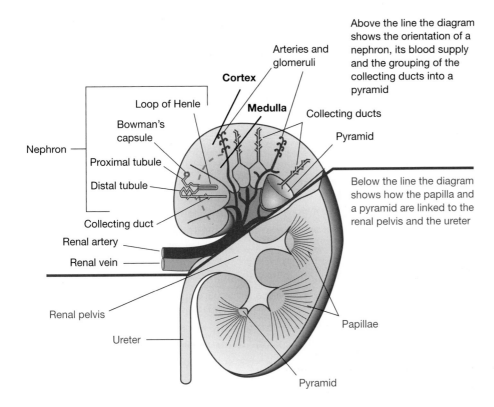

Figure 13.2(a)
Diagram illustrating the overall organization of the kidney.

303

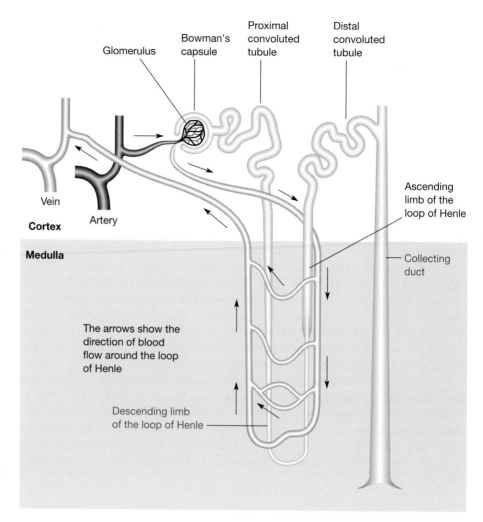

Glomerulus

Bowman's
capsule

Proximal
convoluted
tubule

Distal
convoluted
tubule

Vein

Cortex   Artery

Ascending
limb of the
loop of Henle

Medulla

Collecting
duct

The arrows show the
direction of blood
flow around the loop
of Henle

Descending limb
of the loop of Henle

Figure 13.2(b)
Diagram illustrating the regions of the
nephron and the orientation of the
capillaries serving the loop of Henle.

Vascular control systems operating in the kidneys

A number of controls operate in the kidney to regulate the blood volume, salt
content and blood pressure. The major regulator of water reabsorption is the
peptide hormone vasopressin, also known as antidiuretic hormone (see Table
12.2). By activating adenyl cyclase this hormone increases the permeability of the
collecting ducts to water through a protein kinase-dependent phosphorylation of
membrane proteins. As we shall see in section 13.10 there is a complex interplay
of factors regulating blood pressure and salt content. When the salt content or
the pressure is reduced the capillaries serving the cortical area secrete renin
which converts angiotensinogen into angiotensin I. Further conversion to
angiotensin II leads to vasoconstriction increasing the blood pressure (see Figure
12.8a). The angiotensin II also stimulates the adrenal cortex to secrete aldosterone which increases Na^+ reabsorption from the distal convoluted tubule
raising the osmolarity of the blood. These angiotensin II effects are opposed by
bradykinin which inhibits the angiotensin-converting enzyme. A hormone called
natriuretic peptide is secreted by the atrium of the heart in response to an elevated blood pressure. This peptide inhibits the secretion of renin by the renal
cortex capillaries. There are also specific controls of phosphate reabsorption by
the kidneys. Parathyroid hormone is secreted in response to a drop in blood calcium levels and this decreases reabsorption of phosphate as well as stimulating
production of calcitriol, the active form of vitamin D.

13.2 Structure and functions of the various regions of the kidney tubule

Each kidney tubule and its associated collecting duct form one of the many functional units, or nephrons, that make up the mammalian kidney. The fluid enters the tubule through a knot of capillaries called the glomerulus which is effectively an ultrafilter retaining proteins and cellular elements within the vascular system but allowing water, ions and small organic solutes through into the cup-shaped top of the tubule known as Bowman's capsule. The first twisted section of the nephron in the kidney cortex is known as the proximal convoluted tubule. The cells lining this part of the tubule are similar to those in the intestinal epithelium, because they have extensive microvilli and are linked to neighbouring cells by tight junctions. Thus the luminal surface of these cells is in the form of a brush border whereas the basolateral membrane which borders the capillaries of the vascular system is flat and well supplied with mitochondria to support the Na^+/K^+ ATPase. The proximal tubule connects to the loop of Henle that extends into the medulla and returns to the cortex joining the distal convoluted tubule. The last part of the nephron is a small branch of the collecting duct.

The nephrons form a fan-shaped array with the glomerulus and proximal and distal tubules at the outer edge of the organ and the loops of Henle and the collecting ducts extending from the cortical region deep into the medulla where they are grouped together in papillae. The collecting ducts open through the papillae into a central cavity known as the renal pelvis which narrows down to become the ureter.

Each nephron has its own blood supply with an arteriole leading first to the glomerulus. After supplying blood to the proximal and distal convoluted tubule regions the capillaries then extend into the medulla surrounding the loop of Henle before they return to the cortex and enter a vein (see Figure 13.2b). From this arrangement it should be clear that the oxygen content of the blood supply to the medulla will be substantially less than that in the cortex which explains the dependence of the medulla on glycolysis for its energy supply.

13.3 Characteristics and control of glomerular filtration

The knot of capillaries that forms the glomerulus is surrounded by the cup of tubule cells comprising Bowman's capsule. The basement membrane underlying the Bowman's capsule cells contains pores which allow all of the constituents in the plasma below a molecular weight of about 10,000 to pass into the tubule non-selectively. However, it is important to recognize, as stressed in Chapter 12, that many small molecules and ions travel in the bloodstream bound to proteins, and these will not be able to enter the kidney tubule through Bowman's capsule.

Control of glomerular filtration

The force driving the filtrate through the glomerulus depends on the pressure difference between the capillary and the inside of Bowman's capsule, minus the osmotic effect of the proteins and other large solutes retained in the blood. In the human kidney the net hydrostatic pressure is about 10 kPa and, after subtracting the difference in osmotic pressure (4 kPa), the net filtration pressure is

6 kPa. A relatively small decline in blood pressure will cause a sharp reduction in filtration pressure since the capsule pressure (about 2 kPa) and the difference in osmotic pressure do not change.

Tubular secretion

Any excretion of hydrophobic solutes which are retained in the blood plasma must occur by transcellular transfer across the tubule epithelium. This secretory process is important for the excretion of some drugs. Ammonia is also secreted by the tubule cells which enables the kidneys to control the acid–base balance of the body by releasing protons into the tubule as NH_4^+ ions, thereby preventing the urine from becoming too acid. As described in section 13.7 this involves the uptake of glutamine from the blood and the release of ammonia across the brush border membrane into the tubule lumen. Tubule secretion is also important for the excretion of excess plasma K^+. These K^+ ions are taken up across the basolateral membrane by the Na^+/K^+ ATPase and then released into the tubule lumen across the brush border through K^+ channels.

13.4 Overview of the reabsorption of ions, nutrients and water in the kidney tubule

Reabsorption in the proximal convoluted tubule

Ultrafiltration by the glomerulus passes water, ions and small organic solutes into Bowman's capsule. Figure 13.3 indicates that as the filtrate flows along the proximal convoluted tubule most of the glucose and amino acids are reabsorbed together with sufficient phosphate to maintain the appropriate phosphate concentration in the blood. These processes require the uptake of substantial amounts of Na^+ and Cl^-, although the concentrations of these ions remain high in the tubule because of the passive movement of water from the tubule lumen. The movement of Cl^- in and out of the tubule cells occurs through Cl^- channels and approximately balances the movement of Na^+ in order to prevent the formation of a large potential difference across the cell membrane. The proximal tubule also secretes protons in exchange for Na^+ uptake in order to excrete acid and to recover the bicarbonate ions from the lumen in the form of CO_2. The carbon dioxide reforms bicarbonate (and protons) in the tubule cells and the sodium bicarbonate returns to the blood.

As described below there are a variety of Na^+-dependent transport systems responsible for nutrient reabsorption, and there are also Na^+ channels which permit Na^+ to move from the tubule lumen into the cytoplasm of the tubule cells. All of these entry systems are driven by the transport of Na^+ out of the cytoplasm into the blood by the Na^+/K^+ ATPase on the basolateral membrane, which explains the high metabolic rate of the kidneys. The kidney cortex is well supplied with oxygen so that the full range of central pathways operate in the proximal and distal regions of the kidney tubule. The demand for ATP in the cortex is satisfied by oxidative phosphorylation supported by the TCA cycle and fatty acid oxidation (see Figure 13.4). The cortex is able to use glucose or any other source of acetyl-CoA, such as fatty acids, amino acids or ketone bodies, as a substrate for the TCA cycle.

Kidneys

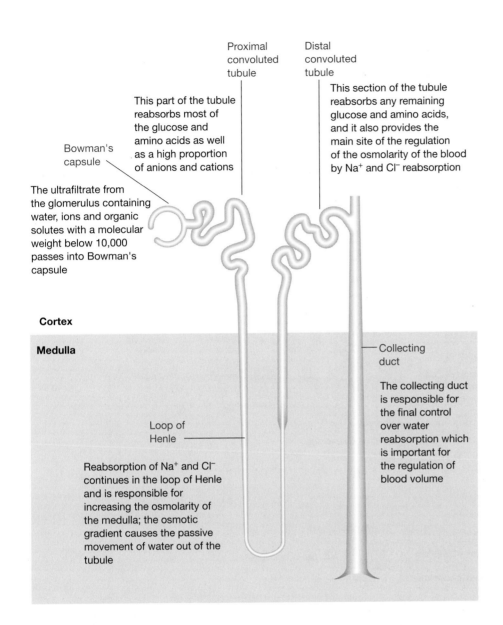

Proximal convoluted tubule

Distal convoluted tubule

This part of the tubule reabsorbs most of the glucose and amino acids as well as a high proportion of anions and cations

This section of the tubule reabsorbs any remaining glucose and amino acids, and it also provides the main site of the regulation of the osmolarity of the blood by Na⁺ and Cl⁻ reabsorption

Bowman's capsule

The ultrafiltrate from the glomerulus containing water, ions and organic solutes with a molecular weight below 10,000 passes into Bowman's capsule

Cortex

Medulla

Collecting duct

The collecting duct is responsible for the final control over water reabsorption which is important for the regulation of blood volume

Loop of Henle

Reabsorption of Na⁺ and Cl⁻ continues in the loop of Henle and is responsible for increasing the osmolarity of the medulla; the osmotic gradient causes the passive movement of water out of the tubule

Figure 13.3
Functions of the different parts of the nephron and collecting duct.

Ion reabsorption in the loop of Henle

Reabsorption of Na⁺ and Cl⁻ continues as the filtrate passes along the loop of Henle in the medulla, and this process is accompanied by the passive movement of water out of the tubule as a consequence of the osmotic gradient. However, the main effect of the tubular reabsorption by the loop of Henle is to increase the osmolarity of the region around the collecting ducts. In the medulla the oxygen supply is relatively poor, so that the epithelial cells lining the loop of Henle rely mainly on the conversion of glucose to lactate as their source of the ATP required for ion transport (see Figure 13.4).

The countercurrent system around the loop of Henle

Although 75% of the salt and water reabsorption occurs in the proximal tubule in osmotically equivalent amounts, the circulatory system around the loop of Henle sets up a countercurrent system by establishing a concentration gradient parallel

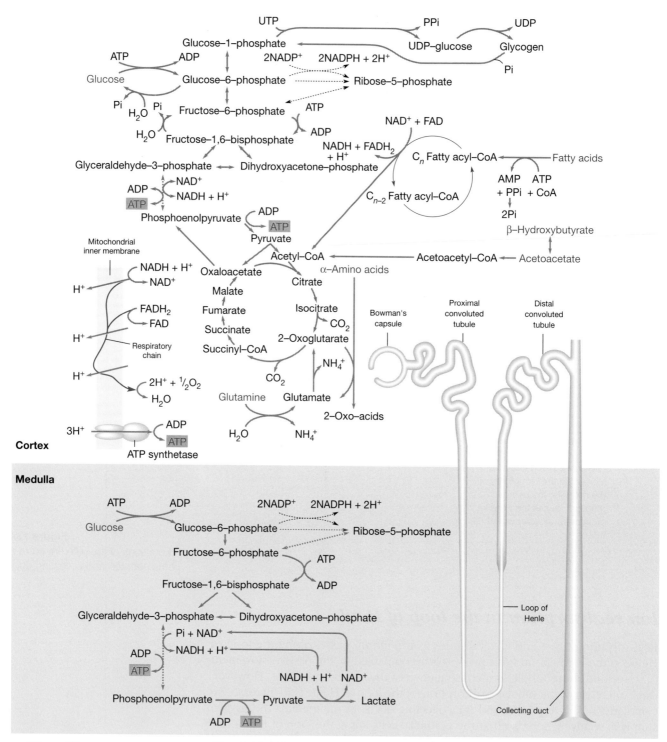

Figure 13.4 Energy-supplying pathways in the various parts of the kidney tubule.

Kidneys

to the loop. The capillary flowing from the glomerulus passes along the ascending portion of the loop where the blood takes up salts and loses water. The salts are moving down a concentration gradient into the blood and the water is moving from the blood into the interstitial space as a consequence of the osmotic difference. As the blood passes the descending part of the loop on the way back to the cortex it loses salts and gains water. In this way the interstitial fluid is provided with a standing gradient.

The distal convoluted tubule controls the osmolarity of the blood

The distal convoluted tubule is again in a well-oxygenated area so that transport is supported by aerobic metabolism. It is this region of the tubule that provides the main control over the osmolarity of the blood, since aldosterone produced in response to angiotensin II stimulates Na^+ reabsorption when the osmolarity is low. It is also in this region that the remaining amino acids and glucose are reabsorbed. However, if the blood glucose level is very high (above $10\,mM$) the reabsorptive capacity of the tubule is exceeded and glucose appears in the urine, as happens in people with untreated diabetes.

Fluid absorption in the collecting ducts

Fluid passing down the collecting duct toward the renal pelvis moves through tissue with a high osmolarity so that water flows from the duct into the extracellular space. The rate of this passive movement is increased by vasopressin which mobilizes additional aqueous pores or channels in the luminal membrane of the cells lining the collecting duct. It is essential for the increased water movement to be transcellular since the opening of paracellular routes could allow the high interstitial concentrations of Na^+ and Cl^- ions to enter the collecting duct.

13.5 Absorption of glucose in the various regions of the kidney tubule

The reabsorption of glucose occurs primarily in the proximal convoluted tubule. Uptake from the tubule lumen is a Na^+-dependent process and the SGLT1 glucose transporter present in the intestine has also been identified in membrane vesicles from kidney cortex. A second Na^+-dependent glucose transporter, SGLT2, is also present in the kidney tubule cells. It is necessary for the tubule cells to accumulate glucose to a concentration above that in the blood because glucose exit across the basolateral membrane occurs by the GLUT 2 facilitative transporter. The driving force for the transcellular transfer of glucose is provided by the inwardly directed Na^+ gradient across the luminal (brush border) membrane. Because the Na^+ ions must be pumped out of the tubule cells by the Na^+/K^+ ATPase on the basolateral membrane, the reabsorption of glucose adds to the demand for ATP in the tubule cells. The overall mechanism responsible for transfer of the glucose from the tubule lumen to the blood is shown in Figure 13.5.

13.6 Amino acid absorption and metabolism by the kidney tubule

Amino acid transport in the kidneys

Amino acid reabsorption occurs mainly in the proximal convoluted tubule but it is a more complex process than the recovery of glucose. This is because the intracellular amino acid concentrations are high relative to those in the blood, and because some amino acids are positively or negatively charged. Uptake of the

Kidneys

Transporters

- Na⁺–dependent amino acid transporter
- Na⁺/K⁺ ATPase
- Na⁺–dependent glucose transporter (SGLT 1)
- Basolateral amino acid transporter
- GLUT 2 glucose transporter

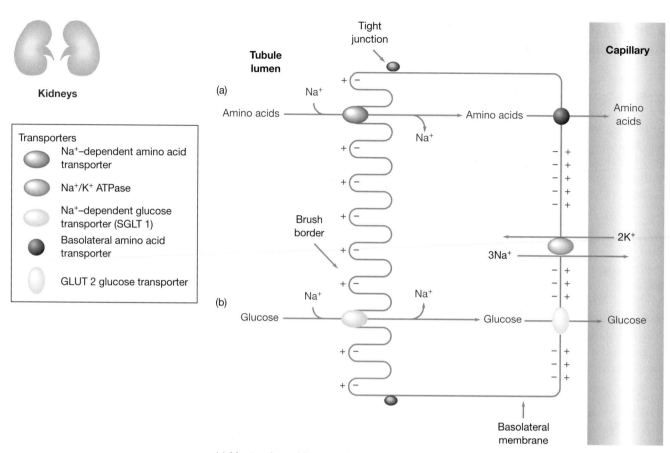

Figure 13.5

Mechanisms responsible for the reabsorption of amino acids and glucose in the kidney tubule.

(a) Most amino acids are reabsorbed against a concentration gradient by Na⁺–dependent amino acid transporters; since the cytoplasmic concentration is higher than that in the blood, transfer across the basolateral membrane is down a concentration gradient.

(b) Glucose is actively reabsorbed from the tubule lumen by SGLT1; transfer from the cytoplasm to the blood occurs down a concentration gradient by GLUT 2.

amino acids occurs against a concentration gradient and generally appears to be driven by the inwardly directed Na⁺ gradient. The range of amino acid transporters found in the small intestine has also been identified in kidney cortex membranes. For the neutral amino acids transfer from the lumen to the vascular system follows the pattern shown in Figure 13.5. The cotransport of the Na⁺ and a neutral amino acid is electrogenic so that it is partly driven by the membrane potential (negative internally). As with glucose transport the ATP required for the amino acid transport in energy terms is that required to pump the Na⁺ ions out of the tubule cells by the Na⁺/K⁺ ATPase on the basolateral membrane.

Transport of negatively charged amino acids could not be supported by the cotransport of a single Na⁺ ion because of the membrane potential and the very high intracellular concentrations of glutamate and aspartate. For these amino acids cotransport of two Na⁺ ions is needed. The exit of K⁺ ions may also be required in order to reorient the transporter binding site to the luminal side of the membrane.

It might appear that the reabsorption of positively charged amino acids could be driven by the membrane potential, but this does not appear to be the case. Probably as a consequence of their high intracellular concentrations the positively charged amino acids still require the cotransport of Na⁺ ions. For these amino acids it is necessary to have an even larger concentration gradient from the cytoplasm to the blood plasma since their exit across the basolateral membrane will be inhibited by the membrane potential. Exit of the positively charged amino acids across the basolateral membrane may require exchange with plasma Na^+ ions.

Peptide transport in the kidneys

Membrane vesicles from kidney cortex have also been shown to have peptide transporters. The high-affinity PepT1 transporter found in the intestine is also expressed in the kidney cortex, and in addition there is a second peptide transporter with a lower substrate affinity, PepT2. The transport of most peptides in the kidney appears to follow the pattern described in section 10.5 for peptide transport in the intestine. Thus neutral peptides require the cotransport of one proton and negatively charged peptides require the cotransport of two protons. The reabsorption of positively charged peptides may be driven by the membrane potential rather than by proton cotransport. The reabsorption of peptides by the kidneys is important for antibiotic treatment because many of these drugs are transported by the peptide transporter, and if PepT1 were not present in the kidney tubules the drugs would be rapidly lost in the urine.

Amino acid metabolism in the kidneys

Although the proximal tubule cells can obtain most of the amino acids they require for protein synthesis from the tubule lumen, those cells in the rest of the tubule have to depend on blood plasma for the amino acids they need for protein synthesis or metabolic pathways such as gluconeogeneis. The basolateral membranes of the tubule cells also appear to have the full range of amino acid transporters to meet these demands.

Amino acid metabolism in the kidneys fulfils three main functions. The most important of these, which is considered in the next section, is the metabolism of glutamine in order to excrete protons as NH_4^+ ions. Amino acids can also serve as a source of substrate for the TCA cycle. Another major metabolic role of amino acids in the kidneys is as a source of substrate for gluconeogenesis.

13.7 Proton secretion by the kidneys and blood pH regulation

Two of the most important ions actively recovered by the kidneys are Na^+ ions and bicarbonate ions. Na^+ can enter the tubule cells from the tubule lumen in exchange for protons, and as shown in Figure 13.6 this process provides the basis for bicarbonate uptake in the form of CO_2. Overall the process is pH neutral as far as the tubule cells are concerned, but recovery of the bicarbonate which crosses back into the capillaries helps to keep the blood from becoming acidic.

Some of the H_2CO_3 and CO_2 is lost in the urine, contributing to an overall loss of protons. A second method of excreting protons results from the buffering action of phosphate ions in the tubule lumen. Most of the phosphate passing through the glomerulus is in the form of HPO_4^{2-} and the Na^+/H^+ exchange permits the addition of a second proton (Figure 13.6). However this technique of proton excretion results in the loss of phosphate, and phosphate excretion by the kidney is carefully regulated (see section 13.8) to balance phosphate intake so that blood levels of calcium and phosphate are maintained within narrow limits.

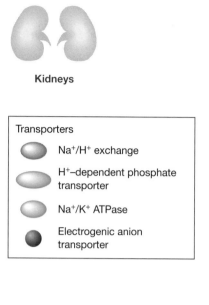

Kidneys

Transporters

- Na⁺/H⁺ exchange
- H⁺–dependent phosphate transporter
- Na⁺/K⁺ ATPase
- Electrogenic anion transporter

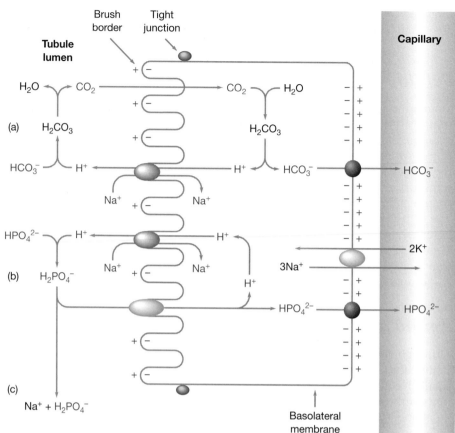

(a) Bicarbonate reabsorption is driven by the Na^+/H^+ exchange which converts the HCO_3^- into carbonic acid; carbonic anhydrase splits H_2CO_3 into H_2O and CO_2 which diffuses into the tubule cell where carbonic anhydrase forms HCO_3^- for export to the blood.
(b) Phosphate reabsorption is driven by the Na^+/H^+ exchange which converts HPO_4^{2-} into $H_2PO_4^-$; once inside the tubule cell it ionizes to HPO_4^{2-} which is exported into the capillary by the electrogenic anion transporter.
(c) In order to export H^+ some $H_2PO_4^-$ remains in the tubule and is excreted with Na^+.

Figure 13.6
The role of proton secretion in the reabsorption of anions.

Glutamine metabolism supports the secretion of protons

A third method of proton excretion is in the form of ammonium ions. NH_3 is secreted into the tubule as a result of the hydrolysis of glutamine, and the Na^+/H^+ exchange provides protons to form NH_4^+ to be excreted with chloride ions (see Figure 13.7a). In order to provide the net secretion of protons together with NH_3 it is necessary for the glutamate produced as a result of the hydrolysis of glutamine to be completely metabolized to CO_2 and water as shown in Figure 13.7(b). If glutamine were merely hydrolysed to glutamate the release of the NH_3 would be associated with the production of a proton so that there would be no net proton secretion. The catabolism of glutamine by the kidneys and the secretion of NH_3 is probably the most important mechanism that the kidneys have for regulating the pH of the blood.

13.8 Control of Ca²⁺ and phosphate reabsorption by the kidneys

The Ca^{2+} and phosphate levels in the blood are maintained within fairly narrow limits by hormonal controls. Bone salts provide a reservoir of 99% of the calcium and phosphate in the body, and the level of these ions in the blood is regulated by the parathyroid hormone and by the peptide calcitonin which is secreted by the thyroid gland. The parathyroid glands secrete their peptide hormone in response to a decline in plasma Ca^{2+} levels. This hormone stimulates the release of calcium phosphate from bone, increases Ca^{2+} absorption from the intestine and increases the reabsorption of Ca^{2+} by renal tubules. In order to raise the plasma Ca^{2+} levels without elevating the plasma phosphate, the parathyroid hormone also increases phosphate excretion by the proximal tubule of the kidney. The main way in which calcitonin protects against hypercalcaemia is by suppressing the release of calcium phosphate from bone. In the kidney calcitonin stimulates phosphate excretion. Under some conditions calcitonin also increases the reabsorption of Ca^{2+} from the loop of Henle, presumably to prevent too sudden a drop in plasma Ca^{2+} levels when release from bone is inhibited. Although the mechanisms responsible for the hormonal regulation of Ca^{2+} reabsorption in the kidney tubule are not clear, it seems likely that both parathyroid hormone and calcitonin control Ca^{2+} channels in the brush border membrane of the tubule cells. Once the Ca^{2+} has entered the cytoplasm from the tubule lumen it can be transported across the basolateral membrane into the blood by a Ca^{2+}/Na^+ exchange or an ATP-dependent Ca^{2+} pump.

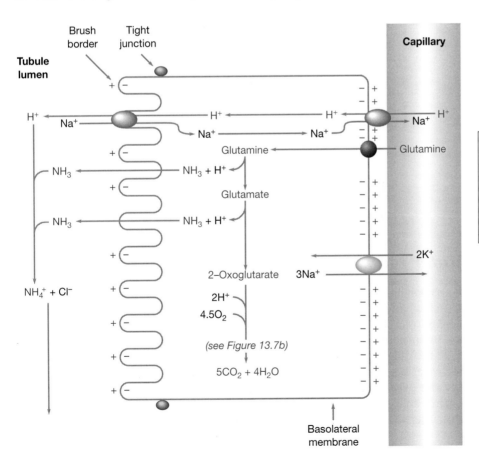

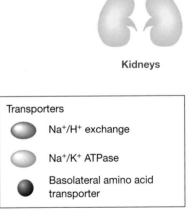

Figure 13.7(a)
The role of glutamine metabolism buffering the pH in the tubule.

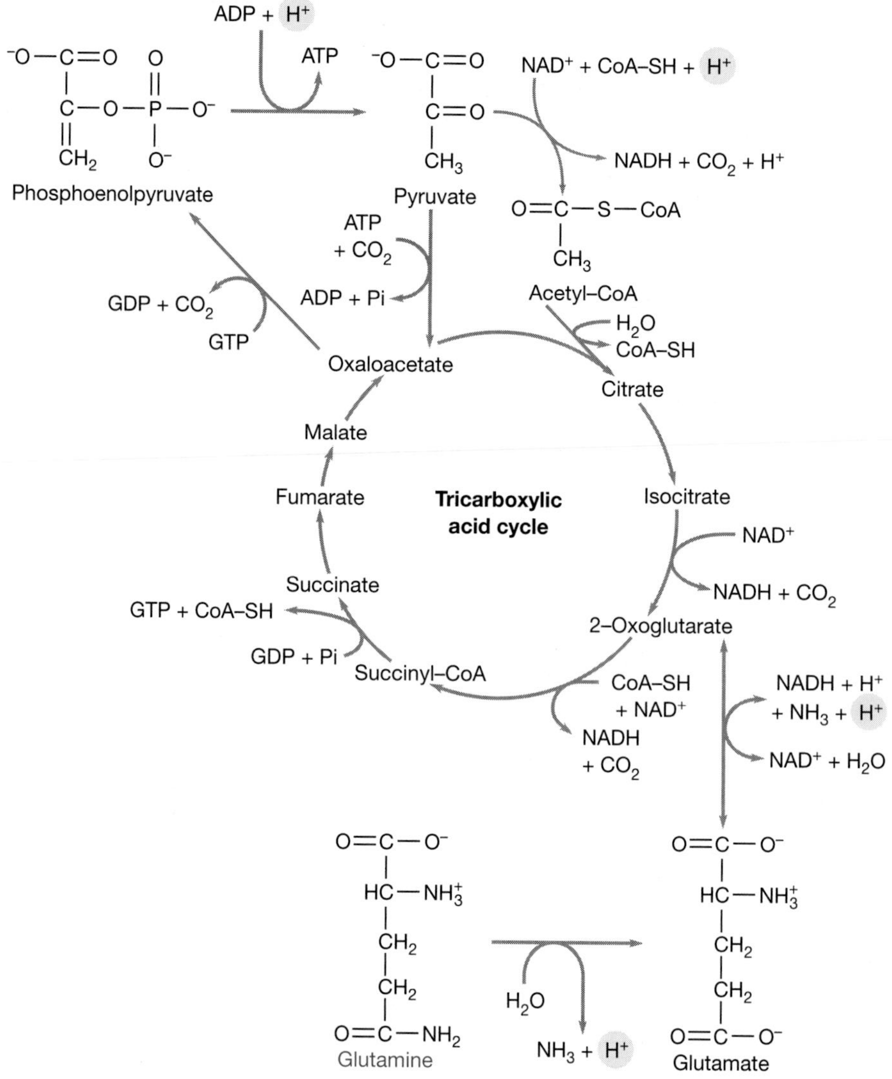

Kidneys

Figure 13.7(b)
Pathway showing why the complete oxidation of glutamine is necessary so that the ammonia released can neutralize acid in the tubule lumen.

ADP + H$^+$

ATP

Phosphoenolpyruvate

Pyruvate

ATP + CO$_2$

ADP + Pi

GDP + CO$_2$

GTP

Oxaloacetate

NAD$^+$ + CoA–SH + H$^+$

NADH + CO$_2$ + H$^+$

Acetyl–CoA

H$_2$O

CoA–SH

Citrate

Malate

Fumarate

Tricarboxylic acid cycle

Isocitrate

NAD$^+$

NADH + CO$_2$

Succinate

2–Oxoglutarate

GTP + CoA–SH

GDP + Pi

Succinyl–CoA

CoA–SH + NAD$^+$

NADH + CO$_2$

NADH + H$^+$ + NH$_3$ + H$^+$

NAD$^+$ + H$_2$O

Glutamine

H$_2$O

NH$_3$ + H$^+$

Glutamate

13.9 Water reabsorption in the various regions of the tubule

Water reabsorption in the kidney cortex

It was pointed out at the beginning of this chapter that the movement of water out of the lumen of the kidney tubule can only occur if the osmolarity of the luminal fluid is lower than that in the surrounding tissue. Figure 13.8 indicates that there is a substantial osmolarity gradient in the extracellular fluid surrounding the tubules from the outer cortex to the inner medulla. Despite this, nearly three-quarters of the water absorption occurs in the cortex through the proximal convoluted tubule because this is where most of the solutes are reabsorbed. The transfer of ions and organic solutes out of the lumen automatically reduces the lumen osmolarity so that water will move out of the lumen through the tight junctions.

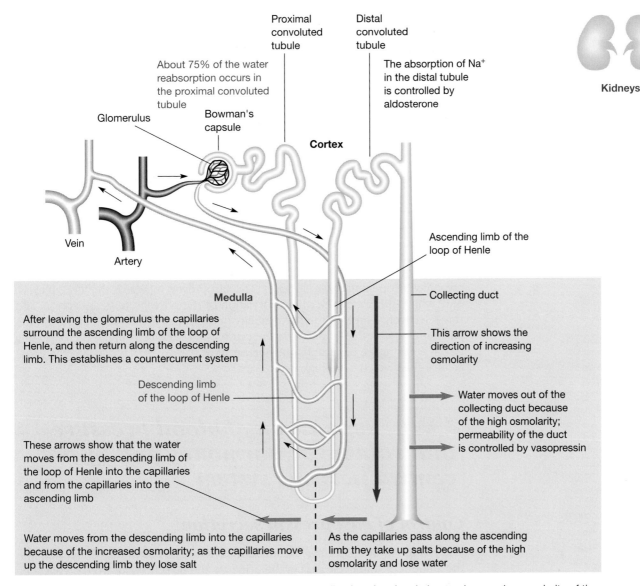

Figure 13.8 Water reabsorption along the tubule and in the collecting duct in relation to changes in osmolarity of the surrounding fluid.

Water reabsorption in the loop of Henle

Water continues to move out of the tubule in the descending loop of Henle because of the increasing osmolarity in the surrounding extracellular fluid, despite the fact that there is no active salt transport in this region. As the urine moves up the ascending loop of Henle the conditions are reversed. The salt content of the lumen is higher than that in the interstitial fluid, but the permeability of the ascending loop of Henle to Na^+ and Cl^- is greatly increased so that the salt moves out of the lumen. In the thick section of the ascending loop of Henle Cl^- appears to be transported against an electrochemical gradient, but this may be a secondary consequence of the electrical potential difference created by the increased activity of the Na^+/K^+ ATPase on the basolateral membrane.

Water reabsorption in the distal convoluted tubule

By the time that the urine has reached the distal convoluted tubule in the cortex most of the organic solutes have been reabsorbed. As a consequence the absorption of Na^+ ions in this region will depend on the operation of the Na^+/K^+ ATPase and the Na^+ movement will be accompanied by Cl^- ions driven by the membrane potential. This salt movement continues to provide an osmotic gradient for further water absorption in the distal tubule.

The final control over water retention

In the collecting duct there is additional active absorption of Na^+ ions, and as the urine moves down toward the medulla there is a further increase in the osmolarity of the interstitial fluid. As a consequence water will move out of the tubule. However, in this region the permeability of the epithelial layer is controlled by the secretion of the antidiuretic hormone vasopressin which increases the permeability by opening aqueous pores. The vasopressin increases the level of cyclic AMP which stimulates the phosphorylation of the pore protein, aquaporin, and this selectively increases the permeability of the apical membranes of the epithelial lining to water. After entering the cytoplasm of the cells lining the collecting ducts, pores in the basolateral membrane allow the water to move into the extracellular fluid which has a high osmolarity.

13.10 Regulation of blood pressure and volume by hormones and by the central nervous system

Control of vasopressin secretion

The volume of the blood will be influenced by the amount of fluid ingested and the amount of water released in the urine. As the fluid flows down the collecting duct into the renal medulla where the osmolarity is high, water will be drawn out of the urine. The rate at which this occurs depends on the permeability of the epithelial layer lining the duct, and as indicated in the previous section this is regulated by vasopressin. The release of vasopressin is stimulated by osmotically sensitive neurones located in the hypothalamus. As the osmolarity decreases, vasopressin secretion is reduced and the secretion is also inhibited by pressure receptors in the heart when the blood pressure is high. Reductions in blood pressure result in increased vasopressin secretion.

Renin is secreted in response to low blood pressure

Renin secretion, which prompts the activation of the angiotensin system, is secreted in response to low blood pressure or a drop in the osmolarity of the blood. As indicated in Figure 12.8(a) renin activates the angiotensin system which increases vasoconstriction and also causes the release of aldosterone from the adrenal cortex. The aldosterone stimulates the transport of salt from the tubule lumen into the interstitial spaces and thus into the blood. This will compensate for the loss of salts as a result of the increase in glomerular filtration owing to the rise in pressure caused by vasoconstriction.

The role of the kidneys in the renin–angiotensin system

There are a number of ways in which the blood pressure can be altered and the kidneys themselves are involved in the renin–angiotensin control system, although it is now clear that endothelial cells in other parts of the body are capable of releasing renin in response to increases in blood pressure. Nevertheless, the endothelial cells at the base of the glomerular capillaries (the juxtaglomerular cells) are the main source of renin secretion in response to a fall in blood pressure. Renin secretion can be stimulated in several ways. The pressure receptors in the arteriole can report a fall in pressure to the CNS which will stimulate renin release directly through adrenergic β_2-receptors. Alternatively, the pressure receptors can alter the endothelial cell membrane potential directly causing renin release. Reduced blood pressure also activates production of the local hormone prostacyclin which in turn activates adenyl cyclase, forming cyclic AMP which causes renin release. Renin is responsible for forming angiotensin I, and once this has been produced the angiotensin-converting enzyme on the membrane surface converts it into angiotensin II, which increases the blood pressure by vasoconstriction (see Figure 12.8a) and promotes reabsorption of Na^+ and Cl^- by stimulating the secretion of aldosterone. The secretion of renin is inhibited by the secretion of natriuretic peptide in the heart in response to high blood pressure. The effects of the activation of the renin–angiotensin system are inhibited by the vasodilator bradykinin (see Figure 12.8b).

The effects on the kidneys of the vasoconstriction mediated by the renin–angiotensin system are not simple. For example, constriction of the efferent arterioles coming from the glomerulus would have the effect of reducing the net filtration pressure and therefore potentially reducing fluid loss. On the other hand, if the stimulation of vasoconstriction by angiotensin II was more general it could increase the capillary pressure entering the glomerulus, thus raising the filtration rate. It is also true that the effects of the renin–angiotensin system will be complicated by the secretion of the hypothalamic peptide hormone vasopressin which promotes water retention by the collecting ducts in response to low blood pressure or high osmolarity, thus balancing out at least some of the angiotensin II effects. Alcohol, which has a strong diuretic effect, promotes water loss by inhibiting the secretion of vasopressin.

13.11 Basic metabolic interrelationships between the kidneys and other tissues

The kidneys have a close association with the blood since they play an important role in maintaining its composition, volume and pressure. The controls that operate to regulate the blood pressure are also influenced by the CNS through its regulation of the secretion of hormones such as vasopressin.

However, it is important to recognize that the kidneys also have close links with the liver and the small intestine. Ions and hydrophilic nutrients which have been absorbed by the small intestine or produced by the liver can only be retained in the blood if the kidney tubules reabsorb them from the tubule after they pass through the glomerulus. The liver and intestine produce the nitrogen waste products, urea and uric acid, which are excreted by the kidneys because they are not reabsorbed. Large intakes of fluid by the intestine must also be eliminated in a controlled way by the kidneys.

The kidneys also have a special relationship with muscle. A key factor in this interrelationship is the release of glutamine by the muscles largely as a function of their activity. Strenuous muscular activity is also associated with the production of lactate which increases the acidity of the blood. By oxidizing the glutamine and releasing the ammonia into the tubule lumen the kidneys are able to excrete protons and help to maintain the acid–base balance of the body.

Maintenance of the plasma levels of Ca^{2+} and phosphate also depend on the relationship between the kidneys and the small intestine. Parathyroid hormone stimulates Ca^{2+} absorption by the intestine and its reabsorption by the kidneys as well as its release from bone.

The interrelationships between the kidneys, liver and the small intestine are intensified during and immediately after feeding. Absorption of large amounts of glucose and amino acids puts a greatly increased reabsorption load on the kidneys, and the less effective the liver is in moderating the rises in nutrient levels, the harder the kidneys must work to reabsorb the nutrients from the tubule lumen.

Figure 13.9 shows the main relationships between the kidneys and the other tissues we have considered in this section of the book. Although they are not mentioned in the figure it is important to note the crucial role played by the kidneys in relation to drugs administered either by mouth or intravenously. With either type of administration the drug will only be effective if reabsorbed to some extent by the kidney tubules. However, it is also important to have a method of eliminating the drugs or their metabolites so that they do not remain trapped in the body.

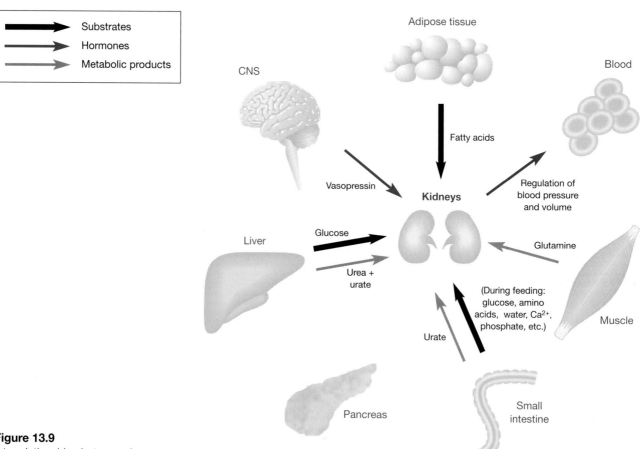

Figure 13.9
Interrelationships between the kidneys and other tissues.

E X E R C I S E S

1. What is the role of the glomerulus?

2. How is energy provided for the absorption of glucose and amino acids by kidney tubules?

3. What is responsible for the metabolic differences between the loop of Henle and the proximal and distal convoluted tubules?

4. What is the driving force for the movement of water out of the lumen of the kidney tubule?

5. Why is most of the water absorbed in the proximal convoluted tubule?

6. Explain how glutamine metabolism can permit the excretion of protons by the kidney.

7. How are phosphate ions reabsorbed?

8. How is water reabsorption in the collecting duct controlled?

9. What is the role of the renin–angiotensin system in the control of blood pressure?

10. Why is secretion of compounds by the tubules important for excretion in the kidneys?

Further reading

Baveral, G., Ferrier, B. and Martin, M. (1995) Fuel selection by the kidney: adaptation to starvation, *Proceedings of the Nutrition Society* **54**, 197–212.

Dibona, G.F. & Kopp, U.C. (1997) Neural control of renal function. *Physiological Reveiws* **77**, 75–197.

Frayn, K.N. (1996) *Metabolic Regulation: A Human Perspective*, Portland Press, Chapter 3.

Friedman, P.A. (1998) Codependence of renal calcium and sodium transport. *Annual Review of Physiology* **60**, 179–197.

Garty, H. & Palmer, L.G. (1997) Epithelial sodium channels: function, structure and regulation. *Physiological Reveiws* **77**, 359–396.

Morel, F. & Doucet, A. (1986) Hormonal control of kidney functions at the cell level, *Physiological Reviews* **66**, 377–468.

Sasaki, S., Ishibashi, K. & Marumo, F. (1998) Aquaporin-2 and -3: representatives of two subgroups of aquaporin family colocalized in the kidney collecting duct. *Annual Review of Physiology* **60**, 199–220.

Soltoff, S.P. (1986) ATP and the regulation of renal cell function, *Annual Review of Physiology* **48**, 9–31.

White, D.A. and Baxter, M., eds (1994) *Hormones and Metabolic Control*, 2nd edition, Arnold, Chapters 9 & 10.

Withersohn, G. & Guder, W.G. (1986) Renal substrate metabolism, *Physiological Reviews* **66**, 469–497.

Integration and control of tissue metabolism

How the integration and control of tissue metabolism can be altered

Integration of the metabolism of the various body tissues depends on a range of hormonal controls which are regulated by the CNS.
The metabolic balance between the different tissues is altered substantially by the absorption of food and exercise, and it can be disrupted by trauma or diseases which affect hormonal controls.

14.1 Overview of the metabolic interactions among different tissues

The first part of this book considered the general organization of the central metabolic pathways in a mammalian cell and the details of carbohydrate, lipid and nitrogen metabolism. Part 2 covered the specialized metabolic features of eight different tissues, and now it is important to see how the metabolism of these tissues is integrated to serve the functions of the body as a whole. In Chapter 5 it was pointed out that metabolism can supply four of the body's major requirements: energy, biosynthetic precursors, protection and the molecules which operate control mechanisms. In order to meet these requirements the metabolism of the various tissues of the body is highly integrated. Much of this integration is achieved through a wide range of hormonal controls, and the release of these chemical messengers is coordinated by the CNS. It is also becoming increasingly clear that many local chemical messengers are needed to transmit the signals from the circulating hormones to the particular enzymes that are being regulated. These second messengers have a very short half-life and most operate in an autocrine manner within the cell, but there are also some that operate between adjacent cells producing paracrine effects.

Principal metabolic contributions of the eight tissues

The eight tissues we have considered can be divided into two groups in terms of their principal contributions to the metabolic requirements of the body. Thus the supply of energy and biosynthetic precursors is provided by adipose tissue, liver, and small intestine whereas protection and control depend on particular functions of the blood, brain, kidneys, muscles and pancreas. However such attempts at classification are always artificial and as indicated in the preceding chapters the liver has some important control functions and the blood, kidneys and muscles also fulfil some supply functions.

The contribution made by any individual tissue toward satisfying a particular metabolic requirement may change dramatically under different conditions. The last part of this book considers the integration of tissue metabolism in the post-absorptive period and the way the metabolic balance between tissues is influenced by nutrient absorption, severe exercise, starvation, trauma and certain diseases which affect hormonal controls. By looking at the ways in which the body's metabolism is perturbed under different conditions it is possible to gain some insight into the main features of metabolic integration and control. The extremes of severe exercise and starvation also highlight the number of parallel metabolic pathways that can be mobilized to meet an emergency situation.

The effects of trauma and disease

Trauma and diseases such as cancer, diabetes, hypo- or hyperthyroidism and disorders of the pituitary and adrenal glands can seriously distort the overall metabolic integration in the body. Trauma produces an immediate disruption of the metabolic balance between tissues, and this is normally followed by a slow recovery phase. The effects of cancer operate over a much longer time scale, although the disruptive effects can often be similar to the immediate effects of trauma. Diseases such as diabetes which are due to a breakdown in the normal hormonal controls can cause rapid changes in metabolism which need to be corrected quickly.

Energy supply

In order to supply all the cells in the body with energy it is essential to maintain appropriate substrate concentrations in the blood. So far as glucose is concerned it is important that the concentration should be maintained within reasonably narrow limits. Too low a concentration would put the brain at risk, and too high a concentration would cause the loss of glucose in the urine, as well as a number of other potentially damaging effects. However it is important to remember that delivery of the glucose to the metabolic pathways within cells requires a transporter to move it across the cell membrane as well as having it delivered by the blood.

Although glucose is capable of supplying energy to all cells, the body does not rely solely on glucose for energy supply so that the availability of fatty acids must also be maintained. Since triacylglycerol provides the body's main energy reserve, a sudden heavy demand for ATP could endanger blood glucose levels if fatty acids were not available. These considerations show that energy supply for the body as a whole requires metabolic integration of the liver and adipose tissue as well as the participation of the small intestine, especially during nutrient absorption. Furthermore, if substrate supply is to be controlled properly, it is essential to have the participation of the hormones from the pancreas and the adrenal glands and a carefully controlled blood volume and pressure.

The supply of biosynthetic precursors

Biosynthetic precursors are required in all cells, except erythrocytes, in order to support the constant renewal of cell organelles, membranes, enzymes and other macromolecules. The liver plays a central role in this function by maintaining amino acid concentrations in the blood and supplying membrane constituents such as cholesterol and fatty acids. Nevertheless the liver needs contributions from the small intestine, adipose tissue, kidneys and muscle to provide the full complement of precursors. Also hormonal controls provided by the pancreas and other endocrine glands help to maintain the appropriate balance between the various biosynthetic precursors.

Protection

The metabolic basis of the protection provided for the body is rather more difficult to define. Some obvious elements of protection are provided by the blood such as the clotting mechanism and the synthesis of antibodies. The fight or flight response to danger is a high-profile form of protection organized by the CNS that depends on the muscles but also requires an integrated back-up involving the liver, adipose tissue, kidneys and a range of hormonal secretions. More subtle forms of protection are provided by the barrier function of the digestive tract, the detoxification processes in the liver and the excretion of foreign compounds and potentially harmful waste products by the kidneys.

The molecular basis of control

At one time the molecular basis of control could be described in fairly simple terms. Hormones are synthesized by endocrine cells and secreted into the circulatory system to produce specific effects on other tissues at a distance. Other simpler chemical messengers are synthesized by neurones and produce their controlling effects at synapses or over short distances at the nerve endings in tissues. Even at the outset these descriptions were over-simplified because it was known that the same molecules could produce different effects in different organs. Some tissues were totally unaffected by particular hormones and in the various tissues where a particular hormone was effective it often had several quite distinct actions. We now know that the explanation for these apparent inconsistencies is provided by the receptors for the chemical messengers and by the actions of second messengers that transmit the signals from the receptor to the enzyme that is being regulated. There are also examples of enzyme cascades that link hormone receptors to the enzymes that are being controlled. Recently it has been found that mitogen-activated protein kinase enzyme cascades are involved in signal transmission from cell-surface receptors, particularly in stress-activated pathways. The requirement for specific receptors and second messengers might suggest that providing metabolic controls for the body was an internal matter for the cells of each tissue that did not need integration with other tissues. However, this is not the case since the purpose of the controls is to coordinate the metabolic activities of the various tissues so that they work together to support the needs of the whole organism rather than operating independently.

Metabolic integration in the postabsorptive state and during feeding

Before considering the overall hormonal regulation of metabolism and the effects of trauma and disease, it is useful to summarize the integration of carbohydrate, lipid and amino acid metabolism in the tissues we considered in Part 2. Figures 14.1, 14.2 and 14.3 illustrate the interrelationships among the eight tissues for the three main areas of metabolism during the postabsorptive period. The box in each of these figures also illustrates the way in which the tissue interrelationships are altered by absorption of large amounts of carbohydrate, lipid or protein. The metabolic interactions between tissues in the fed state are influenced by the composition of the diet, and in many cases the changes are quite subtle. In order to illustrate the principles involved, three extreme situations are shown, namely the

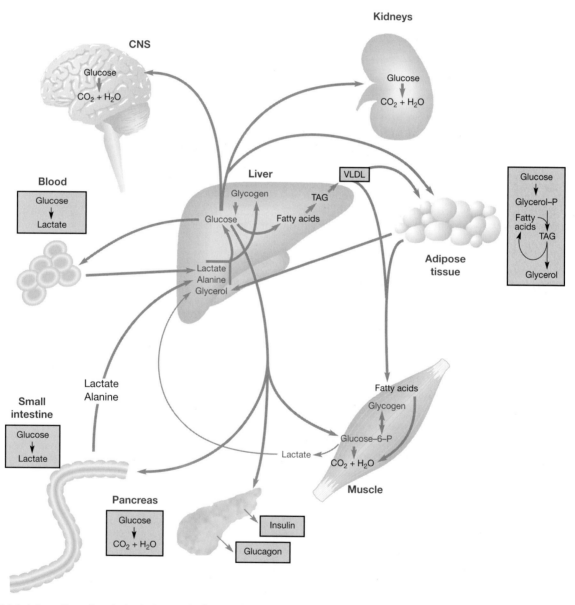

Figure 14.1 Integration of carbohydrate metabolism in the postabsorptive period. TAG, triacylglycerol.

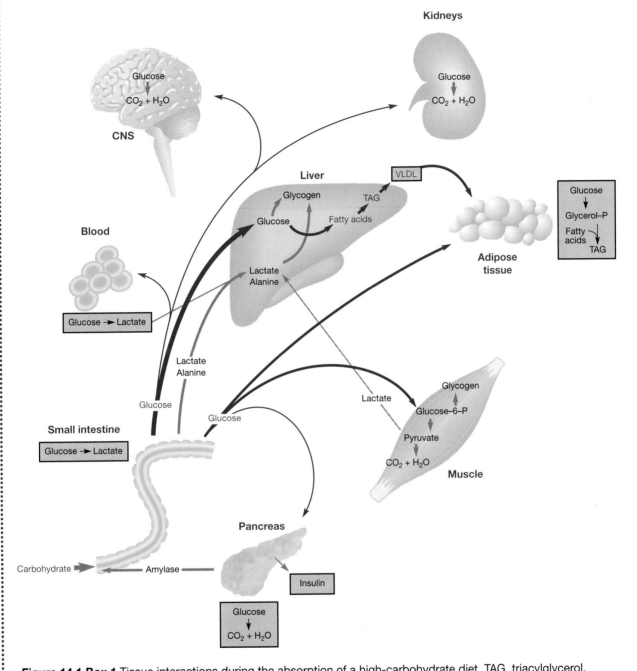

Figure 14.1 Box 1 Tissue interactions during the absorption of a high-carbohydrate diet. TAG, triacylglycerol.

absorption of excessive levels of carbohydrate, lipid or protein. These examples will help to indicate the effects that absorption of mixed diets consisting predominantly of each of the three main types of nutrient are likely to produce.

As illustrated in Chapter 16 the one factor that can alter the body's response to diets containing excessive amounts of carbohydrate, lipid or protein is severe exercise. In addition to using up the excess substrates, strenuous exercise on a regular basis increases glycogen deposition in skeletal muscle and is also responsible for increasing the mass of muscle protein.

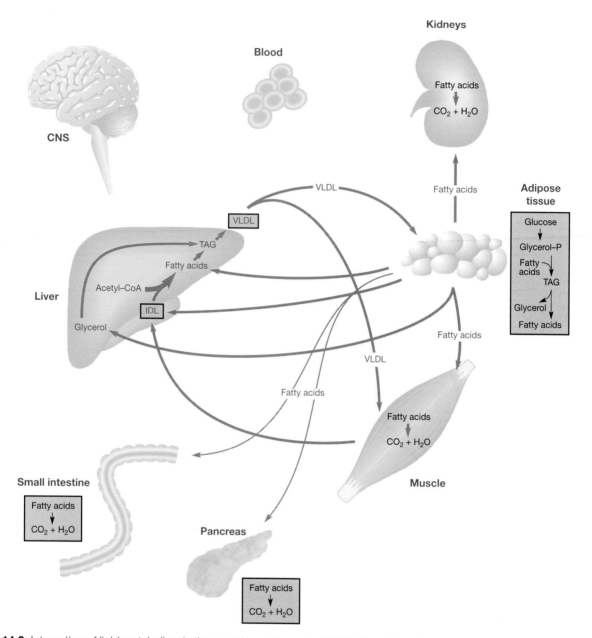

Figure 14.2 Integration of lipid metabolism in the postabsorptive period. TAG, triacylglycerol.

14.2 Integration of carbohydrate metabolism in the postabsorptive state

Figure 14.1 shows that in the postabsorptive state all of the tissues are receiving glucose from the liver. Furthermore, the blood cells, small intestine and adipose tissue are sending gluconeogenic precursors (lactate, alanine and glycerol) back to the liver. It is important to recognize that the interactions shown in Figure 14.1 between the carbohydrate metabolism of the various tissues are a snapshot of

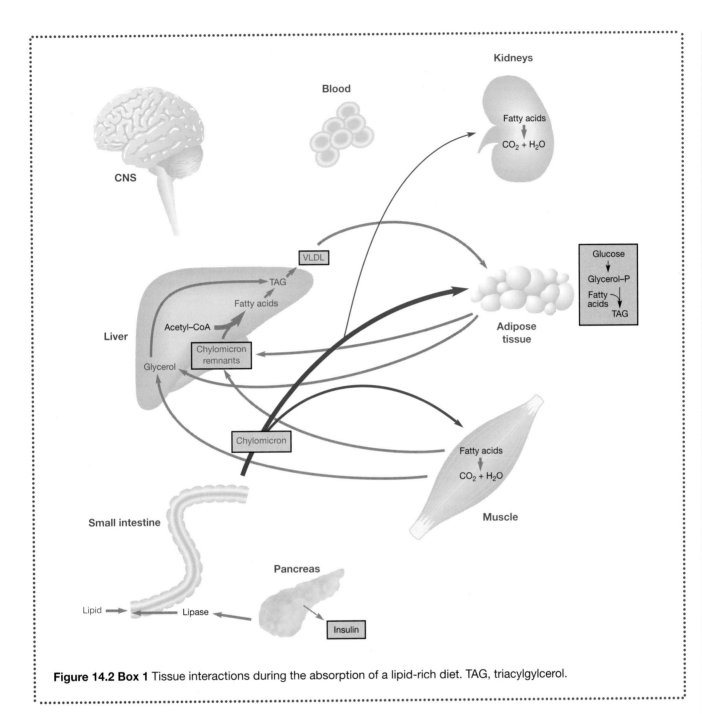

Figure 14.2 Box 1 Tissue interactions during the absorption of a lipid-rich diet. TAG, triacylgylcerol.

what is happening rather than an indication of a steady state. During the post-absorptive period conditions are continually changing. Thus, when the glucose available to the liver exceeds that required to maintain the blood glucose concentration some will be converted into fatty acids, but when there is a slight shortage of glucose there will be a net loss of glycogen and fatty acid synthesis will stop. It is also clear that the operation of the fatty acid cycle in adipose tissue means that it will use glucose plus fatty acids to form triacylglycerol, and at the same time will be releasing glycerol for gluconeogenesis in the liver. The way that the blood cells and the intestine metabolize glucose means that all of the glucose carbon from these tissues returns to the liver in the form of lactate.

The effects of a high-carbohydrate diet

Box 1 in Figure 14.1 shows the way in which the postabsorptive interactions between tissues are altered when a large amount of glucose is available from a carbohydrate-rich meal. Amylase secreted by the pancreas will convert starch into maltose and isomaltase removes the glucose residues at the α–1,6 branchpoints. The disaccharidases on the intestinal brush border membranes will hydrolyse the maltose to glucose. Sucrose and lactose will also be converted into hexoses for absorption. When a meal containing a high level of carbohydrate is consumed, the relationships between carbohydrate metabolism in the various tissues changes substantially. The liver receives a heavy load of glucose through the hepatic portal vein. Since all of this excess glucose cannot be removed from the blood by the liver immediately, it will serve as a source of glucose for all the other tissues. The increased concentration of blood glucose will stimulate insulin secretion by the pancreatic β-cells and this will increase glucose transport into many cells, particularly those in muscle and adipose tissue. Muscle will use any excess glucose to top up the muscle glycogen levels. In adipose tissue the increased glucose will largely be converted into glycerol-3-phosphate, promoting the storage of additional fatty acids in the form of triacylglycerol. If the high-carbohydrate diet contains substantial amounts of sucrose, the liver will also be receiving a heavy load of fructose through the hepatic portal vein. Under these conditions the liver will not be able to metabolize all of the fructose so that some will reach the adipose tissue and muscle.

In the liver the first call on the surplus glucose is to replenish the glycogen used up during the postabsorptive period. Somewhat surprisingly the favoured substrates for glycogen synthesis are the lactate from red blood cells and the intestine and the alanine from intestine and muscle. The main fate for the excess glucose in the liver is conversion into fatty acids for triacylglycerol synthesis and release in VLDL. It is also worth noting that not all hepatocytes will be metabolizing glucose in the same way. The most aerobic ones are likely to be forming fatty acids and synthesizing glycogen from three-carbon precursors by the gluconeogenic pathway. The less well-oxygenated cells around the hepatic vein may be using the excess glucose directly for glycogen synthesis. In addition it should be noted that the synthesis of fatty acids will use glucose-6-phosphate directly by the pentose phosphate pathway to form the NADPH necessary for the fatty acid synthesis pathway (see Figure 3.5).

14.3 Integration of lipid metabolism in the postabsorptive state

Figure 14.2 shows the relationships between the various tissues in the metabolism of fatty acids and triacylglycerol in the postabsorptive state. The principal interactions involve the liver, adipose tissue and muscle, although there will be some utilization of fatty acids by the kidneys, small intestine and pancreas. It is important to note that the fatty acids distributed by the liver are in the form of VLDL whereas those released from the adipose tissue are free fatty acids transported in blood plasma bound to albumin. Figure 14.2 does not show the transfer of cholesterol from the liver by LDL or its recovery by HDL (see section 6.11).

The effects of a high-lipid diet

Box 1 in Figure 14.2 shows that a meal that consists primarily of an excessive amount of lipid will distort the interactions between tissues with respect to the metabolism of fatty acids and triacylglycerol. The initial effect will be a massive production of chylomicrons by the intestine. This high density of chylomicrons is likely to prolong the time needed for the adipose tissue to store the fatty acids they contain, particularly because of the shortage of carbohydrate. As a consequence lipoprotein lipase in the capillaries serving other tissues will release the chylomicron fatty acids to serve as energy-supplying substrates. This will have the effect of inhibiting glucose utilization, so that it will be preserved for the CNS and the blood cells. As the chylomicrons lose their triacylglycerol, the liver will receive excessive levels of chylomicron remnants. Clearing these remnant lipoproteins will flood the hepatocytes with fatty acids and cholesterol. Many of the fatty acids will be exported to the adipocytes in VLDL, and it is also likely that the high fatty acid concentrations will lead to the production of some ketone bodies by the liver. Overall the effects of the increased availability of fatty acids for the supply of energy will mean that more glucose is available to form glycerol-phosphate for the storage of triacylglycerol in the adipose tissue.

An additional consequence of a high-lipid intake not shown in Box 1 in Figure 14.2 is that circulating levels of LDL will rise. Although LDL is important for the transfer of cholesterol to peripheral tissues, excessive levels of LDL lead to above-normal cholesterol levels in the blood. This puts the vascular system at risk, as pointed out in section 12.9, because the LDL can contribute to the formation of foam cells in blood vessels serving the heart and the brain.

14.4 *Integration of amino acid metabolism in the postabsorptive state*

The interrelationships between tissues with respect to amino acid metabolism in the postabsorptive state are shown in Figure 14.3. All the tissues, except for the red blood cells, will be converting some of the circulating amino acids into tissue protein. The composition of the amino acid mixture is controlled by the liver with some help from muscle and the small intestine. At all times some amino acid catabolism will be occurring in the liver, muscle and intestine. Some of the carbon skeletons of the amino acids are converted into fatty acids in the liver and sent to adipose tissue as VLDL. The nitrogen released as a result of this catabolism is converted into urea in the liver and excreted by the kidneys. Nitrogen is released from the CNS and muscle as glutamine which is then converted into alanine plus ammonia by the intestine, or oxidized to $CO_2 + H_2O$ + ammonia in the kidneys. The ammonia formed from glutamine by the kidneys is excreted in the urine in order to reduce the acidity of the blood.

The effects of a high-protein diet

Box 1 in Figure 14.3 shows the effects of a diet containing excessive levels of protein. Absorption of peptides and amino acids by the small intestine will

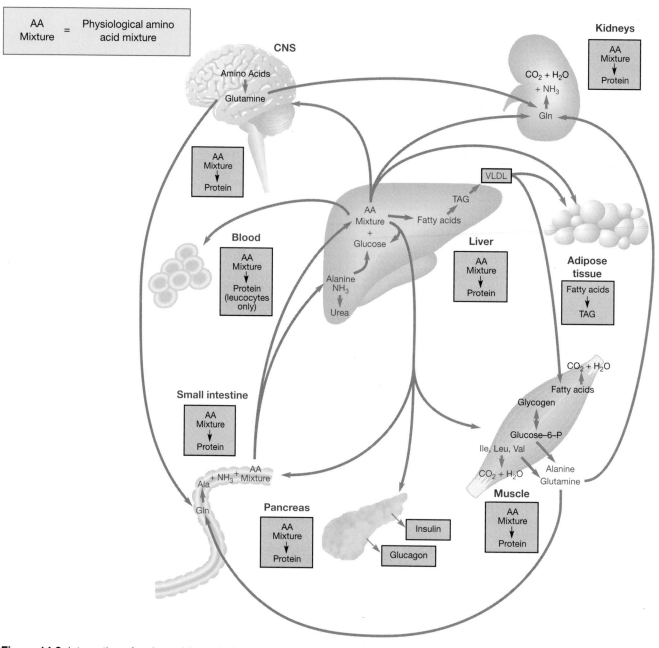

Figure 14.3 Integration of amino acid metabolism in the postabsorptive period. TAG, triacylglycerol.

greatly increase the amino acid levels reaching the liver in the portal blood. This results in a large increase in the production of urea by the liver in order to maintain nitrogen balance. Muscles will also have to cope with increased concentrations of the three branched chain amino acids. As a consequence there will be a greatly increased production of glutamine by muscle. This glutamine will be converted into alanine and ammonia in the small intestine, and these substrates will augment the supply of nitrogen for the urea cycle in the liver. Once the nitrogen has been removed from the excess amino acids, the carbon skeletons will be fed into the central metabolic pathways as TCA cycle constituents or released as acetyl-CoA. Probably the most significant change caused

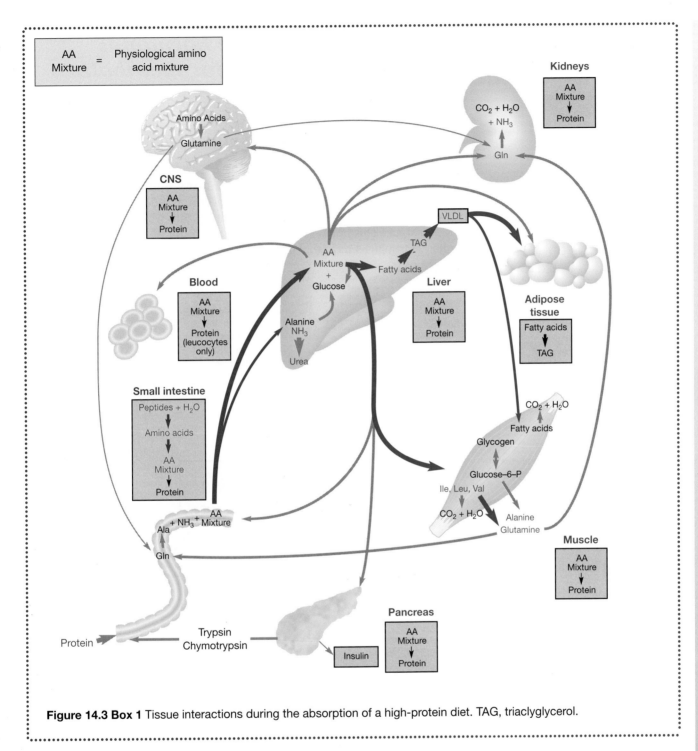

Figure 14.3 Box 1 Tissue interactions during the absorption of a high-protein diet. TAG, triaclyglycerol.

by excessive protein intake is the increased conversion of the acetyl-CoA into fatty acids by the liver. These fatty acids, which will be released as triacylglycerol in VLDL, will then supply fatty acids for the formation of additional triacylglycerol in the adipose tissue. In contrast to the effects of a high-lipid diet, there will be no shortage of glucose for glycerol-phosphate production in adipose tissue since the high rates of amino acid catabolism in the liver provide the liver with an excess of substrates for gluconeogenesis.

14.5 Summary of the hormonal controls responsible for metabolic integration

The effects of insulin and glucagon

There are three groups of hormones that have a significant influence on the integration of metabolism (see Figure 14.4). The first group comprises insulin and glucagon which regulate blood glucose concentration. A rise in blood glucose triggers the release of insulin by the pancreatic β-cells which causes a rapid drop in blood sugar. This initial effect is largely the result of changes caused by the binding of insulin to receptors in two tissues: skeletal muscle and adipose tissue.

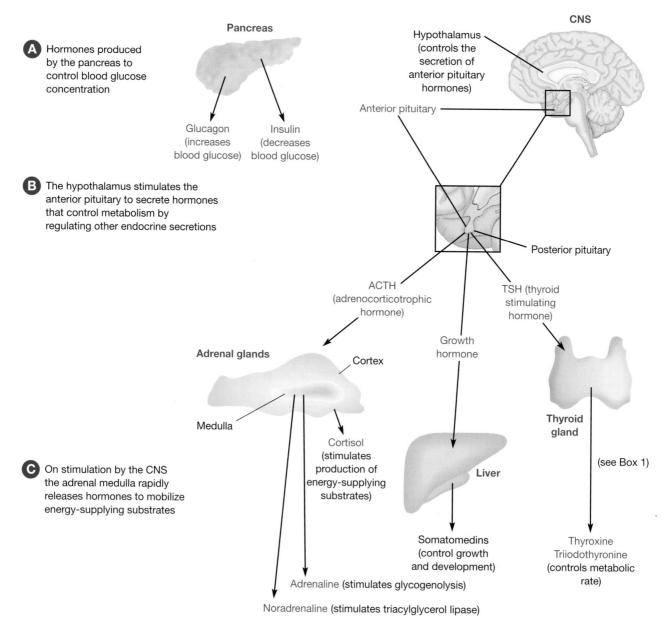

A Hormones produced by the pancreas to control blood glucose concentration

Pancreas

Glucagon (increases blood glucose)

Insulin (decreases blood glucose)

CNS

Hypothalamus (controls the secretion of anterior pituitary hormones)

Anterior pituitary

Posterior pituitary

B The hypothalamus stimulates the anterior pituitary to secrete hormones that control metabolism by regulating other endocrine secretions

ACTH (adrenocorticotrophic hormone)

TSH (thyroid stimulating hormone)

Growth hormone

Adrenal glands

Cortex

Medulla

Cortisol (stimulates production of energy-supplying substrates)

Liver

Thyroid gland

(see Box 1)

C On stimulation by the CNS the adrenal medulla rapidly releases hormones to mobilize energy-supplying substrates

Somatomedins (control growth and development)

Thyroxine Triiodothyronine (controls metabolic rate)

Adrenaline (stimulates glycogenolysis)

Noradrenaline (stimulates triacylglycerol lipase)

Figure 14.4 Summary of hormonal secretions that regulate metabolism.

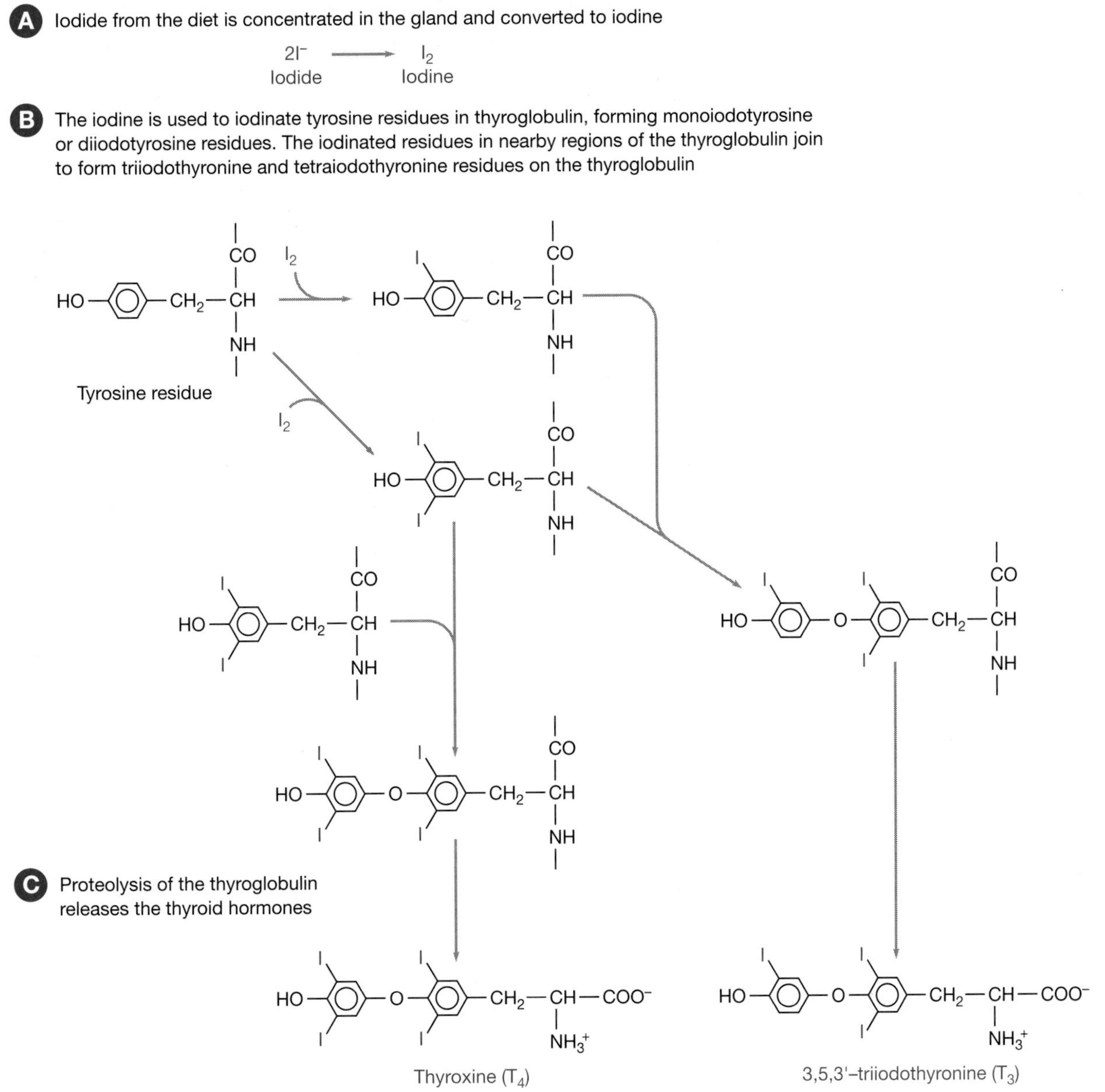

A Iodide from the diet is concentrated in the gland and converted to iodine

$$2I^- \longrightarrow I_2$$
Iodide   Iodine

B The iodine is used to iodinate tyrosine residues in thyroglobulin, forming monoiodotyrosine or diiodotyrosine residues. The iodinated residues in nearby regions of the thyroglobulin join to form triiodothyronine and tetraiodothyronine residues on the thyroglobulin

C Proteolysis of the thyroglobulin releases the thyroid hormones

Thyroxine (T$_4$)

3,5,3'–triiodothyronine (T$_3$)

Figure 14.4 Box 1 Synthesis of thyroid hormones in the thyroid gland.

In both cases the initial consequence of insulin binding is to mobilize additional glucose transporters and deliver them to the plasma membrane. As a result the permeability of the cell membranes to glucose is increased and the blood glucose concentration is immediately reduced. Other consequences of the binding of insulin to receptors follow, but they need not concern us in this simple example. So far three tissues are involved: the pancreas that secreted the insulin and the muscle and adipose tissue where the effects were produced. The CNS may also participate because it can detect a rise in blood glucose and signal to the pancreas to secrete insulin.

When the blood glucose falls the pancreatic α-cells will secrete glucagon which will cause a rapid rise in blood sugar. This time the hormone will produce its initial effects by combining with a receptor in the liver and triggering a cascade of enzyme actions to activate the glycogen phosphorylase enzyme degrading liver glycogen. The consequent rise in glucose phosphates will lead to increased glucose release from the liver through the action of glucose-6-phosphatase. So the insulin effect on muscle and adipose tissue that reduces blood glucose is balanced by the glucagon effect on the liver that elevates it.

The secretion of insulin by the β-cells of the pancreas occurs in response to a rise in blood glucose concentration (see Figure 9.4). Once it is released into the blood, insulin acts in a variety of ways to reduce the blood concentration of glucose and amino acids. Insulin's most immediate effect is the mobilization of GLUT 4 transporters in muscle and adipose tissue which opens the cytoplasm of these tissue to glucose and immediately increases the total volume in which the blood glucose is distributed. Glucagon, which is secreted by the α-cells of the pancreas in response to a drop in blood glucose concentration, raises blood glucose by stimulating glycogenolysis and gluconeogenesis in the liver.

Anterior pituitary hormones

A second group of hormones which affect metabolism much more slowly are the hormones synthesized by the anterior pituitary. The anterior pituitary hormones are responsible for controlling the secretion of hormones by the adrenal cortex, the thyroid gland, the liver and the male and female reproductive glands.

Four of the six hormones produced by the anterior pituitary gland are trophic hormones, which means that they are responsible for the formation and secretion of hormones by endocrine cells in other parts of the body. Adrenocorticotrophic hormone (ACTH) controls the production of a range of steroid hormones by the adrenal cortex. There are two main groups of corticosteroids, the glucocorticoids and the mineralocorticoids, and ACTH is chiefly concerned with the regulation of glucocorticoid secretion. The principal metabolic effects of the glucocorticoids, of which cortisol is the most important, are to increase the availability of energy-supplying substrates. These effects are relatively slow because they result mainly from a stimulation of the synthesis of the enzymes responsible for hormone-sensitive lipolysis of triacylglycerol in adipose tissue and gluconeogenesis in the liver. Cortisol also increases the breakdown of muscle protein, which supplies substrates for gluconeogenesis by the liver.

Thyrotrophic hormone, which is also known as thyroid-stimulating hormone (TSH), stimulates the growth of the thyroid gland in the neck, and production of the thyroid hormones, thyroxine and triiodothyronine. The thyroid gland has the capacity to concentrate iodine, and this is used to iodinate tyrosine residues in thyroglobulin, a glycoprotein synthesized within the thyroid gland (see Figure 14.4, Box 1). In order to release the thyroid hormones the thyroglobulin undergoes proteolysis in lysosomes within the gland. Thyroxine and triiodothyronine are released into the blood from the thyroid, but they circulate through the body largely bound to either thyroxine-binding globulin or albumin. Triiodothyronine is the most active of the two hormones and most tissues can deiodinate thyroxine to form triiodothyronine. The thyroid hormones have a major effect on body metabolism because they regulate the overall metabolic rate. This regulation occurs in two ways. The hormones act indirectly by stimulating the synthesis of enzymes in energy-supplying pathways and they also act more rapidly in mitochondria by increasing the activity of the respiratory chain. Overall the effect of the hormones is to increase the capacity of the body's energy-supplying pathways. A deficiency of thyroid hormone secretion, hypothyroidism, results in a reduction of the basal metabolic rate. Excess thyroid hormone secretion, hyperthyroidism, increases the metabolic rate above the normal level.

Growth hormone, or somatotrophin, also has an overall effect on metabolism in the body because it is responsible for regulating growth and development.

However, it does this by stimulating the production by the liver of peptide growth factors, known as somatomedins. Growth hormone does have some direct effects on substrate supply by stimulating the mobilization of fatty acids in adipose tissue and the production of glucose by the liver.

The other three anterior pituitary hormones are concerned with the regulation of reproductive organs. Prolactin is responsible for stimulating the production of milk by the mammary glands. Follicle-stimulating hormone and luteinizing hormone are responsible for the growth and development of the gonads, and they also control the secretion of sex hormones by these organs.

It is important to recognize that the secretion of the anterior pituitary hormones is controlled by the hypothalamus region of the brain (see Figure 14.4). This means that the CNS controls the production and release of the anterior pituitary hormones, although it should also be noted that there is direct feedback inhibition of ACTH and TSH release by cortisol and the thyroid hormones, respectively.

Hormones produced by the adrenal medulla

The third group of hormones, adrenaline and noradrenaline, are formed by the adrenal medulla as a consequence of stimulation of the sympathetic nervous system. Although these hormones are released into the blood they act in an analogous way to neurotransmitters and many of their effects have been considered in previous chapters. Adrenaline stimulates the release of glucose by the liver as well as the mobilization of muscle glycogen. Noradrenaline is responsible for the activation of the hormone-sensitive triacylglycerol lipase in adipose tissue. Thus, both of these hormones are responsible for increasing the availability of energy-supplying substrates.

14.6 Hormonal controls of carbohydrate metabolism in the fed and postabsorptive states

Because glucose is a basic energy-supplying substrate for all cells, there are profound differences in glucose metabolism between the fed and postabsorptive states. The way in which the integration of carbohydrate metabolism in the postabsorptive state is affected by feeding is illustrated in Figure 14.1.

Control of blood glucose concentration

As described in Chapter 5 the basic control over blood glucose concentration is provided by the liver. Since the transport of glucose across the hepatocyte plasma membrane is near equilibrium, the cytoplasmic concentration mirrors that in the blood. The glucokinase K_m for glucose is about twice the normal blood concentration so that the rate at which it is phosphorylated is very sensitive to small concentration changes. Although glucose-6-phosphatase activity is limited to the lumen of the endoplasmic reticulum, it does not appear to be subject to specific controls, and consequently glucose in the hepatocyte cytoplasm will be cycling at a fairly high rate between the free and phosphorylated form. This process makes it easy for the liver to switch from glucose uptake to glucose release in response to a small change in blood glucose concentration. However, as summarized in Table 14.1, the liver's control over blood glucose is strongly regulated by hormone secretion. Details of the phosphorylation steps responsible for these controls are shown in Figure 14.5. Insulin and glucagon are not only responsible for controlling the formation and breakdown of liver glycogen but are also important for the regulation of the glycolytic pathway, as well as for the formation and

Table 14.1 Summary of the controls of carbohydrate metabolism

Glucose metabolism is controlled in two main ways:

1. by the regulation of blood glucose concentration;
2. by regulating glucose entry into the tissues where it is metabolized.

Tissues responsible for the regulation of blood glucose concentration

	Control mechanism
Adrenal cortex	Secretes cortisol on stimulation by ACTH
Adrenal medulla	Secretes adrenaline on stimulation by CNS
CNS	Stimulates release of adrenaline and glucocorticoids
Liver	Removes blood glucose when the concentration is high
	Supplies blood glucose when the concentration is low
Pancreas	Releases insulin when the concentration is high
	Releases glucagon when the concentration is low

Tissues in which the controls over glucose metabolism operate

	Metabolic effect of the control
Adipose tissue	Insulin stimulates glucose entry and triacylglycerol synthesis
Liver	Insulin stimulates glycogen synthesis
	Cortisol stimulates gluconeogenesis
	Adrenaline and glucagon stimulate glycogenolysis
	Glucagon stimulates gluconeogenesis
Muscle	Adrenaline stimulates glycogenolysis
	Insulin stimulates glucose entry, catabolism and glycogen synthesis

Tissues in which an increase in activity may change glucose metabolism

	Change in metabolism
Blood	Increased glycolysis because of faster transport of O_2 and CO_2
Muscle	An increase in muscular activity increases glucose metabolism
Kidneys	Increased exercise causes more rapid excretion of ammonia and H^+
Small intestine	Carbohydrate absorption will increase the delivery of glucose and lactate to other tissues

eventual fate of acetyl-CoA. Adrenaline is responsible for the mobilization of liver glycogen even when the blood glucose concentration is too high to trigger the secretion of glucagon. In this way adrenaline is able to override the normal control of glucose concentration by the liver in anticipation of future muscle activity.

1 Insulin mobilizes GLUT 4 glucose transporters from the endoplasmic reticulum to the plasma membranes of muscle and adipose tissue.

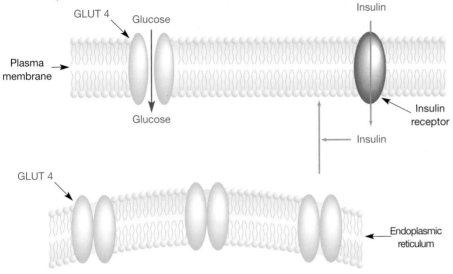

2 Insulin stimulates the phosphatase which activates glycogen synthetase in the liver by removing the phosphates which inactivate the enzyme.

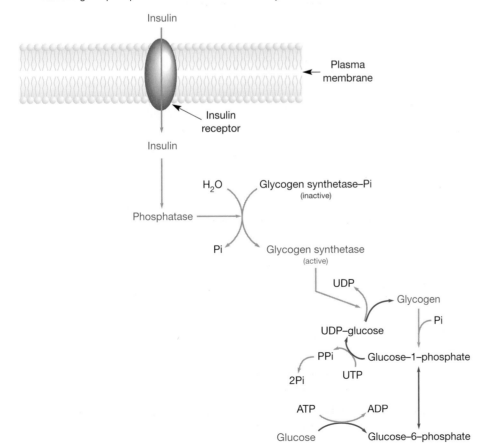

Figure 14.5(a)
Details of the hormonal controls of carbohydrate metabolism by insulin.

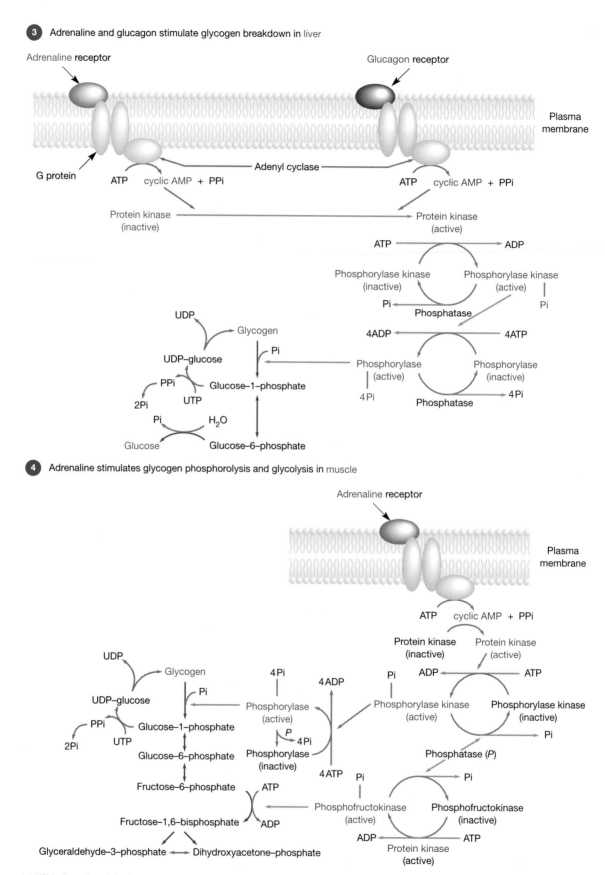

Figure 14.5(b) Details of the hormonal controls of carbohydrate metabolism by adrenaline and glucagon.

The glucocorticoids have indirect effects on glucose production by the liver by stimulating enzyme synthesis and the mobilization of substrates from muscle for gluconeogenesis.

Hormonal control of glucose metabolism in adipose tissue and muscle

The metabolism of glucose in muscle and adipose tissue is also strongly dependent on hormonal controls. The most direct effects result from the control of glucose transport across the plasma membranes of these cells by insulin. Figure 14.5(a) shows that insulin mobilizes the GLUT 4 glucose transporter in both of these tissues, and as a consequence the glucose-6-phosphate levels in both tissues will rise rapidly. In adipose tissue this will increase the storage of triacylglycerol by supplying glycerol-3-phosphate at a higher rate. In muscle, on the other hand, the fate of the glucose will depend on the level of muscle activity. During contraction glucose will be used to supply ATP; if the muscles are at rest it can be used to replenish glycogen stores. In the absence of any demand for glucose the rise in glucose-6-phosphate will inhibit hexokinase, causing the cytoplasmic level of free glucose to rise and inhibit entry of the sugar into the muscle cells. The other direct hormonal effect on muscle is caused by the secretion of adrenaline which prepares the muscles for activity by stimulating glycogen phosphorylase to mobilize glycogen reserves. There are also indirect hormone effects that influence carbohydrate metabolism in muscle. For example, the thyroid hormones stimulate the synthesis of enzymes for the energy-supplying pathways and may also increase the capacity of the mitochondria for oxidative phosphorylation. Glucocorticoids such as cortisol appear to have an inhibitory effect on energy supply in muscle and, as described later in this chapter, they act to mobilize muscle protein for gluconeogenesis by the liver.

Hormonal control of glucose metabolism in the postabsorptive state

When there is no glucose absorption from the intestine the blood level will tend to decline as the non-hepatic tissues continue to use glucose. This change will lead to the breakdown of liver glycogen to replenish the lost glucose. The phosphorolysis of glycogen will also be promoted by glucagon secretion from the pancreatic α-cells. The CNS, kidneys and pancreas will be oxidizing glucose to CO_2 and water, as will the oxidative muscle fibres, and the latter may also be using the glucose to replenish lost muscle glycogen. In adipose tissue the glucose will largely be used to form glycerol-3-phosphate for the synthesis of triacylglycerol. The blood cells and glycolytic muscle fibres, on the other hand, will be converting glucose to lactate which returns to the liver to serve as a substrate for gluconeogenesis. The small intestine is rather a special case because most of the glucose it metabolizes will be converted to lactate or alanine to serve as substrates for gluconeogenesis by the liver. It should be recognized that although the blood glucose level may decline slightly it will be maintained at a concentration sufficient to ensure that some insulin is still secreted by the pancreatic β-cells. The liver may also be converting some of its glucose into fatty acid to be exported as triacylglycerol in VLDL. However, this is only likely to occur when liver glycogen levels are very high. More probable carbon sources for the fatty acid synthesis in the liver are the lactate arriving from the intestine and blood cells or the alanine from intestine or muscle. The glycerol returning to the liver as a result of the hydrolysis of triacylglycerol by lipoprotein lipase in adipose tissue or muscle, as well as that released by lipase action within the adipocyte, will also enter the glycolytic pathway in the liver. When the liver is exporting triacylglycerol, the glycerol will be phosphorylated to provide the necessary glycerol-3-phosphate. However, when glucose is in short supply the glycerol will probably serve as a substrate for gluconeogenesis (see Figure 2.4).

The effects of carbohydrate absorption

When carbohydrate is being absorbed by the small intestine, the picture changes. As indicated in Figure 5.4 glucose will be taken up by the liver and converted into glycogen or triacylglycerol for release as VLDL. However, as shown in Box 1 in Figure 14.1 a high carbohydrate intake will distort this pattern. Under these conditions the dietary glucose will satisfy the glucose requirements of most tissues directly, and a high proportion of the glucose will be converted into fatty acids in the liver. The combination of a high blood glucose and the consequent increase in insulin secretion will further stimulate triacylglycerol storage by adipose tissue. During feeding, galactose which is absorbed will continue to be metabolized by the liver, as will low levels of fructose. However, the fructose from a large intake of sucrose will enter the adipose tissue and provide a further stimulus to the adipose tissue to store triacylglycerol.

14.7 Hormonal regulation of lipid metabolism in the fed and postabsorptive states

In the postabsorptive state there is a balance between the formation and hydrolysis of triacylglycerols in adipose tissue (see Figure 14.2). Whether or not triacylglycerol synthesis and hydrolysis are in balance is largely dependent on the ratio of lipogenic and lipolytic hormone concentrations. As summarized in Table 14.2, insulin stimulates triacylglycerol formation by promoting glucose entry and reducing the level of cyclic AMP, whereas noradrenaline and adrenaline increase the activity of hormone-sensitive triacylglycerol lipase by stimulating adenyl cyclase. The catecholamines tend to be secreted largely in response to exercise, fear or excitement, etc., whereas insulin release is governed by the blood glucose concentration. The fact that the net synthesis and breakdown of triacylglycerol are regulated on a different basis provides the body with a safety factor in terms of energy supply. Because catecholamine secretion is governed by a real or anticipated increase in energy demand it will increase the rate of fatty acid release at any given insulin concentration. As indicated in Chapter 16, full muscle power requires plentiful supplies of both glucose and fatty acids. Thus, the most favourable energy supply for rapidly contracting muscles will be provided by relatively high levels of insulin to promote glucose entry into muscle cells and the secretion of catecholamines to increase the circulating levels of fatty acids in the blood.

Figure 14.6 shows that there are other ways in which insulin can promote the formation of triacylglycerol. Insulin can inhibit cyclic AMP synthesis, thereby decreasing the stimulatory effect of the catecholamines on the release of fatty acids by triacylglycerol lipase and it can also stimulate the synthesis of the lipoprotein lipase attached to the walls of the capillaries. The latter effect will increase fatty acid delivery to the adipose tissue from circulating lipoproteins. Stimulation of lipoprotein lipase synthesis also increases the availability of fatty acids to non-adipose tissues.

Table 14.2 Summary of the control of the metabolism of fatty acids and triacylglycerol

The storage and release of fatty acids is controlled in two main ways:

1. by the availability of glucose and fatty acids for triacylglycerol synthesis;
2. by hormones that control the activity of hormone-sensitive triacylglycerol lipase.

Tissues responsible for the control of fatty acid and triacylglycerol metabolism

	Control mechanism
Adrenal medulla	Secretes adrenaline and noradrenaline on stimulation by CNS
CNS	Stimulates release of adrenaline and noradrenaline
Liver	Supplies glucose and synthesizes fatty acids for release in VLDL
	Converts excess fatty acids into ketone bodies
Pancreas	Releases insulin when the glucose concentration is high

Tissues in which the controls of fatty acid and triacylglycerol metabolism operate

	Metabolic effect of the control
Adipose tissue	Insulin stimulates glucose entry and triacylglycerol synthesis
	Noradrenaline and adrenaline stimulate lipolysis of triacylglycerol
Muscle	Increased concentrations of fatty acids stimulate their metabolism and inhibit the utilization of glucose
	High concentrations of ketone bodies inhibit utilization of fatty acids and glucose

Tissues in which an increase in activity may change fatty acid and triacylglycerol metabolism

	Change in metabolism
Muscle	An increase in muscular activity increases catabolism of fatty acids or ketone bodies
Kidneys	Increased availability of fatty acids or ketone bodies inhibits glucose metabolism
Small intestine	Lipid absorption increases the delivery of fatty acids to adipose tissue in chylomicrons

Hormonal control of lipid metabolism in the postabsorptive state

In the postabsorptive state the main source of fatty acids for triacylglycerol synthesis in adipose tissue will be from the VLDL released by the liver. While the liver is reducing the blood glucose to the normal 5 mM concentration any excess sub-

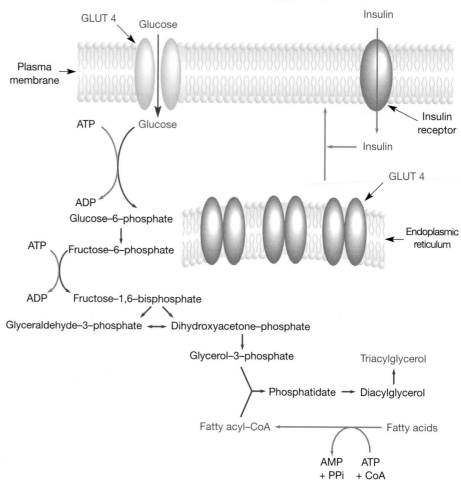

① Insulin mobilizes GLUT 4 glucose transporters from the endoplasmic reticulum to the plasma membranes of adipocytes. As a result of the increased rate of glucose entry and conversion to glycerol-3-phosphate the rate of triacylglycerol synthesis is stimulated

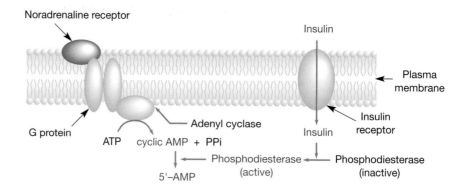

② Insulin reduces the level of cyclic AMP by stimulating phosphodiesterase and this decreases the release of fatty acids by the hormone-sensitive lipase in adipocytes.

Figure 14.6(a)
Details of the regulation of lipid metabolism by insulin.

strates not required for glycogen synthesis or to provide energy for the liver cells will be converted into triacylglycerol and released as VLDL. Both of the principal energy-supplying substrates, glucose and fatty acids, will be available to muscle, but fatty acids can only be used by cardiac muscle and the type I and type II oxidative fibres. The relative rates of oxidation of fatty acids and glucose by these fibres depend on the amounts available to the muscle. In the postabsorptive state

3 Noradrenaline and adrenaline stimulate the formation of cyclic AMP which activates protein kinase A and this converts the hormone-sensitive triacylglycerol lipase into its active form, releasing the first fatty acid

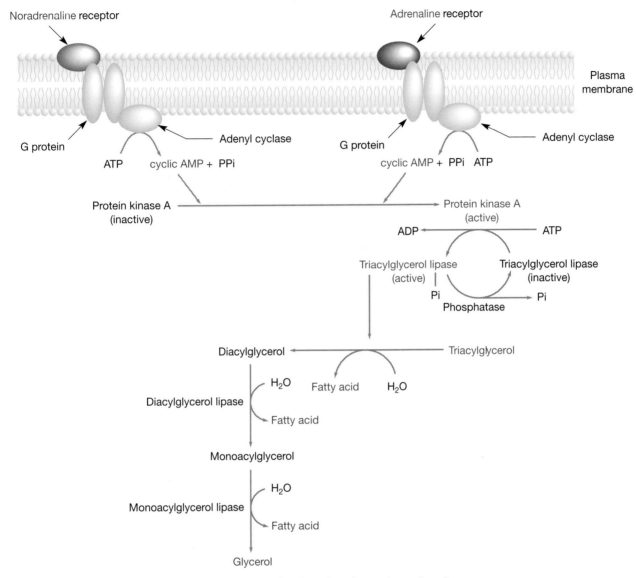

Figure 14.6(b) Details of the regulation of lipid metabolism by adrenaline and noradrenaline.

circulating fatty acid levels (bound to albumin) tend to be relatively low as a result of the inhibition of fatty acid release by insulin (see above) so that glucose will be the preferred fuel. However, when the blood fatty acid levels rise, as a consequence of catecholamine secretion or a decline in blood glucose, then the rate of fatty acid catabolism will increase. This, in turn, will inhibit uptake and metabolism of glucose by muscle cells. The reciprocal relationship between the utilization of these two energy-providing substrates is known as the 'glucose/fatty acid cycle'. Nevertheless it is important to remember that high concentrations of both substrates are required for strenuous exercise.

The effects of lipid absorption

The principal changes that occur in lipid metabolism in the fed state are a shift away from the approximately balanced position of the triacylglycerol/fatty acid cycle in adipose tissue. The increased absorption of glucose raises the blood glucose concentration and as a consequence the insulin level will increase. These changes promote increased storage of triacylglycerol. Also, lipid absorption will increase the release of chylomicrons from the intestine providing adipose tissue with an additional supply of fatty acids. The high glucose levels will also lead to increased release of triacylglycerol in VLDL by the liver. The increased availability of triacylglycerol in the blood reaching the adipose tissue means that the lipoprotein lipase will be releasing fatty acids into the adipocytes at a higher rate, further promoting the storage of triacylglycerol. It is probable that these changes in the fed state will also mean that there is increased synthesis of triacylglycerol in other tissues such as muscle, kidney, intestine, pancreas as well as in liver. Box 1 in Figure 14.2 shows that during the absorption of a high-fat diet the adipose tissue is not able to clear all the fatty acids from the chylomicrons so that these lipoproteins will also be supplying other tissues with fatty acids.

The other change in lipid metabolism in the fed state is likely to be an increase in the absorption of cholesterol. The effect of this will be to reduce cholesterol synthesis in the liver. If the dietary intake of cholesterol is very high, or if the dietary cholesterol fails to inhibit synthesis in the liver, a high fat intake may lead to deposits of cholesteryl esters in the endothelial lining of blood vessels. This effectively narrows the vessels decreasing the blood flow and increasing the potential danger of clots blocking blood vessels in the heart or brain (see section 12.9).

14.8 Effects of hormones on amino acid metabolism and protein synthesis in the fed and postabsorptive states

All cells, with the exception of mature red blood cells, are constantly resysnthesizing their constituent proteins so that they require an adequate supply of the full complement of amino acids. Consequently, the appropriate concentrations of all 20 amino acids in the blood must be maintained. For the non-essential amino acids this is relatively simple since any excesses or deficiencies will be corrected by synthesis or breakdown in the liver or the small intestine. For the essential amino acids, the solution is not so simple. Excessive concentrations of individual essential amino acids can be overcome by increased catabolism either in the liver or, in the case of the branched chain amino acids, in muscle. Deficiencies of essential amino acids in the postabsorptive state can only be remedied by increased protein degradation. This is most likely to occur in muscle and can be achieved in the short term without any significant decrease in muscle strength. However, protein degradation is a rather wasteful way of meeting the deficiency of a single amino acid since it will result in excessive levels of all the other amino acids. The integration of amino acid metabolism in the various tissues is illustrated in Figure 14.3. Table 14.3 summarizes the role of the various tissues in controlling amino acid metabolism.

A major feature of tissue integration in nitrogen metabolism is concerned with nitrogen excretion. Most of the nitrogen released during the catabolism of amino acids and nucleobases must be transported to the liver where it is converted into urea which is then excreted by the kidneys. The kidneys also secrete some ammonia as a means of excreting excess protons without acidifying the urine. The principal ways in which nitrogen is delivered to the liver from other tissues is as glutamine or alanine, the two commonest amino acids in the blood.

Table 14.3 Summary of the control of amino acid metabolism and protein synthesis

The metabolism of amino acids and proteins is controlled in three main ways:

1. growth requires an increase in protein synthesis;
2. nitrogen balance requires that amino acid intake is matched by amino acid catabolism;
3. adequate supplies of all 20 amino acids must be obtained from the diet or protein degradation to support protein synthesis.

Tissues responsible for the control of protein synthesis and amino acid metabolism

	Control mechanism
CNS	Stimulates release of growth hormone and TSH
	Stimulates muscular activity causing increased glutamine synthesis
Liver	Supplies non-essential amino acids
	Metabolizes excess amino acids and releases the nitrogen as urea
	Synthesizes and releases growth factors
Muscle	Metabolizes excess branched chain amino acids
Pancreas	Releases insulin when amino acid concentrations are high

Tissues in which the regulation of protein synthesis and amino acid metabolism operate

	Metabolic effect
Muscle	Forms glutamine and alanine in order to send ammonia to the liver
	Breaks down muscle protein to supply amino acids for protein synthesis and gluconeogenesis during starvation
Kidneys	Metabolize glutamine to $CO_2 + H_2O$ and release NH_4^+ to control blood pH
Small intestine	Converts glutamine into alanine plus ammonia

Tissues where an increase in activity may change protein synthesis and amino acid metabolism

	Change in metabolism
Liver	Excessive intake of amino acids results in the formation of fatty acids and an increased production of urea
Muscle	Synthesizes muscle protein in response to growth factors, regular exercise and high protein intake
Small intestine	Digestion and absorption of protein increases the delivery of amino acids to the blood in an approximately physiological mixture

Glutamine is produced by the CNS and muscles in order to export ammonia released during the catabolism of amino acids and nucleobases. Some of the glutamine reaching the kidneys is deaminated and the resulting 2-oxoglutarate is then completely oxidized by the TCA cycle in order to achieve the net excretion of protons together with the ammonia. The other tissue that metabolizes large amounts of glutamine is the small intestine, which uses it as an energy source. In this case catabolism of glutamine ends with the release of the nitrogen into the hepatic portal blood as alanine or ammonia. When this nitrogen reaches the liver it is converted into urea.

Hormonal effects on amino acid metabolism

The major hormonal effects on amino acid and protein metabolism are produced by insulin. This hormone increases the rate of amino acid transport into adipose tissue, liver and muscle. It also stimulates the rate of protein synthesis in these tissues, possibly at the initiation stage of translation. Growth hormone stimulates the production of somatomedins by the liver and these peptides stimulate protein synthesis in the body as a whole. The thyroid hormones also stimulate protein synthesis, although in this case there is considerable evidence for a selective increase in the synthesis of specific enzymes. Cortisol and the other glucocorticoids have a general inhibitory effect on protein synthesis in muscle and as a consequence they release amino acids from muscle protein which provides the liver with substrates for gluconeogenesis. The hormonal controls of amino acid metabolism and protein synthesis are shown in Figure 14.7.

Integration of amino acid metabolism in the fed state

In the fed state peptide uptake by the intestine will increase the blood amino acid concentrations, and it also stimulates the rate of protein synthesis in the intestine itself, probably as the result of an increase in cytoplasmic amino acid concentrations. The increased amino acid concentrations in the blood will stimulate amino acid catabolism by liver and muscle. In addition it is clear that higher circulating amino acid levels increase the rate of protein synthesis, particularly in muscle. Thus, it appears that the absorption of dietary protein will tend to increase the synthesis of muscle protein, providing increased muscle strength, a store of protein which can be used as a reserve supply of essential amino acids and an energy source during starvation. Box 1 in Figure 14.3 indicates that the three main consequences of a high-protein diet are increased amino acid catabolism, the formation of additional triacylglycerol by the liver and a general stimulation of protein synthesis. However it is important to note, as indicated in the next section, that these changes only apply in a healthy individual where nitrogen balance is maintained.

14.9 The metabolic effects of trauma, physical injury or surgery

The effects of shock

The shock associated with an accident or a sudden physical injury causes an immediate disruption of the metabolic balance between tissues. This is caused by the stimulation of the sympathetic nervous system which causes a massive

1 Insulin increases the rate of amino acid transport into adipose tissue, liver and muscle. Although the mechanism is unclear, the insulin effect may be due to the stimulation by insulin of the synthesis or mobilization of amino acid transporters.

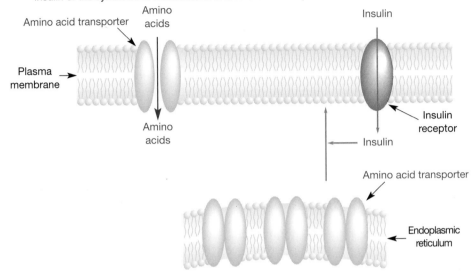

2 Insulin reduces the level of cyclic AMP by stimulating phosphodiesterase and this may be responsible for the effect of insulin on protein synthesis since cyclic AMP-dependent phosphorylation of initiation factors may inhibit their activity.

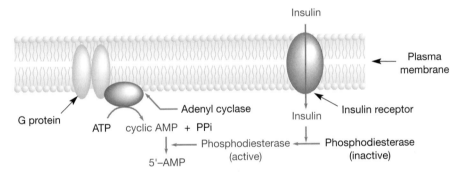

3 Growth hormone stimulates the formation of insulin-like growth factors by the liver. These factors increase the rate of protein synthesis in the body which increases the uptake of amino acids from the blood.

4 Cortisol increases the rate of protein breakdown in muscle. This releases additional amino acids into the blood, increasing vascular amino acid concentrations, and makes more amino acids available for gluconeogenesis.

Figure 14.7
Details of the hormonal control of amino acid metabolism.

release of adrenaline and increases the heart rate and blood pressure. The sympathetic stimulation of the pancreatic islet cells increases glucagon release and inhibits the secretion of insulin. As a consequence there will be a rapid rise in blood glucose concentration. In addition, the release of noradrenaline by the sympathetic pathways stimulates the release of fatty acids from adipose tissue. The effect of shock on the nervous system also stimulates the hypothalamus to secrete vasopressin and the neuropeptides that control the secretion of anterior pituitary hormones. Vasopressin helps to raise the blood pressure by reducing the elimination of water in the urine, the secretion of ACTH stimulates the release of cortisol by the adrenal cortex and growth hormone increases the release of fatty acids from adipose tissue. The overall initial metabolic effect of the trauma is to mobilize glucose and fatty acids from the liver and adipose tissue, respectively. Although the corticosteroids take longer to produce their effects, the increased protein catabolism in muscle caused by cortisol will release amino acids for gluconeogenesis. Because the elevation in blood glucose concentration is associated with an inhibition of insulin secretion, most tissues apart from the blood and CNS will use the fatty acids as an energy source rather than glucose. The initial response to trauma is associated with a reduction in the utilization of energy-supplying substrates, probably due to a drop in body temperature.

Surgery can also produce a reaction similar to the shock caused by injury or fright. Even the anticipation of an operation or the administration of an anaesthetic may precipitate the sort of sympathetic response produced by trauma or a serious injury. The initial effect of trauma may only last for a few hours, although if the injuries are serious, involving extensive burns for example, the reduction in metabolic rate may continue for as long as a day.

The recovery phase

After the initial response to trauma ends, the body switches to a highly active metabolic state in order to support recovery from the injuries. This is partly due to an increase in body temperature, but the extra energy is supplied mainly to support tissue repair. Stimulation of the anterior pituitary by the hypothalamus may be responsible for the elevation of the metabolic rate as a result of the stimulation of thyroid hormone secretion by TSH. The alterations in the metabolic interactions between tissues in the recovery phase shown in Figure 14.8 are similar to those in the initial response to trauma. However, the high rate of substrate utilization in the recovery phase places extra demands on liver, muscle and adipose tissue. Although glucose is not the main energy-supplying substrate for most tissues, there is a strong demand for it because it is used as a glycolytic substrate by damaged tissue and leucocytes. The lactate produced by these cells returns to the liver increasing the rate of gluconeogenesis.

The requirement for a high rate of gluconeogenesis also demands continuing mobilization of muscle protein, and the recovery phase is characterized by a negative nitrogen balance. This is even true when a high-protein diet is being consumed, and is probably the result of a reduction in protein synthesis because of the high rate of cortisol secretion by the adrenal cortex. The negative nitrogen balance occurs despite an increase in insulin secretion during the recovery phase, and the relative ineffectiveness of insulin under these conditions may be due to a decrease in the number of insulin receptors in muscle and adipose tissue. Another reason for the increased breakdown of muscle protein is probably the demand for extra glutamine. Recovery from injury or a serious infection requires an increase in cell proliferation, and glutamine is needed in order to synthesize the nucleotides required for nucleic acid synthesis (see section 4.9). Figure 14.8 indicates that some of the glutamine produced by muscle is used in the proliferation of antibody-producing lymphocytes and other white blood cells.

Despite the increased production of glucose by the liver, fatty acids are still the main energy-supplying substrate for the body during the recovery phase. The activity of the hormone-sensitive lipase in adipose tissue continues to be stimulated by the release of adrenaline and noradrenaline by the sympathetic nervous system. Normally the high blood glucose concentration would promote the resynthesis of triacylglycerol in the adipocytes. However, as mentioned above, the insulin secreted during the recovery phase seems to be less effective in adipose tissue, and as a consequence there is a net loss of triacylglycerol from adipose tissue during the recovery phase. As a consequence those individuals with relatively large fat deposits are in a better position to survive trauma, severe injury and serious operations.

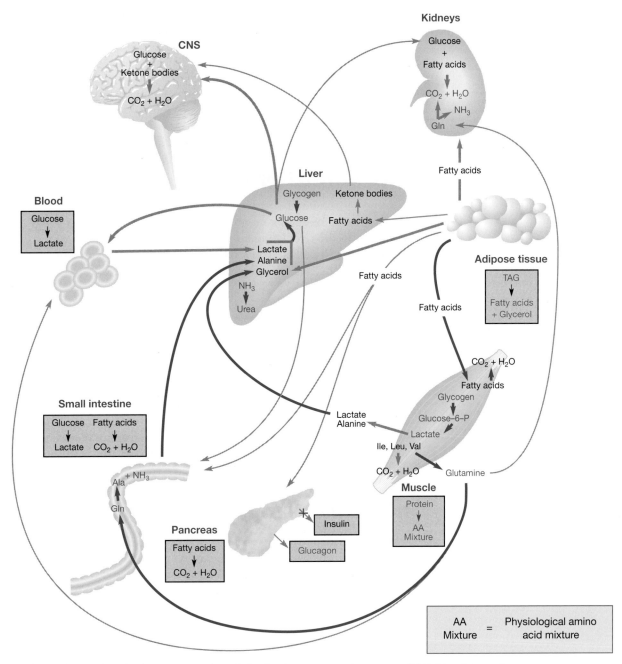

Figure 14.8 Tissue interactions in the recovery phase following trauma or major surgery. TAG, triacylglycerol.

14.10 Metabolic effects of cancer

The growth of tumours associated with many types of cancer can also cause a serious disruption in the normal metabolic balance between tissues. These changes are similar to those occurring during starvation (see Chapter 15). The condition is called cachexia and is characterized by a negative nitrogen balance and the net loss of stored triacylglycerol. The tumours produce cachexin, a protein that promotes the decline in body weight. These effects are probably assisted by the growth-promoting cytokines which stimulate cell division. It seems probable that the causes of weight loss in cancer are due to an increased secretion of cortisol which reduces the rate of protein synthesis in muscle, and to the stimulation of the sympathetic neurones in adipose tissue which activates the hormone-sensitive lipase. The reduction in muscle protein supports gluconeogenesis and helps to meet the increased demands for glutamine to support the tumour growth as well as the protective activities of lymphocytes.

14.11 Diseases that disturb the hormonal integration of metabolism

Humans are subject to a number of diseases that are characterized by a serious alteration in the circulating level of a particular hormone, and to conclude this chapter we will consider several examples of the ways in which such diseases alter the integration of metabolism.

Diabetes mellitus

This disease is characterized by abnormally high levels of blood glucose which, if ignored, can result in the loss of water and glucose in the urine. As described in the previous chapter, the kidney tubules normally reabsorb all of the glucose passing through the glomerulus, but when the blood glucose concentration is above 12 mM the reabsorption capacity is exceeded. There are two fundamentally different forms of diabetes mellitus, an insulin-dependent form and a non-insulin-dependent form. The former occurs in the young and is associated with a loss of weight. The latter, which is more common, occurs in middle-aged and elderly people who are often overweight.

Insulin-dependent diabetes mellitus

Insulin-dependent diabetes mellitus (IDDM) is characterized by the failure of the pancreatic β-cells to secrete insulin and appears to be due to the destruction of these cells by the immune system. As a consequence the elevation of blood glucose following a meal will persist since there is no insulin to stimulate glycogen synthesis in the liver. Furthermore, since insulin is absent, GLUT 4 will not be mobilized to the plasma membranes of muscle and adipose tissue, and this severely restricts the utilization of glucose by both of these tissues. As a consequence muscle must rely on other energy-supplying substrates, and this increases the catabolism of muscle protein as well as the utilization of fatty acids.

In adipose tissue the lack of GLUT 4 results in decreased storage of triacylglycerol, and the fact that the high blood glucose is associated with an increase in the circulating fatty acid levels indicates that there is increased activity of triacylglycerol lipase in the adipocytes. The elevation in lipase activity is probably due to noradrenaline secretion as a consequence of stress which stimulates the sympathetic nerve pathways to adipose tissue and the adrenal medulla. The rise in fatty acid levels has two further consequences: it reduces the utilization of glucose, and leads to the production of ketone bodies by the liver. The rise in vascular ketone body concentrations reduces the blood pH, and can cause severe acidosis.

As soon as the IDDM has been diagnosed, it can be treated in a satisfactory way by regular insulin injections at least once a day. It should be recognized, however, that these injections are less effective at maintaining a stable blood glucose concentration than the controlled release of insulin by the pancreatic β-cells into the portal vein.

Non-insulin-dependent diabetes mellitus

Non-insulin-dependent diabetes mellitus (NIDDM) is not due to the absence of insulin secretion by the pancreatic β-cells, but to a decrease in its effectiveness as a regulator of the blood glucose concentration. It seems likely that there is a genetic basis for this condition, which is present in one-tenth of elderly humans. The decreased effectiveness of insulin causes the blood glucose to exceed the normal level, which stimulates the release of additional insulin. The combination of a high blood glucose and increased insulin promotes the storage of triacylglycerol by adipose tissue even though the insulin is less effective than normal. Consequently those suffering from NIDDM are often overweight. There are also changes in liver metabolism because of the decreased effectiveness of insulin. The balance between glycogen synthesis and phosphorolysis is shifted so that there is net release of glucose by the liver at a higher blood glucose concentration. In addition, the extra circulating glucose promotes the release of VLDL by the liver so that many non-hepatic tissues will use fatty acids in preference to glucose, pushing the blood glucose concentration even higher.

Those individuals with NIDDM can alleviate their excessive blood glucose levels by carefully managing their diet. They must restrict their carbohydrate intake and avoid sucrose. The latter point is particularly important because diabetics appear to have increased levels of fructose transporters in the small intestine and adipose tissue. Overall, those with NIDDM must reduce their calorie intake in order to avoid obesity. Some drug treatments help to reduce the high blood glucose in NIDDM by stimulating insulin secretion by the pancreatic β-cells or increasing its effectiveness. As NIDDM patients get older they may also need to be injected with insulin if their insulin secretion decreases.

Hypothyroidism

Those individuals with low levels of circulating thyroid hormones have a reduced basal metabolic rate and are termed hypothyroid. If this condition occurs in the young, growth is severely restricted, a condition known as cretinism. Hypothyroid adults suffer from myxoedema which is often characterized by obesity and fluid retention. Mild hypothyroidism in adults can result from deficient supplies of iodide in the diet. This is usually compensated for by an enlargement of the thyroid gland, a condition known as goitre, which is a consequence of increased levels of TSH. Severe myxoedema, on the other hand, is usually due to the destruction of the thyroid hormone-producing cells and must be treated by regular administration of thyroid hormones. The reduction in basal metabolic rate in hypothyroidism is responsible for obesity because of the general reduction in the energy requirements of the body as a whole.

Hyperthyroidism

Excessive production of thyroid hormones causes an elevation in metabolic rate as well as increased stimulation of the sympathetic nervous system and a rise in heart rate. There are a number of causes of this condition, which is also called Graves' disease. In severe cases it may be due to a thyroid tumour. Mild hyperthyroidism may be a consequence of the over-production of TSH by the pituitary. The increase in metabolic rate results in increased release of glucose by the liver as a consequence of glucagon secretion and stimulation of triacylglycerol lipase in adipose tissue by noradrenaline. When the thyroid hormone levels become very excessive the condition is known as thyrotoxicosis, which is associated with a decrease in the efficiency of oxidative phosphorylation. Hyperthyroidism is usually treated by removal of the thyroid gland or destruction of the hormone-producing cells by drug treatment. Patients treated by either of these methods must then have their thyroid hormone levels maintained by carefully monitored doses of the hormones.

E X E R C I S E S

1. Compare the fate of dietary galactose, glucose and fructose.

2. Compare the way the liver deals with an increase in the glucose concentration in the hepatic portal vein at the beginning and end of a high-carbohydrate meal.

3. How does insulin regulate the storage of triacylglycerol by adipocytes?

4. List the metabolic effects of adrenaline secretion.

5. What is the connection between a high triacylglycerol intake and the level of blood cholesterol?

6. Explain why an excessive protein intake can increase the storage of triacylglycerol.

7. Explain why those with untreated diabetes are very thin if they have IDDM and overweight if they have NIDDM.

8. List the causes of weight loss as a result of trauma.

9. What are the functions of the glutamine produced by muscle?

10. Explain the difference between hypothyroidism and hyperthyroidism.

Further reading

Blumer, K.J. & Johnson, G.L. (1994) Diversity in function and regulation of MAP kinase pathways, *Trends in Biochemical Sciences* **19**, 236–240.

Cano, E. & Mahadevan, L.C. (1995) Parallel signal processing among mammalian MAPKs, *Trends in Biochemical Sciences* **20**, 117–122.

Crabtree, G.R. & Schreiber, S.L. (1996) Three-part inventions: intracellular signaling and induced proximity, *Trends in Biochemical Sciences* **21**, 418–422.

Frayn, K.N. (1996) *Metabolic Regulation: A Human Perspective*, Portland Press.

Frayn, K.N., Coppack, S.W. & Humphreys, S.M. (1995) Fuel selection in white adipose tissue, *Proceedings of the Nutrition Society* **54**, 177–189.

Gould, G.W. & Holman, G.D. (1993) The glucose transporter family: structure, function and tissue-specific expression, *Biochemical Journal* **295**, 329–341.

Exton, J.H. (1997) Phospholipase D: Enzymology, mechanism of regulation and function. *Physiological Reviews* **77**, 303–320.

Hodgkin, M.N., Pettitt, T.R., Martin, A., Michell, R.H., Pemberton, A.J. & Wakelam, M.J.O. (1998) Diacylglycerols and phosphatidates: which molecular species are intraccellular messengers? *Trends in Biochemical Sciences* **23**, 200–204.

Houslay, M.D. & Milligan, G. (1997) Tailoring cAMP-signalling responses through isoform multiplicity, *Trends in Biochemical Sciences* **22**, 217–224.

Lee, H.C. (1997) Mechanisms of calcium signaling by cyclic ADP-ribose and NAADP. *Physiological Reviews* **77**, 1133–1164.

Robinson, M.J. & Cobb, M.H. (1997) Mitogen-activated protein kinase pathways, *Current Opinion in Cell Biology* **9**, 180–186.

Rolfe, D.F.S. & Brown, G.C. (1997) Cellular enegy utilization and molecular origin of standard metabolic rate in mammals. *Physiological Reviews* **77**, 731–758.

Vanhaesebroeck, B., Leevers, S.J., Panayotou, G. & Waterfield, M.D. (1997) Phosphoinositide 3-kinases: a conserved family of signal transducers, *Trends in Biochemical Sciences* **22**, 267–272.

Walsh, B.T. & Devlin, M.J. (1998) Eating disorders: progress and problems. *Science* **280**, 1387–1390.

White, D.A. & Baxter, M., eds (1994) *Hormones and Metabolic Control*, 2nd edition, Arnold, Chapters 5 & 6.

Wickman, K. & Clapham, D.E. (1995) Ion channel regulation by G proteins. *Physiological Reviews* **75**, 865–885.

Woods, S.C., Seeley, R.J. Porte Jr., D. & Schwartz, M.W. Signals that regulate food intake and energy homeostasis. *Science* **280**, 1378–1383.

Woscholski, R. & Parker, P.J. (1997) Inositol lipid 5-phosphatases – traffic signals and signal traffic, *Trends in Biochemical Sciences* **22**, 427–431.

The influence of starvation on tissue metabolism

The body's response to starvation is to mobilize its energy reserves in a carefully controlled manner.

Because muscle protein is used as a source of substrates for gluconeogenesis, exercise complicates the metabolic response to starvation.

15.1 Changes in tissue metabolism as a function of the length of time without food

The object of this chapter is to show how starvation alters the interactions between the eight tissues that we have considered in Part 2. As indicated in Chapter 5 the principal energy reserves in the body are the adipose tissue stores of triacylglycerol and muscle protein. Consequently these two sources must provide the body with energy-supplying substrates during extended periods of starvation. It is also crucial that the body's other three main requirements continue to be met. For example, the resynthesis of cell constituents requires that adequate levels of all 20 amino acids should be available. In order to support the body's integration and the protective functions provided by the blood, it is essential that the blood glucose should be maintained for the CNS and the red blood cells. It is useful to consider the metabolic effects of starvation because similar changes also occur as a result of trauma or surgery (see section 14.9).

The effects of starvation depend on the length of time without food

The metabolic changes that occur during starvation are continuous, but before describing them in detail it may be helpful to divide the time without food into a number of arbitrary periods. After the food from a meal has been absorbed, the supply of nutrients from the intestine ends and we enter the postabsorptive period which continues until the next regular meal. If this meal is missed the individual will enter the initial period of starvation during which liver glycogen is rapidly depleted, and this may last for up to 24 hours. During the next two or three days, which constitute the early period of starvation, there are marked metabolic changes, chiefly characterized by a 10-fold rise in ketone body concentrations. The following week or two can be considered an intermediate period of starvation in which ketone body concentrations rise further and the rate of muscle protein depletion is substantially reduced. After starvation has continued for two to three weeks conditions stabilize and the final period of prolonged starvation can continue for a long as two months in some cases. Eventually death occurs, usually as a result of weakness in respiratory muscles or because of pneumonia.

In the initial period of starvation the reserves of glucose stored in the liver are rapidly exhausted. Individuals who follow a regular pattern of meals will normally store enough glycogen in their liver to support the blood glucose over the period from the last meal of the day until the time they normally eat their first meal the next day. As this glycogen reserve is depleted, gluconeogenesis comes into play to help maintain blood glucose levels. In order to minimize the body's utilization of glucose and amino acids to supply energy, fatty acids are released from adipose tissue stores in order to satisfy as much of the requirement for energy-supplying substrates as possible. The increased availability of fatty acids for those tissues that can use them conserves glucose for the CNS and the red blood cells. Fatty acid oxidation also minimizes the use of the amino acids from muscle protein as a general energy source so that blood levels of amino acids can be maintained to support protein synthesis, even though this may be occurring at a reduced rate. In addition it is important that the vascular concentrations of some of the amino acids should be protected so that they can continue to serve as substrates for gluconeogenesis. As indicated in section 7.5, the driving force for the release of fatty acids stored in the form of triacylglycerol is the increase in noradrenaline levels and the decrease in insulin. Both of these changes accelerate the exit of fatty acids from adipose tissue by reducing the rate of triacylglycerol synthesis and increasing the rate of triacylglycerol hydrolysis as a consequence of the rise in cyclic AMP levels.

The data presented in Figure 15.1 show that the most dramatic change in the concentrations of energy-supplying substrates during the early and intermediate periods of starvation is the increase in ketone body levels. Total ketone body concentrations in the blood rise from 0.02 mM in the fed individual to more than 6 mM after two weeks without food. Since all aerobic tissues, including the CNS, are able to metabolize ketone bodies if they are present, the rise in the concentrations of these alternative substrates (acetoacetate and 3-hydroxybutyrate) has a massive glucose-sparing effect. In this way virtually all the blood glucose, which is maintained at about 4 mM (80% of the normal concentration), is available for the blood cells and the CNS. It is important to recognize that although the CNS mitochondria can oxidize ketone bodies to produce ATP, the neurones must have some glucose in order to provide ATP by glycolysis in the axons and dendrites which often extend a long distance from the cell body where most of the mitochondria are located. Fatty acid concentrations in the blood increase to about four times the normal fed level after three days of starvation, but after that they do not increase much further. This is because of the large-scale conversion of fatty acids into ketone bodies that takes place in the liver.

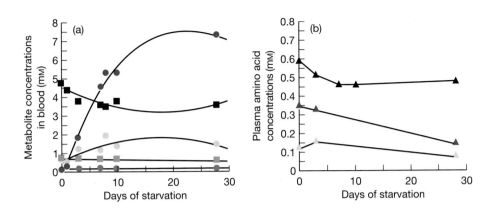

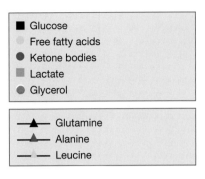

Figure 15.1
Changes in the concentrations of blood constituents during starvation: (a) energy-supplying metabolites; (b) amino acids.

Hormonal changes during starvation

The hormonal changes that occur in starvation are chiefly signalled by the decline in blood glucose. This reduces insulin secretion (although even in prolonged starvation some insulin is still secreted) and increases the production of glucagon. As a consequence of the reduction in vascular insulin concentration and the release of noradrenaline by the sympathetic neurones in adipose tissue, the triacylglycerol lipase in adipose tissue is stimulated, increasing the release of free fatty acids and glycerol. The rise in glucagon also stimulates gluconeogenesis in the liver. In prolonged starvation the kidneys become a major site of gluconeogenesis using the increased glutamine release from muscle. The additional glutamine production by muscle is largely due to amino acid release as a result of protein catabolism. The additional branched chain amino acids must undergo catabolism in the muscle and the resulting ammonia leaves the muscles as glutamine. The other amino acids produced by the catabolism of muscle protein are released into the blood and many of these can serve as gluconeogenic precursors in the liver. The intestine also metabolizes the extra glutamine converting it into alanine which, together with the glycerol from the adipose tissue, provide particularly valuable substrates for gluconeogenesis by the liver. The other change that occurs in starvation as a consequence of hormonal effects is a decline in the basal metabolic rate. This appears to be due to a reduction in the level of the active form of the thyroid hormone, 3,5,3'-triiodothyronine, which is produced by deiodination of thyroxine, the primary product of the thyroid gland. The reduction in basal metabolic rate cuts the overall utilization of the energy-supplying substrates and serves to protect muscle protein levels during periods of prolonged starvation by reducing amino acid catabolism.

15.2 Changes in the relative importance of the various energy-supplying substrates as the ketone body concentration rises

In addition to serving as energy-supplying substrates, ketone bodies also inhibit glucose utilization and the mobilization of amino acids from muscle protein. Once they have entered a cell the ketone bodies will be converted into acetyl-CoA in the mitochondrial matrix. When the acetyl-CoA level exceeds the substrate requirement for the TCA cycle, citrate begins to accumulate in the matrix and will be exported into the cytoplasm where it will inhibit the phospho-fructokinase step in glycolysis. Although some amino acid catabolism is necessary to provide oxaloacetate for the TCA cycle, the rise in acetyl-CoA caused by catabolism of ketone bodies prevents additional amino acids from being converted into acetyl-CoA.

It might be assumed that the rise in vascular ketone body concentrations that occurs after the first two days of starvation indicates that their rate of production by the liver continues to increase, but this does not appear to be the case. Instead the higher concentrations in the blood are indicative of a slower rate of ketone body oxidation by muscle. This change may be partly due to the decrease in basal metabolic rate. The high ketone body concentrations reached at the end of the intermediate period of starvation decrease the rate of glucose utilization by the CNS, so that as much as two-thirds of its energy requirements are met by ketone body oxidation. High ketone body concentrations also increase their utilization by the kidney cortex and the small intestine as well as inhibiting the catabolism of the amino acids derived from muscle protein. Ketone bodies are formed by the liver in order to prevent blood levels of fatty acids from rising to the point where the integrity of membranes may be at risk. However the negative aspect of increased ketone body concentrations is the reduction of blood pH which can lead to a highly damaging level of acidosis especially in IDDM. The kidneys must combat the reduction in blood pH caused by the ketone bodies by metabolizing increased amounts of glutamine.

15.3 Changes in carbohydrate metabolism during starvation

As indicated at the beginning of this chapter, the most dramatic changes in carbohydrate metabolism occur in the initial and early phases of starvation. This is illustrated in Figure 15.2. During the postabsorptive period liver glycogen is broken down to maintain the blood glucose concentration at about 5 mM. When liver glycogen becomes depleted, gluconeogenesis by the liver becomes the main process supplying blood glucose and the vascular concentration declines to about 4 mM. The main substrates for this glucose synthesis consist initially of the lactate and alanine supplied to the liver by the small intestine, the blood cells and muscle. However, as the liver glycogen begins to run out other amino acids are used as substrates. Furthermore, because the blood glucose concentration declines and increasing amounts of fatty acid are released from the adipose tissue the liver will also receive substantial amounts of glycerol which can be used for gluconeogenesis.

The hormonal effects responsible for the changes in carbohydrate metabolism are largely a consequence of the decline in insulin levels and the increased secretion of glucagon. The stimulus for glycogenolysis in starvation is largely due to the increase in cyclic AMP caused by glucagon, although the lower insulin levels help to reduce glycogen synthetase activity. The main contribution that declining insulin levels make is to restrict the use of glucose by muscle and adipose tissue by decreasing the mobilization of the GLUT 4 transporters to the plasma membranes of these cells. This change is particularly important for maintaining the glucose supply to the CNS and the red blood cells. In addition to stimulating glycogenolysis glucagon also stimulates gluconeogenesis by the liver and this effect becomes more pronounced when the liver glycogen becomes exhausted.

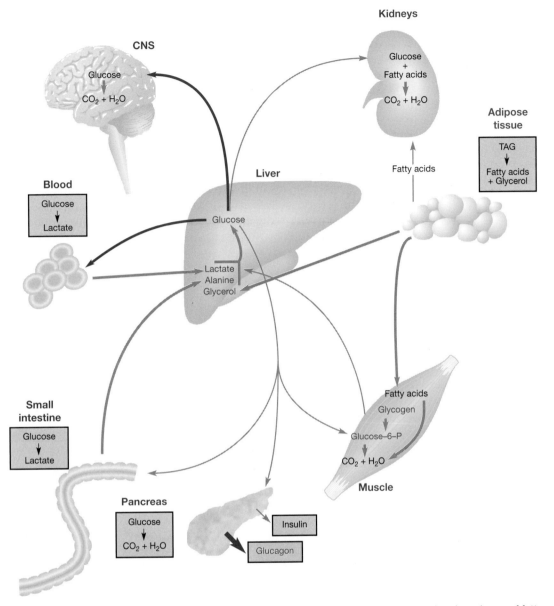

Figure 15.2 Changes in carbohydrate metabolism after liver glycogen is exhausted. During exercise the release of fatty acids and glycerol from adipose tissue is increased, more muscle glycogen is used and more lactate is returned to the liver for gluconeogenesis. TAG, triacylglycerol.

In the intermediate and prolonged stages of starvation the supply side of carbohydrate metabolism is restricted to gluconeogenesis in the liver and kidneys. Glucose utilization is mainly limited to the CNS and the erythrocytes. In these later stages the glucose production by the kidneys becomes particularly significant, with glutamine providing the major source of the glucose carbons.

The effects of exercise on carbohydrate metabolism during starvation

The initiation of exercise during the initial or early phases of starvation will speed up the changes in carbohydrate metabolism. As a consequence the liver glycogen will be exhausted more quickly, so that it will be necessary to achieve maximal rates of gluconeogenesis more rapidly. If exercise occurs in the later stages of starvation, it will have little effect on carbohydrate metabolism. Under these conditions the rate of gluconeogenesis will already be high, so that the only significant change is likely to be a result of the increased availability of glycerol which can replace some of the amino acids as a substrate for gluconeogenesis.

15.4 Changes in lipid metabolism during starvation

The principal changes in lipid metabolism occur in the early stage of starvation when the release of fatty acids from the adipose tissue increases by a factor of four. This is associated with a progressive increase in the production of ketone

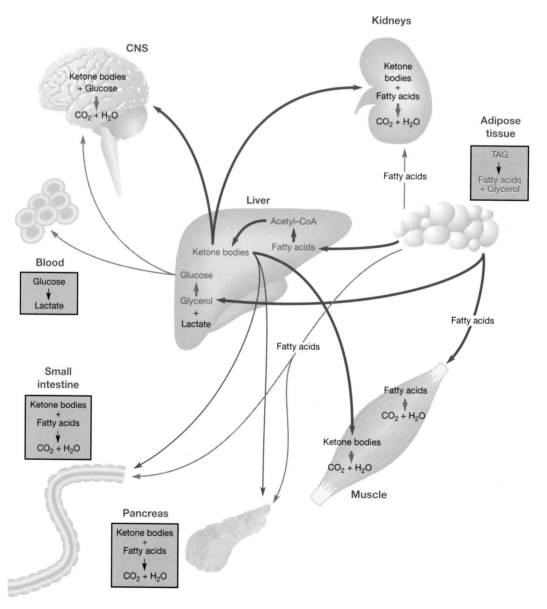

Figure 15.3 Lipid metabolism during starvation. Exercise increases the rate of triacylglycerol (TAG) breakdown by adipose tissue.

bodies by the liver in response to the elevated plasma fatty acid levels (see Figure 15.3). The increased production of free fatty acids by the adipocytes results from the increase in cyclic AMP resulting partly from the production of noradrenaline by the sympathetic neurones and partly as a result of the decline in the vascular insulin concentration. The lower insulin level restricts glucose entry into the adipocyte because of the reduced mobilization of GLUT 4, which reduces the availability of glycerol-3-phosphate for triacylglycerol synthesis, and it also prevents the decrease in cyclic AMP caused by insulin (see Figure 14.6).

As indicated in earlier chapters, the rise in the availability of fatty acids inhibits the utilization of glucose by tissues such as muscle and kidney cortex. As the blood concentrations of ketone bodies rise this inhibition is reinforced and additional tissues such as the intestine and the CNS are switched away from glucose to the use of ketone bodies as major energy-supplying substrates.

The effects of exercise on lipid metabolism during starvation

When exercise occurs during starvation it is likely that a further increase in the activity of the hormone-sensitive triacylglycerol lipase of adipose tissue will occur. In this case the extra fatty acids will be used to support muscle contraction since the capacity of the liver to form ketone bodies will already be operating at or near its maximal rate. The additional stimulus for triacylglycerol breakdown will come from the secretion of adrenaline and additional noradrenaline from both the adrenal medulla and the nerve endings in adipose tissue.

15.5 Alterations in amino acid metabolism during starvation

The most quantitatively important phase of amino acid metabolism during starvation is in the early stage when increasing amounts of muscle protein are being mobilized to serve as substrates for gluconeogenesis. However, by the third day the loss of muscle protein begins to decline. This probably occurs partly to prevent a dangerous loss of muscle strength, and also to protect the supply of amino acids for protein synthesis. The decrease in protein breakdown in muscle as starvation proceeds is only possible because the CNS uses progressively more ketone bodies, thereby reducing the requirement for glucose supplied by gluconeogenesis. The stimulatory effects of the glucocorticoids on the breakdown of muscle protein are important at the beginning of starvation but they appear to be countered by the decline in metabolic rate caused by the decrease in the thyroid hormone level.

Once the initial burst of protein loss from muscle has occurred, the main features of amino acid metabolism are the production of glutamine by muscle and the CNS, and its metabolism in the kidneys and the small intestine (see Figure 15.4). Glutamine and the alanine produced from it by the intestine continue to serve as important sources of carbon for gluconeogenesis throughout starvation.

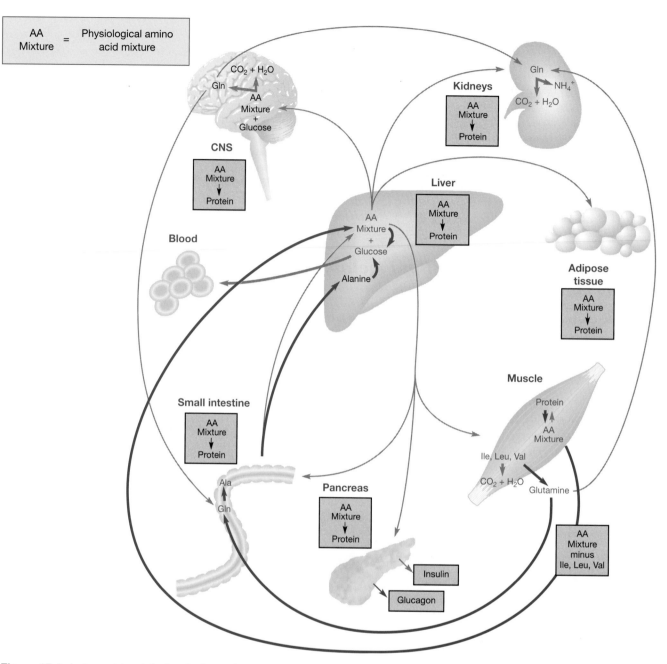

Figure 15.4 Amino acid metabolism in the early stages of starvation. As starvation continues there is a decrease in the rate at which muscle protein is broken down. Exercise also reduces the rate of muscle protein catabolism.

The effects of exercise on amino acid metabolism during starvation

The imposition of a period of exercise during starvation will modify amino acid metabolism by increasing glutamine production. This will help to increase the capacity of the kidneys for gluconeogenesis. If the exercise occurs during the early stage of starvation it will probably inhibit the loss of muscle protein at least on a temporary basis.

15.6 Changes in tissue interrelationships as a function of the length of starvation

There are substantial changes in the tissue interactions during the various stages of starvation. In the initial stage (Figure 15.5a) the liver is the main participant with the assistance of changes in the secretion of insulin and glucagon by the pancreas. During the early phase the adipose tissue also becomes important as

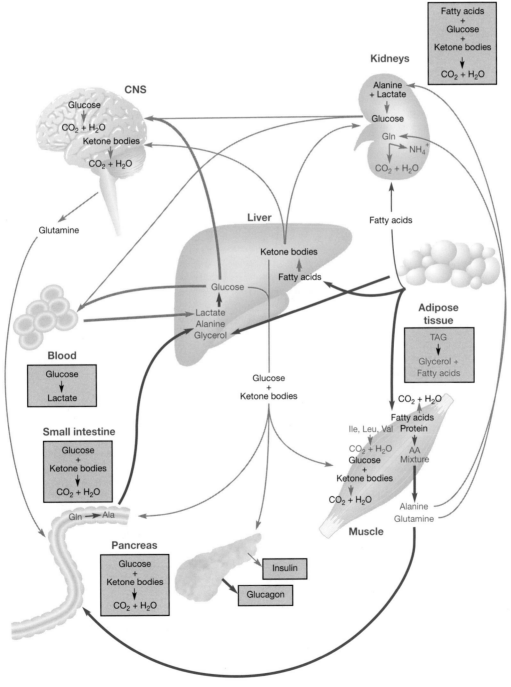

Figure 15.5(a) Tissue interrelationships in early starvation, TAG, triacylglycerol.

the supplier of fatty acids together with muscle which is providing a major carbon input for gluconeogenesis. As the release of fatty acids increases, the liver again becomes the major player because although it continues to produce glucose by gluconeogenesis, it is now forming vast amounts of ketone bodies for all of the tissues except the red blood cells.

The changes in the metabolic interactions between tissues that occur during prolonged starvation are illustrated in Figure 15.5(b). The first set of changes in the transition from the early stages to prolonged starvation involve substituting fatty acid mobilization and gluconeogenesis for the release of liver glycogen. The second set of changes are associated with the use of ketone bodies by most tissues and the reduction in both metabolic rate and protein mobilization from muscle.

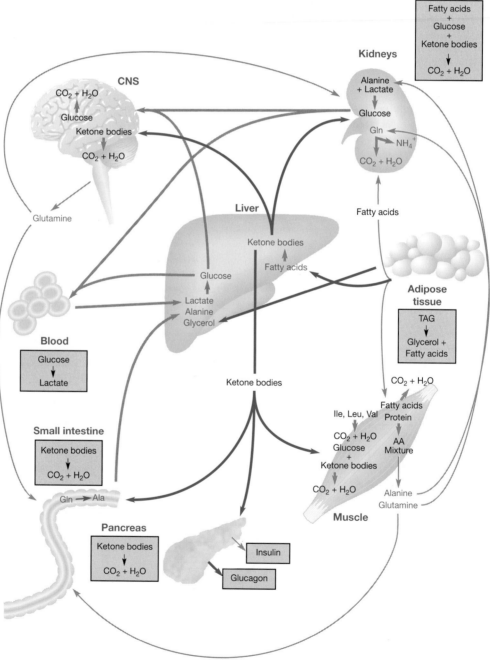

Figure 15.5(b) Tissue interrelationships during prolonged starvation, TAG, triacylglycerol.

EXERCISES

1. What is responsible for the release of fatty acids from adipose tissue during starvation?

2. Why do the vascular ketone body concentrations continue to rise during starvation when there is no longer an increase in vascular fatty acid concentrations?

3. Indicate the sources of carbon for gluconeogenesis in the various stages of starvation.

4. Why is there an increase in glutamine production during starvation even when muscular activity is minimal?

5. List the hormonal changes that occur in the various stages of starvation.

Further reading

Baverel, G., Ferrier, B. and Martin, M. (1995) Fuel selection by the kidney: adaption to starvation, *Proceedings of the Nutrition Society* **54**, 197–212.

Cahill, G.F.J. (1976) Starvation in man, *Clinical Endocrinology and Metabolism* **5**, 397–415.

Frayn, K.N. (1996) *Metabolic Regulation: A Human Perspective*, Portland Press, Chapter 7.

Henry, C.K.J. (1990) Body mass index and the limits of human survival, *European Journal of Clinical Nutrition* **44**, 329–335.

White, D.A. and Baxter, M., eds (1994) *Hormones and Metabolic Control*, 2nd edition, Arnold, Chapter 4.

How does exercise alter the metabolic balance?

CHAPTER 16

Maximum power output during exercise can only be maintained for a few seconds since it depends on anaerobic contraction. Prolonged exercise at a strenuous level depends on the supplies of muscle glycogen as well as fatty acids and glucose.

16.1 Overview of the effects of exercise on the metabolic interactions between tissues

In contrast to the metabolic effects of nutrient absorption or starvation, which aim to provide the most efficient storage or release of energy-supplying substrates, severe exercise requires all the energy-supplying systems to operate at the maximum rate. The heart rate is increased and blood pressure is elevated during exercise in order to provide the fastest possible delivery of oxygen and substrates to the muscles. Vasoconstriction of the blood vessels serving the digestive system directs the blood primarily to the muscles, liver and adipose tissue. The type of substrate used by the muscles will depend on the time over which the strenuous exercise is spread as illustrated in Table 16.1.

The nervous system plays a key role in controlling the changes that occur during exercise. In addition to the direct stimulation of the muscles by the appropriate motor neurones, stimulation of the sympathetic nervous system is responsible for the increase in heart rate, the vasodilation that occurs in muscles and the constriction of the blood vessels supplying many of the internal organs. Stimulation of the adrenal medulla results in the secretion of adrenaline which stimulates the rate and force of the heart beat directly as well as increasing the rate of glycogenolysis in both liver and muscle. Stimulation of the sympathetic

Table 16.1 Changes in muscle metabolism as a function of the duration and severity of exercise

Initial energy source	Sustainable energy source	Duration of exercise
Rest		
Glucose	Blood glucose	No limit
Mild exercise (e.g. walking)		
ATP, phosphocreatine	Blood glucose, fatty acids	Hours
Strenuous exercise (e.g. jogging, swimming, playing tennis)		
ATP, phosphocreatine	Fatty acids, glycogen	15–120 min depending on fitness
Severe exercise with maximum power (e.g. running upstairs, sprinting)		
ATP, phosphocreatine	Glycogen	10–15 s

nervous system also releases noradrenaline from the adrenal medulla and nerve endings in adipose tissue, causing lipolysis of stored triacylglycerol by the hormone-sensitive lipase.

Sprinting

Maximum power output is required for sprinting or running up stairs and can only be sustained for a very short time. This requires rapid contraction of all three muscle fibre types (I, IIA and IIB). Since the type IIB (glycolytic) fibres have a relatively poor blood supply, they must rely on anaerobic glycolysis to meet the demand for ATP. It would appear that the development of fatigue, which occurs in less than half a minute at full power, may be due to the drop in pH caused by lactate production rather than depletion of muscle glycogen.

Sustained aerobic exercise

If vigorous exercise, such as running or cycling, is sustained over a long period the required ATP must be supplied in quite a different manner. Sustained exercise must rely on aerobic metabolism and because of the limited size of the glycogen stores it requires a combination of fatty acids and glucose as substrates. The supply of blood glucose from the liver is not adequate to support glycolysis and muscle glycogen must be used as the main substrate for the glycolytic pathway in muscle fibres during contraction. Only a limited supply of glucose is available from liver glycogen, so that gluconeogenesis must take place in the liver to ensure that the blood glucose level is maintained. In any case, exercise supplies substrates for gluconeogenesis since the type IIB muscle fibres always produce lactate which is returned to the liver to be converted back into glucose. In order to protect the glucose supply for the CNS and the red blood cells it is important for the fatty acid levels in the blood to rise so that glucose utilization by the muscles is inhibited.

Export of ammonia from muscles during exercise

Increased rates of muscle contraction also increase the rate of ammonia production from adenine deamination (see Figure 8.5) and amino acid catabolism. The extra ammonia results in a more rapid release of glutamine by the muscles. This indirectly increases the availability of energy-supplying substrates for the muscles in two ways. First of all, the rise in the rate of glutamine catabolism by the kidneys enables them to excrete additional protons together with the ammonia that is released. Complete oxidation of the 2-oxoglutarate produced by complete deamination of the glutamine allows the kidneys to reduce their requirement for both glucose and fatty acids. It should be recognized that ammonia secretion during glutamine catabolism by the kidneys increases the capacity for anaerobic glycolysis by limiting the drop in vascular pH caused by lactate production. The extra glutamine formed by the muscles during exercise also provides an alternative substrate for the intestine which converts much of the glutamine into alanine to serve as a substrate for gluconeogenesis by the liver.

Hormonal changes during exercise

Numerous hormonal changes are associated with vigorous exercise, but the most important for substrate supply are the increases in adrenaline, noradrenaline and glucagon. The concentrations of these hormones are increased by three to four times during several hours of sustained exercise, and these changes are accompanied by a decline in insulin levels because of the fall in blood glucose. Adrenaline initially causes a rapid breakdown of liver glycogen which occurs even before the level of glucose in the circulation has begun to fall. The increase in cyclic AMP caused by adrenaline is also responsible for an increase in the rate of glycogenolysis in skeletal muscle, although glycogen phosphorylase activity is also stimulated by the rise in 5'-AMP concentration which occurs during rapid muscle contraction. The resulting rise in glucose phosphate levels reduces the utilization of blood glucose by muscle, thus helping to maintain an adequate supply of glucose for the CNS and the erythrocytes. Noradrenaline produced as a consequence of the stimulation of the sympathetic neurones in adipose tissue stimulates the activity of the hormone-sensitive lipase which, together with the reduction in glucose entry into adipocytes due to the decline in GLUT 4 mobilization by insulin, results in the release of free fatty acids and glycerol. The latter returns to the liver where the other major metabolic effect of the hormone changes takes place, namely increased gluconeogenesis. The elevated glucagon levels initially signal the degradation of liver glycogen, but as this becomes depleted gluconeogenesis from lactate, glycerol and alanine is stimulated by glucagon and becomes a major source of blood glucose. The other hormone that is secreted during strenuous exercise is cortisol which acts much more slowly, but is probably responsible for the release of amino acids from muscle protein during sustained exercise.

16.2 Comparison of the effects of moderate versus severe exercise

Exercising at the maximum rate

The metabolic consequences of exercise depend on both the severity and the duration of the exercise. Thus, sprinting or running up stairs, which require maximum power output, depends on the most effective and readily available sources

371

of ATP. Muscle contains about three times as much phosphocreatine as ATP and by rephosphorylating ADP the phosphocreatine can maintain the maximum rate of contraction for up to 4 s. At that point anaerobic glycolysis will take over to produce the ATP by the conversion of glycogen to lactate which gives the highest rate of ATP production by a metabolic pathway. In principle anaerobic glycolysis should be able to continue until it has exhausted the store of glycogen in the muscles, but this does not occur, probably because fatigue is caused by the drop in pH resulting from the production of lactate. Nevertheless, it is clear that the only substrate used for the short bursts of activity at the maximum rate is glycogen, which comes from within the muscle cells. It should also be noted that the overall yield of ATP per glucose residue from glycolysis is 50% higher from glycogen (three ATPs) than from glucose (two ATPs).

Sustained exercise

Sustained exercise, on the other hand, requires the use of substrates and oxygen coming from outside the cell. This allows the muscles to oxidize glucose completely to CO_2 and water, but under these circumstances the maximum power output is reduced substantially. If the period of exercise extends for hours rather than minutes, it becomes essential for fatty acid oxidation to become a major source of energy for the production of ATP. The use of the combination of fatty acids and glucose further reduces the maximum power output (to less than 50% of maximum), but it does make it possible to continue a moderate rate of exercise for many hours. If the period of strenuous exercise continues without a break, it eventually stops when the muscle glycogen has been used up. This is because the type IIB glycolytic fibres cannot take up glucose from the vascular system rapidly enough to support their normal rate of contraction. Table 16.1 summarizes the variations in muscle metabolism as a function of the length and severity of the exercise.

16.3 The influence of fitness on the metabolic effects of exercise

The metabolic effects of exercise can be modified significantly by achieving a high level of fitness. Regular exercise stimulates the formation of additional muscle protein as well as improving the reserves of glycogen and triacylglycerol in muscle. Keeping fit also improves the circulation of oxygen and substrates to the muscles through the vascular system. These changes can be illustrated by the fact that a trained individual who is exercising at the same rate as an untrained person can continue to exercise for a substantially longer time before reaching the point of exhaustion.

The reserves of glycogen and triacylglycerol in muscle are also influenced by the diet consumed during the period of training. The glycogen content of muscle can be nearly doubled by changing from a normal mixed diet to a high-carbohydrate diet for a number of days. Conversely a low-carbohydrate diet can cut the glycogen content of skeletal muscle by more than 60%. These changes in muscle glycogen also have dramatic effects on the length of time an individual can continue sustained exercise. Thus, if a healthy trained individual with muscle glycogen content of about $100\,\mu mol/g$ exercises at a level that can only be continued for 2 h, this time can be extended by 50% if the muscle glycogen is doubled by consumption of a high-carbohydrate diet. Conversely, a low-carbohydrate diet would cut the period during which this level of exercise could be sustained by 50%.

16.4 Alterations in carbohydrate metabolism as a consequence of exercise

The changes in carbohydrate metabolism that are important during exercise occur principally in muscle and liver. As illustrated in Figure 16.1, the liver switches from its normal role of controlling blood glucose to the export of glucose produced by both glycogenolysis and gluconeogenesis. This alteration is initiated by the secretion of adrenaline, and then reinforced by the secretion of glucagon as the level of blood glucose falls. The rate of gluconeogenesis is also supported by the arrival at the liver of increasing amounts of lactate, alanine and eventually glycerol.

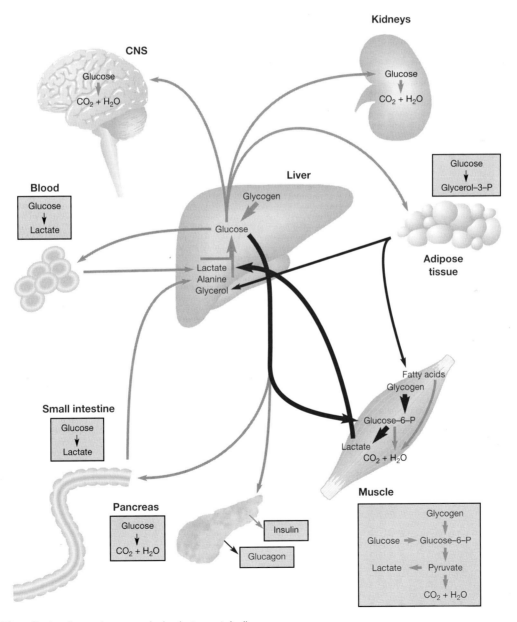

Figure 16.1 The effects of exercise on carbohydrate metabolism.

In the muscles glycogenolysis begins to occur as soon as the rate of glycolysis exceeds the entry rate of glucose from the blood. The maximum time during which full power output by anaerobic glycolysis can be maintained is at least partially explained by the need to export lactate from the type IIB fibres into the blood. This process, like the entry of glucose, is limited by the ratio of the volume of the muscle cells to the plasma membrane surface area. Eventually the rise in the cytoplasmic lactate concentration will cause a reduction in intracellular pH.

16.5 Exercise effects on lipid metabolism

For short periods of exercise at maximum power, lipid metabolism plays no significant part in substrate supply. However, for sustained exercise, when energy-supplying substrates from the blood are becoming important, the release of fatty acids from adipose tissue does play a significant role. The triacylglycerol lipase activity is increased by the rise in the cyclic AMP level caused by the secretion of adrenaline and noradrenaline. The activity of the lipase will also be increased by the decline in insulin levels which also allows cyclic AMP levels to rise. In prolonged exercise fatty acids will provide up to 60% of the total substrate, but the power output is lower than can be achieved with glycogen or glucose as the principal substrate. Figure 16.2 illustrates the changes in lipid metabolism during sustained exercise.

16.6 The influence of exercise on amino acid metabolism

Amino acid metabolism during exercise fulfils two main functions: supplying substrates for gluconeogenesis, and removing excess ammonia from the muscles. As mentioned in section 8.7 the rate of release of ammonia by the purine nucleotide cycle is related to the extent of muscle activity. The formation of glutamine provides the main mechanism for the transfer of this ammonia to the kidneys, or to the liver by way of the small intestine. The production of glutamine is particularly important during the anaerobic phase of contraction because of the reduction of the blood pH as a result of the rate of lactate formation. As indicated in section 13.6, glutamine metabolism in the kidney permits the secretion of ammonia into the kidney tubule lumen together with protons.

Alanine is also released by muscle during exercise and its conversion to glucose by the liver gives rise to the glucose/alanine cycle. Thus the liver receives alanine from muscle through the vascular system in two ways, direct transfer from the muscles and by the conversion of glutamine to alanine in the small intestine. Figure 16.3 indicates the changes in amino acid metabolism that occur during exercise. Cortisol secretion also stimulates the release of amino acids from muscle protein, although this is probably only important during prolonged periods of exercise and must be limited in order to protect muscle strength.

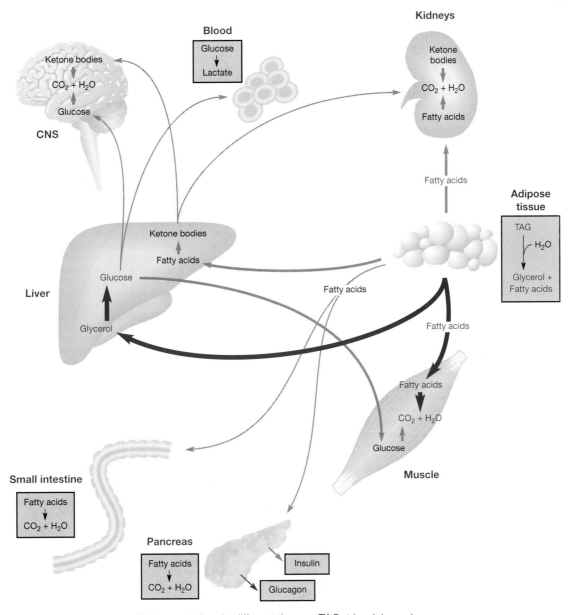

Figure 16.2 Influence of exercise on lipid metabolism in different tissues. TAG, triacylglycerol.

16.7 Effects of exercise on the interactions between tissues during anaerobic and prolonged exercise

Figure 16.4 compares the effects of high-power anaerobic and prolonged aerobic exercise on the interactions between tissues. As indicated above, anaerobic exercise (Figure 16.4a) chiefly involves the liver, pancreas and CNS with the muscles, whereas prolonged exercise (Figure 16.4b) must also involve the adipose tissue. In addition, the kidneys and intestine also make important contributions to metabolism during prolonged exercise.

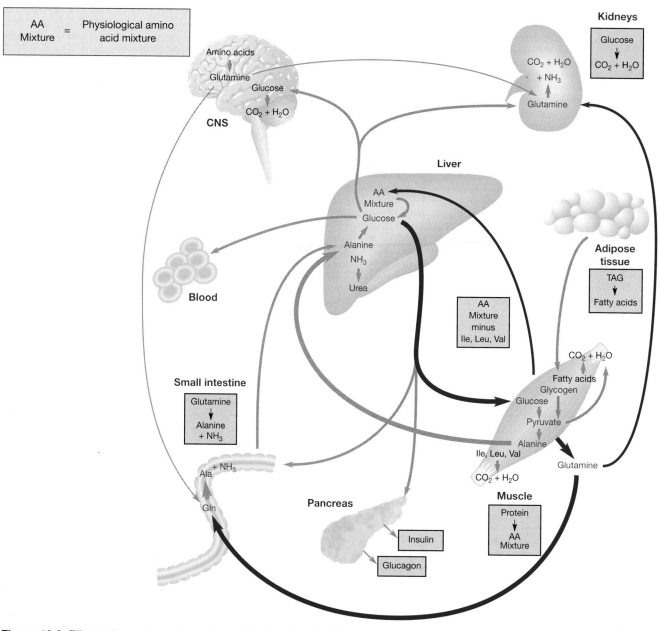

Figure 16.3 Effects of exercise on the amino acid metabolism in different tissues. TAG, triacylglycerol.

In anaerobic exercise glycogen is virtually the only substrate used to provide ATP. Nevertheless the release of glucose from the liver and the associated rise in insulin are essential to provide glucose for the CNS and the erythrocytes as well as permitting a rapid recovery of muscle glycogen during a pause in muscle activity. Glutamine metabolism by the kidneys moderates the drop in vascular pH and in the intestine glutamine metabolism produces alanine which provides an additional substrate for gluconeogenesis.

Prolonged exercise requires fatty acid release from adipose tissue as well as the stimulation of gluconeogenesis by glucagon released by the pancreas. The increased fatty acid release from adipose tissue enables the liver to form ketone bodies during prolonged exercise, and these help to reduce the utilization of glucose by the CNS and other tissues.

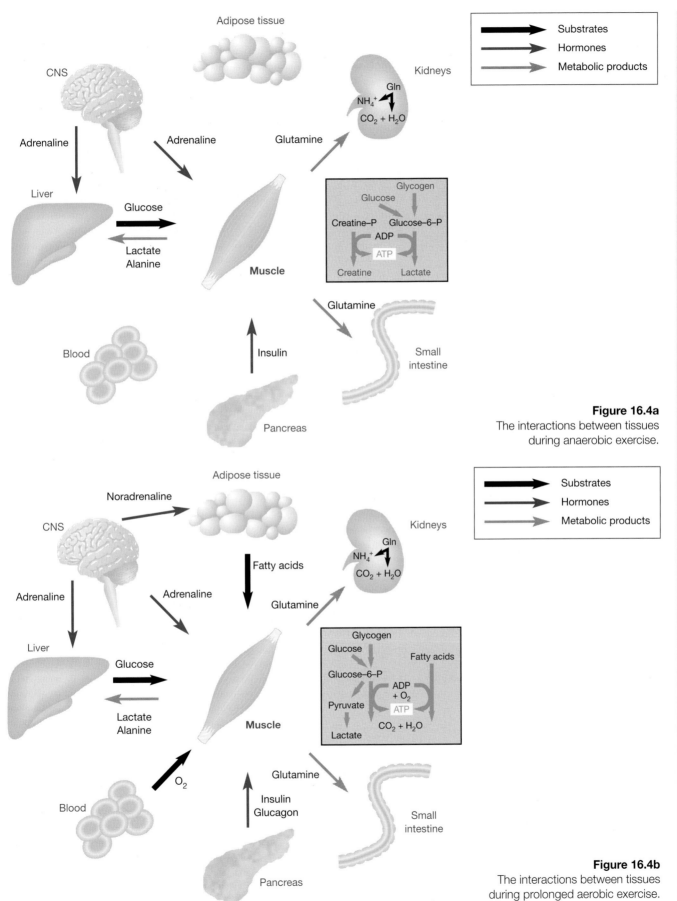

Figure 16.4a
The interactions between tissues during anaerobic exercise.

Figure 16.4b
The interactions between tissues during prolonged aerobic exercise.

EXERCISES

1. Why does maximum power output by muscle depend on anaerobic glycolysis?

2. Describe how glutamine metabolism helps to moderate the decline in vascular pH during strenuous exercise.

3. How does the extent of the glycogen reserves in muscle influence the length of time that strenuous exercise can continue?

4. Compare the fuel utilization in sprinting and prolonged exercise.

5. What are the effects of adrenaline during exercise?

Further reading

Booth, F.W. & Tomason, D.B. (1991) Molecular and cellular adaption of muscle in response to exercise: perspectives of various models, *Physiological Reviews* **71**, 541–585.

Dyck, D.J., Putnam, C.T., Heigenhauser, G.J.F., Hultman, E. & Spriet, L.L. (1993) Regulation of fat–carbohydrate interaction in skeletal muscle during intense aerobic cycling, *American Journal of Physiology* **265**, E852–E859.

Frayn, K.N. (1996) *Metabolic Regulation: A Human Perspective*, Portland Press, Chapter 7.

Spurway, N.C. (1992) Aerobic exercise, anaerobic exercise and the lactate threshold, *British Medical Bulletin* **48**, 569–591.

Stanlet, W.C. & Connett, R.J. (1991) Regulation of muscle carbohydrate metabolism during exercise, *FASEB Journal* **5**, 2155–2159.

White, D.A. & Baxter, M., eds (1994) *Hormones and Metabolic Control*, 2nd edition, Arnold, Chapter 7.

References to figures are identified by F following the page number, e.g 6F for Figure 1.1 on page 6. If one of the entries for a subject is particularly important it is in bold type; bold type is also used for figures showing the molecular structure of the indexed item.